741.942 OPP †

D1587134

WITHDRAWN

WIMBLEDON SCHOOL OF ART
MERTON HALL ROAD, SW19 3QA
Tel : 540 0231

WEEKLY

10 JUL

741.942 OPP

OPPÉ

English drawings

Wimbledon School of Art
5403900144231

ENGLISH DRAWINGS AT WINDSOR CASTLE
STUART AND GEORGIAN PERIODS

BY A. P. OPPÉ

PHAIDON

WIMBLEDON SCHOOL OF ART
LIBRARY

WILLIAM BLAKE: THE ASSUMPTION. 1806 (Cat. No. 63)

ENGLISH DRAWINGS

· STUART AND GEORGIAN PERIODS ·

IN THE COLLECTION OF

HIS MAJESTY THE KING

AT WINDSOR CASTLE

BY

A. P. OPPÉ

LONDON

THE PHAIDON PRESS LTD

All rights reserved by Phaidon Press Ltd
1 Cromwell Place, London, SW7

1950
MADE IN GREAT BRITAIN
TEXT PRINTED BY TONBRIDGE PRINTERS LTD · TONBRIDGE
PLATES PRINTED BY HENRY STONE & SON LTD · BANBURY
BOUND BY KEY & WHITING LTD · LONDON

CONTENTS

PREFACE 7

INTRODUCTION 9

CATALOGUE

Drawings by Members of the Royal Family 19

Drawings by known artists 22

Anonymous Drawings 107

SUPPLEMENT: Drawings by Paul and Thomas
Sandby acquired since 1947 113

APPENDIX: Portrait Sketches by the Dightons 118

PLATES 123

CONCORDANCE 207

INDEX OF PERSONS AND SUBJECTS 210

INDEX OF PLACES 214

PREFACE

THIS volume contains the drawings in the Royal Library by British artists and foreigners working in England who were born with a few exceptions before 1786. The intention is to cover the periods before the Victorian, the few exceptions being artists whose work is irrevocably intermingled with those of the earlier period. Architectural and Military drawings, to which separate volumes will be devoted, have been omitted from detailed consideration, but the names of the artists have been included with references indicating where their drawings may be found. Paul and Thomas Sandby have been the subject of a previous catalogue, but notes on the important drawings acquired or recognized since the date of that catalogue are given in a separate Supplement at the end of this volume. Foreign artists have been omitted when their work has been included in previous catalogues, except where further drawings of English interest by them have been recognized or fresh information has been gained. The limit between drawings and miniatures has been hard to fix; here, as elsewhere, some overlap seems inevitable. It is necessary to add that only such drawings are included as have been definitely assigned to the Royal Library.

The work was undertaken during the war when Mr. A. C. Sewter, to whom it was entrusted, had been called up for service after making some progress with the drawings by Hogarth and Rowlandson. I owe more than gratitude to Sir Owen Morshead for constant help and kindness at a time when work at Windsor meant a welcome relief from the cares of London, and conditions for study in the Royal Library were, paradoxically enough, easier than at normal times. The work was interrupted before the end of the war, partly through its own increase in scale which led to the separate publication of the drawings by Paul and Thomas Sandby, and of those in the Royal Library by Hogarth together with the others which had necessarily been studied in their connexion. From the resumption of the volume I have been dependent on Miss Scott-Elliot for assistance which amounts to collaboration. Since the material of this catalogue was too varied in content, condition and size to lend itself, as in the other cases, either to photographing as a whole or to removal en masse for study where the appropriate equipment for reference and comparison was available, it has fallen to her to secure system and continuity in the work. Many valuable suggestions are also due to her, and she has relieved me almost entirely of the onerous tasks of checking, indexing, etc. In the references to the Archives, Miss Mary Mackenzie, the Registrar, has given much help.

Acknowledgements for information given with regard to individual details have been made, I hope invariably in the appropriate places, but, more generally, I am glad to record frequent consultations at the British Museum with Mr. E. Croft-Murray on doubtful attributions and with Mrs. George on caricatures, and help received from Mr. Robinson of the Maritime Museum and Mr. O. Millar, Deputy Surveyor of the King's Pictures, regarding naval drawings and documentation of King Charles I's possessions respectively. Thanks are also due to Messrs. Tooth for permission to reproduce the photograph of a picture by Mercier once belonging to them; to Messrs. Christie for frequent consultation of their old catalogues; and to Dr. I. Grafe for much care in the preparation of a complicated volume.

PAUL OPPÉ

September, 1950

INTRODUCTION

SIR RICHARD HOLMES, the Royal Librarian from 1870 to 1906, writing in the Burlington Magazine, claimed that one of the 'limnings' by Peter Oliver from paintings which were in King Charles I's collection had remained in the Royal possession since it was painted. This was the D'Avalos Allegory, after Titian (No. 461). Unfortunately, he does not give his authorities for this statement, and the list of buyers at the sales of the King's pictures shews that it was sold in common with the other similar limnings. Some of these were recovered at the Restoration, for they re-appear in the Inventories of King James II's possessions, and with them the two original monochromes by Isaac Oliver still in the Royal Collection (Nos. 459 and 460), and the copy of Van Dyck's portrait of Queen Henrietta Maria (No. 271) which was made by Gibson the dwarf and was probably the large miniature seen and mentioned in Evelyn. No doubt because all of these were limnings or miniatures rather than drawings, and were probably still in their original frames, as some of them have remained to this day, none of them found a place in the eighteenth-century catalogue of Drawings in the Royal Library, a composite volume known as 'Inventory A'.

In the oldest part of that inventory, which dates only from the last quarter of the eighteenth century, the list of contents given for a volume of miscellaneous foreign landscapes mentions besides drawings described as 'made by students at Rome'—who may or may not have been English—a drawing 'by Mr. Crone', and another with a punning inscription which was rightly identified by a later Librarian as by Chatelain. Both of these remain in the Library, and they are the only drawings of English origin in the main body of the old inventory except for architectural drawings, which fall outside the scope of the present catalogue, and two of the drawings by Richard Dalton of which more will be said later on. Another inventory or, rather, a catalogue of books, of about the same date, known as 'Inventory B', mentions eight drawings of horses by Sawrey Gilpin which were bound in a volume with the engravings from them, and these too, remain in the Royal Library (No. 273), though the prints have disappeared. Some more English drawings are listed among the contents of miscellaneous portfolios and cases in a later portion of 'Inventory A' which from the watermark cannot be earlier than 1816. The King's own landscape compositions in a guard book (No. 1) are now included, and with them the head of King Charles II by Samuel Cooper (No. 133), which was a present to George III from the Prince of Wales and seems then to have been framed, a single drawing of a horse by Gilpin (No. 272), a landscape by Woollett, a Madonna and Child by Peter Oliver, and large landscapes or seascapes by Bray (No. 88) and Coote Manningham (Nos. 427-431).

There is an obvious reason for the small number of English drawings in the part of King George III's collection which was covered by the Inventory and remains in the Royal Library. It was devoted almost entirely to the Old Masters, and whatever may have been the reasons for amassing those treasures, English drawings were acquired only for their content. From the earliest days of his reign, the King shewed a great interest in representations of strange places, but views of these found their home in his geographical or topographic cabinet, the enormous collection of maps, charts, plans and prints, which passed, about 1820, as the 'King's Maps' with his Library, to the British Museum. That collection seems to have been kept separate from the Drawings and, at any rate latterly, was probably under the charge of a different officer. In it drawings form only a very subsidiary feature; they are scarcely more than a continuation of the early charts and plans which, when, as often, schematic diagram blossoms into picturesque representation of coastlines and natural features, constitute the most valuable and interesting part of the collection. Prints seem to have been preferred to drawings, no doubt as being more careful and definitive, and the drawings themselves show that the compilers were very little concerned with artistic considerations. They range indifferently from the most puerile sketches by amateurs to unrecorded early drawings of Lucca by Canaletto.[1] Some other foreign drawings and a few of the English have merit in themselves, such as a watercolour of the Pont du Gard by William Marlow, and a batch of early Scottish drawings by Paul and Thomas Sandby, which are clearly the product of one of their posthumous sales, except for one primitive drawing by Thomas which carries the unrecorded mark of his patron, William, Duke of Cumberland; but the bulk are only of interest to historians concerned with rarities of name rather than with merit. It is clear that everything that could be classed as topographic was forced into this part of the collection. Grimm's drawings of the Maundy Ceremony in Whitehall, considered to be his most ambitious work and exhibited at the Royal Academy of 1774 were bequeathed to the King by Sir Richard Kaye in accordance, explicitly, with a wish once expressed by the King to Grimm himself.[2] In 1810, when the bequest took effect, the drawings were consigned to the King's Maps, where they remain. Whether this would have been their fate had the bequest taken place earlier, it is impossible to say, for the collection was maintained long after the King had ceased to be capable of taking any interest in it, and only appears to have been closed about 1820, either with his death or on the transfer to the British Museum.

Grimm's drawings are so large that it was found necessary to fold them, in spite of their thick mounts, in order to place them in the volumes which contain the collection. Their still larger size may have saved the drawings by Bray and some of those by Coote Manningham from the same fate, but it may be that the strange history of the two volumes and the parcel of Bruce's drawings of Africa (No. 94) was the reason for their exclusion. The King is said to have secreted them and only to have revealed their hiding-place during one of his rare lucid intervals. In this case, too, it is said that the King, in his zeal for architecture and strange places, expressed the wish that Bruce would make drawings for his collection when he had an audience before he set out on his travels in 1762, but it is clear that the collection as a whole was not the result of commissions nor of any definite plan, but was put together from the most miscellaneous sources, many of the maps and plans still bearing marks of official origin, and those of long obsolete fortifications still being contained in wrappers marked 'secret'.

Their large size may also have accounted for the exclusion of Dalton's drawings of Egypt, etc. (No. 164), from the King's maps, but it may have been his pride in his own work that led him to retain them among the Old Masters under his charge as Keeper of the Drawings, if the King's Maps came under the Librarian when the offices were separated. In any case, a little contemporary gossip about his activities possibly helps to explain the absence of English drawings other than topographic from King George III's Collection. In 1772, Lord Nuneham, who was scarcely the first-comer and was much in contact with artists, wrote to his father, Lord Harcourt: 'The King either will not, or cannot, receive anything unless it is recommended by, or passes through the hands of, that supreme critic in the arts, Dalton, who not unfrequently retains for his own collection or his own profit the drawings and proof plates that are intended for his master, without even shewing them.'[3] This is corroborated so far as concerns his concurrent commercial activities by a letter from Mrs. Delany. Writing in 1772 to Lady Andover from London,[4] she describes an interruption from 'the most impertinent, troublesome, prating man in the world, Mr. Dalton by

---

[1] The name of Pietro Bellotti, which is at the back of one of them, is probably due to a half-instructed confusion with the seventeenth-century figure artist of that name.

[2] R. M. Clay, *S. H. Grimm*, p. 58.

[3] *Harcourt Papers*, Vol. III, p. 107.

[4] *Correspondence*, 1862, 2nd series, Vol. I, p. 430.

name, who has vases, pictures, etc. etc. to dispose of—"*the finest that ever were seen, amazing cheap!*" though extravagantly dear and not to be parted with "*but to oblige her Grace* (Portland) *who is such a connoisseur, such an encourager of virtu*" and much more than I can say, or your ladyship can desire to hear'. At that date, though not yet Surveyor of the Pictures, Dalton was still the King's Librarian, and it was in that capacity that he was acting when denounced by Lord Nuneham.

Queen Charlotte's interest in English drawings was less purely topographical than the King's, and her opportunities for decoration called for less extensive schemes than those with which the King hoped to initiate a new school of English historic art by the patronage of West. Her fondness for Gainsborough's landscape drawings as well as for his portraits was well known. In the sales of her collection in 1819, there were no fewer than twenty-two of his drawings, and the loss of these from the Royal Collection may have weakened it on the artistic side more than did the transfer of all the British drawings in the King's Maps to the British Museum. There should have been among them no fewer than ten out of the series of twelve drawings in coloured chalks which were said to be the only ones made by him in that medium. The Queen received four of them as a gift from the artist when she had expressed such admiration of them that Lord Mulgrave tried to buy the whole set in order to give them to her. At the sale after Gainsborough's death the Queen is said to have bought six of the remainder.[5] Her sales also contained drawings by West and Cipriani, as well as landscapes of other localities besides Windsor by Webber, Cleveley, Serres and others. She had ten views of the Lakes 'representing Different Times of the Day' by the German drawing-master Becker, whom Farington[6] visited at Bath in 1801, and two views by him of Windsor, where he seems to have lived for a time, for a volume of drawings of the neighbourhood was in the Dunn Library, and since dispersed under the name of Sandby. The portraits by Edridge of her family and friends which were at Frogmore when the house was described by W. H. Pyne were not sold with the Queen's collections and effects, but it is impossible to identify any of them with certainty among those now in the Royal Library.

King George IV bought back almost immediately after the sale one of her small copies of portraits by G. P. Harding (No. 310), the brother of her industrious librarian, Edward Harding, who himself made many copies for her, as well as caring for her large library and collection of prints and conducting for her a small private printing press. Some drawings from her collection escaped the sales, perhaps by accident. Such are the eight drawings by the Ladies Spencer (Nos. 594-598), which are expressly noted in the Inventory (about 1840) as having belonged to Queen Charlotte, and the volume of sketches by Lord Aylesford (No. 32) which is inscribed by her as a gift from the artist in 1809.

Another memorial of Queen Charlotte which is noted in the inventory as having been brought from Buckingham Palace in 1828 (together with the volumes and loose drawings by Bruce) illustrates both her affection for the King and her children and the interest of the whole family in art. These are the two red portfolios of drawings by the King when Prince of Wales and by the Princes and Princesses, the seven drawings by the Queen herself, and the book with the Princess Royal's drawings and etchings. The portfolio with the King's drawings as Prince of Wales is mentioned by Pyne as being at Frogmore, and is quite distinct from the volume of large chalk drawings by the King (No. 1) which had already found its place in the inventory. The Queen's own efforts in historical composition, even when her hand was all but guided by her instructor, proclaim that her proficiency was not equal to her interest. It is said[7] that she received lessons from

[5] Whitley, *Gainsborough*, p. 320.
[6] *Diary*, Jan. 17, 1801 (unpublished).
[7] Whitley, *Art and Artists*, I, 174.

Gainsborough, but if there is any truth in this it is likely that they were limited to demonstrations of his 'mopping' process in her presence. Her daughters were more successful performers. The Princess Royal is said to have confined herself to copies, of which those after Ridinger mentioned by Pyne have disappeared, but many flower drawings after prints and some etchings remain in the Royal collection. The Princess Elizabeth, who is represented in this collection only by a group of vignette-like compositions, adventured boldly into allegory with several series which were etched, as *The Progress and Power of Genius*, etc., and gained her much contemporary compliment. It is noticeable that of the list of Royal instructors given by Pyne, and followed with embellishments by Angelo, not one appears to have left any of his work with his pupils, as was customary among drawing masters at that date, excepting only Alexander Cozens, one of whose tracings has found its way in a damaged condition (No. 157) into the Princes' portfolio. Cozens, too, is alone among the drawing-masters of whom there is documentary evidence in the Royal Archives and in the official *Court and City Register*. It may be only a coincidence that the Princesses showed most signs of their activity as artists during the years 1780-1786, when he is officially noted as Instructor to their young brothers, and it was during those years that the example and encouragement of Dr. Fisher, afterwards Bishop of Salisbury, is recorded (see No. 263). A large proportion of the etchings by the Princesses is dated 1785.

There is much fuller information regarding the acquisitions of King George IV. None of these are mentioned in the old Inventories 'A' and 'B', although the former contains entries dating as late as 1840, and was only bound up in 1862 or after; but there are in the Royal archives a whole series of invoices from Messrs. Colnaghi and other printsellers and several from the artists direct. They no doubt formed the Carlton House collection, and were long kept separate from the earlier possessions. The invoices begin as early as 1799 and, with the emergence of a further series since the publication of the Catalogue of the Sandby Drawings, they continue to the death of King George IV in 1830.[8]

Throughout that period the drawings are included in the dealers' invoices with prints, and indeed constitute but a very small fraction of the whole. Even so, a number are included which cannot now be identified, while there are many drawings in the collection which are shewn by inscriptions or dealers' marks upon them to have been similarly bought, but were either procured from other dealers, whose invoices have not been preserved, or were included in the extant invoices in groups under general descriptive headings with or without the names of artists.

By far the largest number of entries in the invoices relate to portraits, and they are almost entirely prints. Clearly the Prince or his Librarian set himself out to form a comprehensive gallery of personages, celebrated or otherwise, such as was made by many collectors at the date whose catalogues were published, either on the occasion of their sales or otherwise, or as his father had caused to be put together of geographical and topographic material. Whether King George III had instituted a similar collection of portraits cannot now be determined, since no list of them was ever drawn up and any that he may have collected have now become merged, or have been dispersed, with King George IV's. No portrait prints are included in either 'Inventory A' or 'B', and as a rule the family drawings such as those by Hamilton (Nos. 283-287), if not later accessions but remaining from the eighteenth century, were omitted both from 'Inventory A', no doubt because they were framed, and from the Lord Chamberlain's Inventories of pictures because of their

---

[8] No fewer than twenty-four drawings by Paul and Thomas Sandby are mentioned in these further invoices, of which eight can be identified with certainty. Other views of Windsor which were invoiced without the names of the artists may relate to drawings by them. This considerably reduces the possibility of regarding any of the drawings by either Paul or Thomas which are in the Royal collection as having been commissioned or purchased by King George III.

comparative insignificance. Apart from his prints, the invoices shew the large sums expended by King George IV on portraits in miniature by Cosway and in enamel by Bone, but these, together with the copies in enamel from pictures by Reynolds or old masters with which the patron and Bone rivalled Charles I and Peter Oliver, lie, like the prints, outside the scope of this catalogue.

In one direction there was an exception to the general preponderance of prints over drawings, and that was in the most individual portion of King George IV's collection, the military uniforms and incidents. Here no doubt prints were not ready to hand, at any rate, with detail, colour and variety, sufficient to suit his purpose. The first drawings of these subjects are invoiced about 1802, so far as is shewn by the records at present available, but the interest was at its height in 1813 and succeeding years, and only becomes sporadic and occasional from about the year of his accession. Most of these drawings are by foreign artists: Langendyk, Finart, Sauerweid and others, and they were received in large and expensive consignments from Colnaghi. But at an early date in the century the Prince obtained through the same source drawings of these subjects as well as character drawings by one or other of the Dightons, and from 1812 he bought them in large numbers from Denis Dighton direct. In 1815 this artist was appointed Military Draughtsman to the Prince Regent. According to Pye,[9] the King's favour continued as long as Sir Benjamin Blomfield remained in office as, *inter alia*, Private Secretary to the King, but after Sir William Knighton had succeeded him (which was in 1822) and had been told that one of Dighton's pictures was priced at 200 guineas, the artist's 'channel of communication with the Prince, the source of his income, became closed'. According to the same story the shock was too much for Dighton's reason; retiring to Brittany with assistance from the Artists' Benevolent Fund, he died in 1827, aged 35. In fact, his exhibits at the Academy only ceased in 1825, and his last invoice to the King, for a drawing of the costume of the 10th Hussars at his usual price of 16 guineas, is dated 1826. By then the King's purchases of military subjects had decreased generally, but they and more considerable drawings were still being bought from time to time from Dighton. It would seem, therefore, that the discontinuance was less sudden and complete than was reported to Pye, and that Dighton's breakdown may be assigned to a less sensational cause than is given by him.

With the decrease in interest in military subjects the purchases of theatrical drawings and portraits seems to have increased. From 1820 there are several items in Colnaghi's invoices which are explicitly described as being 'for the Illustrations of the Stage'. Here again drawings constitute but a small proportion among the prints of similar subjects. In November, 1820, Colnaghi's invoices, which throughout 1813 had contained charges of £3 per week for 'attendance for the arrangement of His Royal Highness' collection of drawings and Prints', specify the binding of 'the first volume elegant in russia, of the Theatrical Portraits'. The binding of the second and third volumes follows soon after. Meanwhile in March, 1820, Edward Harding was engaged in arranging the theatrical portraits, etc., for which he claimed some £400 in June, 1826, and in the correspondence which followed mention is made of the ninth and tenth volumes of theatrical portraits as 'being in a state of forwardness'.

These volumes must have been broken up long since, for few of the theatrical drawings mentioned in the invoices are now traceable. The drawings of theatres such as those by Schnebbelie and Whichelo which form an unduly large proportion of the remaining topographic drawings may have belonged to this part of the collection. Since however most of them are inlaid in larger sheets, it is more likely that they were arranged for extra-illustration. It is clear from the invoices that the Prince and his librarians suffered from the passion for Grangerizing which was prevalent at this period.

---

[9] *Patronage of British Art*, p. 387.

An extra-illustrated De Grammont is expressly mentioned in one of the invoices, and such books would account for the numerous apparent duplicates which occur in the invoices. Whether for this purpose or not, the Regent, without emulating the world-wide appetite of his father, made many purchases of topographic material. French topography is expressly mentioned, but his chief purchases were concerned with London and the royal palaces. Pre-eminent among these is the volume containing the whole series in watercolour of the illustrations by Charles Wild and others to Pyne's *Royal Residences*, which, though it is mentioned in no invoice or catalogue, would appear from the character of its binding to have formed part of the Carlton House Library. This is an outstanding example of the English topographer's art, but the space it occupies in the present volume cannot correspond in any way to its importance, because its contents conform exactly to those of the book as published.

Another aspect of the Prince of Wales as collector might have given more character to the collection had it been more fully preserved. Among the very first drawings invoiced to the Prince by Colnaghi there are batches which are specified merely as five, ten and twelve 'curious, gay drawings', and differentiated according as they were 'coloured', in which case they cost three guineas each, or plain, when they cost six guineas for ten, or in a book, when the latter amount secured a dozen. A fortnight later there are 'two fine, gay drawings' again costing three guineas each, while a month later 'two gay drawings' still cost three guineas each without deserving the additional description of 'fine'. Subsequent invoices are less general in character, but the word 'curious' occurs sufficiently often to shew that it had not yet gained the special technical meaning which it has now acquired in booksellers' catalogues. There are, for instance, 'curious unknown characters' purchased in 1810, a 'curious historical drawing' in 1813, and both Morland's hieroglyphical letter in 1812 (No. 442) and the drawing by Laroon in 1813 (No. 409) are described as curious, the latter being also 'interesting'. Closely akin probably were the 'three drawings of remarkable persons of Berlin', bought in 1801 for seven guineas, and it is possible that '43 sketches by a gentleman artist', bought in 1810 for £6 1s., were of the same type as the 'curious unknown character and a ditto of an old man' bought ten days before for 5s. each. These have not survived, but there are enough examples remaining (No. 734) of the 'beggars' bought about the same time to give an indication of the material that was sold to amuse the Prince, or perhaps merely to relieve the vendor.

The epithet 'curious' might no doubt also cover more important drawings if they contained an element of caricature. Like everyone else at the time, the Prince of Wales had his collection of Hogarth's prints containing a sprinkling of drawings. Colnaghi's invoices mention only three drawings by him, of which two are untraceable, while the third, the 'Dimensions of Garrick and Quin' (No. 351), though certainly 'curious', is in no sense comic, but from other sources it is known that he acquired at some time after 1801 Baker's large collection of prints, which almost certainly contained many of the drawings by Hogarth now in the Royal Collection. Less trustworthy tradition credits him with the purchase of Rowlandson's two Reviews (Nos. 517 and 518) even before they were exhibited, and with a set of sporting roundels which were said to have been used for a screen and have now been dispersed without leaving any record. The invoices only mention Rowlandson on seven occasions at prices ranging from 5s. to £2 10s., but as the two first are described as 'gay', and several of those now in the collection bear unmistakable Colnaghi inscriptions, it is probable that many of the drawings by him besides the four (Nos. 510, 511, 530 and 540) now identifiable were included among the anonymous 'gay' or 'curious' drawings entered in the invoices. One of the most interesting series of drawings in the collection, the ten Roman Carnival scenes (Nos. 21-30) by David Allan, who was known as 'the Scottish Hogarth', may also be classed in this category, as may certainly the drawings by Boyne, Brandoin, Bunbury and Woodward, and the character sketches by the Dightons. Again, like everyone else of the period, the Prince had his volumes of caricature prints, purchasing three from Colnaghi, and no doubt hiring others for a period in the customary way from Fores.

If the word 'curious' had not yet acquired its modern meaning, 'gay' was already used in a sense which it retained at any rate until the middle of the century, though it has now lost it. The drawings and prints of this character can mainly be judged by their titles, and the taste for them seems to have remained with the Regent until a late date, since in 1818 a very long series of purely military drawings is suddenly diversified by 'The Morning Visit', 'The First Kiss of Love' and 'Promenade dans le Jardin d'Amour', each at two guineas. Most of these and many of the 'curious' drawings and prints must have disappeared in a holocaust which took place in 1830. A letter of March 24, 1845, to J. H. Glover, the then Royal Librarian, which is preserved in the Royal Archives (*Vict. Addl. Mss.* T/73), states that on the death of King George IV the contents of 'several drawers full of *Free* prints and drawings the private property of His late Majesty' were destroyed by the writer, Joseph Calkin, himself by order of Sir William Knighton, and with the knowledge and approbation of his successor, Sir Henry Wheatley. More important prints, French, sporting and caricature, and some duplicates, were sold in 1886, but the sale contained only two drawings. These were doubtfully attributed in the catalogue to Rowlandson.

Expenditure on prints and drawings seems from the invoices to have decreased generally with King George IV's accession to the throne. It was at this time that the Royal Library parted with the collection of maps and plans 'as a gift' to the British Museum, and the new King may have been shy of piling up a fresh account in order to replace it. Nor was Sir William Knighton ill-advised in discountenancing expenditure whether on the military drawings of Denis Dighton or of others. The total invoiced expenditure on military drawings alone amounted to well over £5,000; that on prints and drawings together, without counting pictures, enamels or miniatures, would have far exceeded the amount at which Sir Thomas Lawrence's collection could have been obtained in its entirety by the sovereign or the nation. No doubt, despite the memory of earlier extravagances, King George IV would have accepted the generous terms offered by Lawrence in his will, had it become effective before his final illness and his death. As it is, there is no record that the matter was even placed before his successor, King William IV, and, as is well known, the Government refused, in spite of Talleyrand's historic gibe, to spend the small sum asked, £18,000, in acquiring for the British Museum a collection which fully deserved the claim made for it by Lawrence himself, that it was unrivalled in the world. Had it been purchased by the King it would, apart from its wealth of Old Masters, have enriched the Royal Collection with outstanding drawings and watercolours by British artists whose works may now be sought at Windsor in vain.

For the rest of the nineteenth century the Royal Library has no records, and the more important purchases of watercolours by contemporary artists will fall to be described in a further volume. Some information however regarding the acquisition of earlier drawings can be obtained from auction catalogues and other publications. In two directions especially the collections made by King George IV were more than supplemented. Considerable purchases of drawings by Hogarth made at or after the Standly Sale in 1845, and of early drawings by Paul Sandby from the Banks collection in 1876, may be said to have at least doubled the importance of these sections of the collection. Sir Richard Holmes, who made the latter purchase, was also instrumental in securing the important portrait of Queen Elizabeth by Isaac Oliver (No. 457) as well as some of the limnings by Peter Oliver which had belonged to King Charles I. It was probably also owing to him that the Royal Library acquired the four drawings by Blake in which the excellence of the

Assumption (frontispiece) compensates for the shortcomings of the other three, for he was in his younger days sufficiently within the pre-Raphaelite circle to be the subject of a sketch by Rossetti, published by Marillier (*Rossetti*, 1899, p. 219) and now in the British Museum. From 1906 a register of accessions has been maintained, and it will be seen from the numerous references to its entries in this catalogue that the collection of older British drawings has been greatly enriched during the present century, very largely through the knowledge, taste and generosity of H.M. Queen Mary.

STOTHARD : DESIGN FOR A LUNETTE AT BUCKINGHAM PALACE (Cat. No. 600)

CATALOGUE

CATALOGUE

KING GEORGE III (1738–1820)

1. A volume labelled 'Landscapes drawn by H.M.' and containing, between leaves of blue card, forty-five loose and unnumbered drawings in black and white chalk, stump and some wash, on blue-grey paper. The materials and paper are uniform; the drawings are all enclosed within one or more broad ruled black lines, none are inscribed; the sizes vary from about 16½ × 22½ in. (41.9 × 57.2 cm.) down to 11 × 19 in. (27.9 × 48.3 cm.) With the exception of a somewhat formal and abstract view of Windsor Castle, the drawings are compositions, in the classical taste, of trees, park land, temples and shrines (*Figure* 1) and, sometimes intermixed with these, English villages. A ruled line in the architecture is a marked feature. Syon House (*Figure* 2) may be recalled in one view; Kew and Virginia Water perhaps in others.

Emphasis on perspective suggests the instruction of Joshua Kirby, and this is borne out by the general similarity of the compositions to Hogarth's frontispiece to Kirby's *Perspective*, 1761, which was dedicated to King George III as Prince of Wales. Wilson is also frequently recalled, principally in No. 42, which is a reminiscence of his *Baths of Caracalla*.

Entered as 'a Guard Book containing 45 Drawings of Landscapes and ancient Buildings by the King', in 'Inventory A', p. 151 (1816).

Fig. 1. King George III: Architectural study (Cat. No. 1)

2. Eleven compositions, presumably copies, of simple landscape subjects. Five in pencil only, five with added wash and one with pen also. Five are initialled in pencil 'P.W.' Various sizes, on washed mounts.

Contained, with the following (No. 3), in a red imitation Morocco portfolio with brown paper leaves and red silk flaps, which is lettered on the black leather spine 'Drawings by His Majesty when Prince of Wales 1760,' and has the Royal Arms (dating from before 1801) and 'C' in gilt embossed paper on both sides. A paper within in Queen Charlotte's handwriting reads: 'This Port Folio Contains Drawings by the King from His first beginning when He was Prince of Wales. which I have Collected and put into this Port Folio by me. the 9th January 1809.'

A memorandum by J. H. Glover dated August 26, 1828 (Inventory 'A', p. 172), states that the 'Drawings by His Majesty when Prince of Wales 1760; Drawings by the Princes and Princesses; Princess Royal's Drawings and Etchings; Seven Drawings by Her Majesty Queen Charlotte' were among books, prints and drawings which were taken from the Library at Buckingham House by Command of his Majesty and placed in 'Press E'. See also 'Inventory A', p. 144 (later).

3. Thirty-eight compositions, viz., Ornamental Title, twenty-seven buildings in a landscape setting with, above, geometrical theorems in ruled borders and ten similar, but without the geometry and ruled borders. The whole designs within ruled borders measure 7¼ × 4¼ in. (18.4 × 10.8 cm.), the paper cut approximately to uniform size. Some are numbered at foot with numerals up to 4. One drawing, in pencil only, shows clearly the extent of the instructor's handling over the pupil's beginning. The decorative treatment was presumably intended to make the geometry more palatable.

Fig. 2. King George III: Syon House (Cat. No. 1)

These drawings are mentioned in Pyne's *Royal Residences*, 1817, under Frogmore, p. 8, as having been discovered by Queen Charlotte 'about four years ago' and placed in this portfolio in her Library.

They are specifically entered with the preceding (No. 2) on p. 144 of 'Inventory A' and presumably, with No. 2, on p. 172.

KING GEORGE III AND JOSHUA KIRBY

4. A HOUSE WITH A COLONNADE, ETC.

Pen and grey wash, within border. 13½ × 18½ in. (34.6 × 47.5 cm.) *Figure 3*

Inscribed at the back in pen: 'This Drawing was Designed & Executed for my Book on Perspective by His Majesty King George III' (remainder cut off) and initialled on the front at foot 'G.P.W. 1760' (changed from 1761); the feathers below. Right-hand lower corner torn off and joined.

Engraved with the title as given, Plate LXIV, Kirby's *Perspective of Architecture*, 1761.

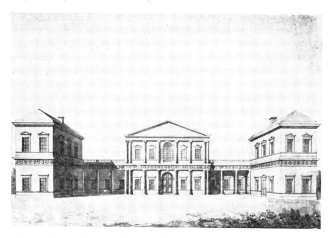

Fig. 3. King George III and Kirby: A house with a colonnade (Cat. No. 4)

This drawing was found in the portfolio containing the previous drawings; but Kirby's inscription and the fact that the margin has been cut down considerably more than is necessary for the portfolio suggest that it does not form an original part of it. It would seem rather to have remained in Kirby's possession. It explains a mysterious sentence in the paragraph on p. 55 of the second part of his *Perspective*, in which Kirby says of his Plate LXIV: 'The Design was made, and completed for me so as to come within the compass of the plate; and I hope I may take, the liberty of saying, that This, and the last finished print in the book, are esteemed by me as the most valuable parts of it'. (Plate LXXIII, the last plate in the book is described (p. 58) as 'little more than one half of a most magnificent design, which was made and given me for this work; and which (if well executed) would make an excellent piece of scenery for a theatre.') In the preface to the work Kirby also says that 'some elegant designs for the perspective' were owed to others than himself. Landscapes exhibited by him were noted by Horace Walpole as said to be by the King.

A drawing, a complete scaled elevation, described in Thomas Worsley's Inventory as 'A drawing of a door etc. done by the King and given me to execute at the Queen's House', is in the collection of Sir William Worsley at Hovingham Hall. It is inscribed 'Invenit, designavit, dedit Georgius III'.

PRINCE EDWARD AUGUSTUS, DUKE OF YORK (1739–1767), Brother of King George III.

5. A COTTAGE with tree, gate, river, etc.

Pencil and grey wash within ruled borders, soiled. 10½ × 13¾ in. (26.7 × 34.9 cm.) Inscribed in the margin below: This Drawing is most humbly Dedicated to Her Royal Highness the PRINCESS by Her most Dutyfull and

Obedient Son EDWARD. Prince Edward Fecit Novr. 21st 1752.

The condition of the drawing seems to show that it does not properly belong to Queen Charlotte's portfolio (see on No. 6), where it has been placed.

QUEEN CHARLOTTE (1744–1818)

6. Seven drawings: the Adoration of the Shepherds, Pygmalion, the Invention of Painting, etc.

Pencil, pen and brown wash on cards with washed borders. *c.* 14 × 17 in. (36 × 48 cm.)

Preserved together within a paper band inscribed in pen: '7 Drawings by Her Majesty' and 'Queen Charlotte' added in pencil. One of a pair of drawings is clearly by the Instructor entirely or almost entirely; the copy of it shews the figures, architecture, etc., schematically outlined for the pupil to follow as far as possible in detail. The other five drawings illustrate the same process of instruction.

The portfolio now containing these drawings is uniform with, but somewhat larger than, that mentioned above under King George III (Nos. 2 and 3). It is lettered 'Drawings by the Princes & Princesses', and its brown leaves, having rotted, have been removed at some date. Glover's memorandum of August 26, 1828, mentions the Queen's drawings separately (Inventory 'A', p. 172).

THE PRINCESS ROYAL, CHARLOTTE AUGUSTA MATILDA (1766–1828)

7. An Album lettered 'Princess Royal's Drawings and Etchings' holds twenty-two large botanical drawings in pen and watercolours, three figure subjects in brown wash, three ornamental flower drawings in pen, five miscellaneous drawings and several etchings. There are now, also, loose in the volume two ornamental floral subjects in watercolour, two pencil flower drawings, one dated 1777, and a sheet of heads and features in pen dated 1793. Most of the drawings are signed in full and inscribed with dates (from 1782 to 1784) and 'Windsor'.

The etchings include one in reverse after a drawing by Giulio Clovio in the Royal Collection (Popham, *Italian Drawings at Windsor*, No. 243), and are dated 1785.

According to information kindly supplied by Mr. W. Blunt, some of the drawings of flowers appear to be copied from the *Illustratio Systematis Sexualis Linnaei* (1777) of John Miller or Müller.

Removed from Buckingham Palace in 1828 (Inventory 'A', p. 172).

A series of twenty-four drawings of flowers and foliage by the Princess Royal in pen and ink and monochrome wash are also preserved at Windsor Castle. They were transferred from Frogmore in 1924.

PRINCE EDWARD, DUKE OF KENT (1767–1820)

8. THREE SEASCAPES

Watercolour. 6¾ × 9½ in. (17.1 × 24.1 cm.)

Uniformly inscribed on the washed mounts: Edward. Feby. 1781.

In Queen Charlotte's portfolio (see on No. 6).

9. LANDSCAPE

Watercolour. Oval, 9¼ × 11¾ in. (23.5 × 29.8 cm.)

Inscribed on washed mount: Edward fecit 1784.

From Queen Charlotte's portfolio (see on No. 6).

These drawings were produced at the time when Alexander Cozens was instructing the young Princes. This was exhibited at the Exhibition of Alexander Cozens' drawings at Sheffield and at the Tate Gallery, 1946, as an example of his method of instruction and as showing his handling, especially in the foliage and distant hills.

10. MOUNTAIN LANDSCAPE with bridge and cottage.

Watercolour and pen over pencil outlines. $14\frac{1}{2} \times 21\frac{1}{2}$ in. (36.8×54.6 cm.) Inscribed on washed mount: E.p. delineavit May 16th 1784.

Also from Queen Charlotte's portfolio (see on No. 6). The Instructor has more successfully disguised his assistance. An etching of Kew Green signed Edward and dated 1785 is also preserved in the Royal Library.

PRINCESS AUGUSTA SOPHIA (1768–1840),
Second daughter of King George III

11. A LANDSCAPE

Pen and grey wash. Oval, *c.* 9×12 in. (23×30 cm.)
(17620)

Inscribed on the washed mount: Princess Augusta Sophia delin. Oct. 1778.
Purchased by H.M. Queen Mary and presented by her to the Royal Library in 1932.

12. A LADY, head and shoulders.

Black and red chalk, within oval. $15 \times 9\frac{1}{2}$ in. (38.1×24.1 cm.)
Signed: Augusta Sophia August 4th 1781.
In Queen Charlotte's portfolio (see on No. 6).
The Royal Library also contains several etchings after old masters (including two drawings by Leonardo da Vinci in the Royal collection etched in reverse) by Princess Augusta, initialled with monogram and dated 1785.

13. A PEASANT GIRL AND BOY (AFTER PIAZZETTA)

Black and white chalk on brown paper, numbered 924 on back in pencil, much stained by damp. $16\frac{1}{8} \times 12\frac{1}{2}$ in. (41×31.5 cm.)
Signed in ink: Augusta Sophia September 1786.
The drawing by Piazzetta is No. 0770 in the Royal Collection.
From Buckingham Palace, No. 924, in (1876) Inventory. Transferred to the Royal Library in 1903. The presence of this and the following drawing in Queen Charlotte's portfolio proves that additions have been made to its contents at a recent date.

14. A GEOMETER (AFTER PIAZZETTA)

Black and white chalk on brown paper. Numbered 934 on the back in pencil. $15\frac{1}{4} \times 12\frac{1}{4}$ in. (36.6×29.5 cm.)
The original drawing by Piazzetta is No. 0757 in the Royal Library; a similar copy after another drawing by Piazzetta (No. 01252) in the Royal Library is in the collection of Sir Robert Witt.
From Buckingham Palace (Number 934 in the 1876 Inventory), where, as a wormhole and a clear impression of the wood of a backboard shew, it had been framed for many years.

PRINCESS ELIZABETH (1770–1840),
Third daughter of King George III

15. Fifty-one vignette compositions of landscape, mainly single buildings, ruins or objects among foliage. *Figure 4*
Grey wash, uniformly mounted on cards.

Fig. 4. Princess Elizabeth: Composition (Cat. No. 15)

Preserved within a band inscribed 'Fifty-one Drawings by Her Royal Highness the Princess Elizabeth' in Queen Charlotte's portfolio mentioned above (No. 6).

THE PRINCES ERNEST AUGUSTUS
(1771–1851)

AUGUSTUS FREDERICK (1773–1843)

ADOLPHUS FREDERICK (1774–1850)
AND ANOTHER

16. Queen Charlotte's portfolio (see on No. 6) contains four gouache drawings mounted on thick boards, three of which ($10\frac{3}{4} \times 14\frac{5}{8}$ in.—27.3×37.1 cm.) are apparently after Paul Sandby, and dated at the back, December 8th 1780, The first, a view of Windsor town and Castle, so inscribed. is similar to the view in the Royal Collection, *Sandby* No. 79, q.v. It is inscribed as the work of His Royal Highness Prince Ernest Augustus, aged 9 years and a $\frac{1}{2}$. The second is inscribed: 'A View of St. Leonard's Hill near Windsor— His Royal Highness Prince Augustus Frederick aged 7 years and $\frac{3}{4}$'; and the third: 'His Royal Highness Prince Adolphus Frederick aged 6 years and $\frac{3}{4}$ a View of a Farm near Windsor'.

Three similar gouaches inscribed at the back with the names of the three younger princes, two of them dated January 26 '81, similar but less Sandby-like in character and without titles, are in the possession of Mr. G. J. K. Little, C.B.E., to whom they have descended with other Royal relics from Robert Hownham, successively Page of the Presence and Page of the Back Stairs from 1784 to 1800.

The fourth gouache is considerably smaller, measuring $6\frac{1}{2} \times 9\frac{1}{2}$ in. (16.5×24.1 cm.), in a somewhat different, drier technique, and is differently inscribed at the back: 'Painted by Prince Ernest and given by him to the P. of Wales 1771'. The subject appears to be the Abbot's kitchen at Glastonbury, but the artist is difficult to identify. The only Prince Ernest other than the prince mentioned above (who was under one year of age at that date) was the younger brother of Queen Charlotte.

It seems improbable that these four gouaches were in the portfolio when it was in Queen Charlotte's possession, but the three first-named at any rate suggest that on this occasion the younger princes received some instruction from Paul Sandby. Whoever he was, the instructor must have completed the drawings.

ROBERT ADAM (1728–1792)

17. A CASTELLATED SINGLE-ARCH BRIDGE OVER A
RIVER AT THE EDGE OF A PARK   *Plate* 24

Watercolour. 16½ × 22 in. (42 × 56 cm.)   (17299)
Acquired 1944.

For similar elaborate inventions by Adam *cf. Architectural
Review*, lvii., 1925, Nos. 338–342 (Bolton); and *Burlington
Magazine*, lxxx., No. 468, March 1942 (Oppé).

ROBERT ADAM AND (?) G. B. CIPRIANI

THE ILLUMINATIONS AT BUCKINGHAM HOUSE FOR THE
KING'S BIRTHDAY, 1763.

18. GENERAL DESIGN OF A TRANSPARENT ILLUMINA-
TION, proposed to have been Executed in the Queens
Garden in Honour of His Majesty's Birthday, The 4th June
1763.   *Plate* 25

Pen and watercolour; pinholes for compass and at key
points. 18⅞ × 49⅜ in. (48 × 125 cm.)   (17643A)

Signed: Robert Adam Architect, at foot left; the title, as
given, written along the top. A scale of feet below.

19. DESIGN OF A TRANSPARENT ILLUMINATION Ordered
By The Queen and Executed in Honour of His Majestys'
Birth Day The 4th June 1763.

Pen and watercolour; pinholes for compass. 18⅞ × 38¾ in.
(48 × 98.4 cm.)   (17643B)

The title, as given, signature, etc., as in the preceding.

20. DESIGN OF A BRIDGE ILLUMINATED IN HONOUR
OF HIS MAJESTY'S BIRTH DAY, The 4th June 1763. By
Order of Her Majesty.

Pen and watercolour; pinholes throughout. 18⅞ × 25¼ in.
(48 × 63.5 cm.)   (17643C)

The title, as given, signature, etc., as in the preceding.

These three designs are connected with an incident which
is fully described in the *Gentleman's Magazine* of June 1763
(Vol. xxxiii., p. 311) and in Watkins: *Memoirs of Queen
Charlotte* (1819, pp. 171–2). The Queen is said to have prepared the illumination as a surprise for the King, who for
that reason was kept at St. James's Palace from Saturday
the 4th, his birthday, until Monday the 6th, and there
entertained by the attendance at court of ladies in the
masquerade costumes prepared for a grand ball given by
the Duke of Richmond on that night. Accordingly the King
knew nothing of the preparations at Buckingham House
until the shutters were suddenly thrown back on his arrival
at 10 o'clock.

The abbreviated design (No. 19) consisting only of three
painted pavilions connected by statues with garlands is
explicitly described as having been carried out. A slighter
design for the full proposal (No. 18) is at the Soane Museum
(Adam Collection, Vol. 49, No. 1). It contains no statues
in the colonnade and several small variations which show
that it, not the example in the Royal Library, was used for
the reconstruction of the subject, with background and
figures, engraved by D. Cunego after Adam, Plate 5 of the
Works (reproduced A. T. Bolton, *The Architecture of Robert and
James Adam*, Vol. i., p. 39; see also p. 48). The design is
correctly stated in the engraving to have been carried out
only in part; but the year is wrongly given as 1762. The
drawing for this plate and a companion, both attributed to
Clérisseau and Zucchi, were exhibited in the collection of
Mr. Leslie Wright at the Royal Academy in October 1949,
Nos. 96 and 100.

The bridge (No. 20) is shown through the arch on the
extreme right of No. 18 with a cupola, etc., surmounting it.
The title suggests that it was actually executed in the
simpler form here shewn.

The designs, entered as four in number in 'Inventory A',
p. 170 (1816), which may have been sent to the Queen by
Adam to commemorate the event can scarcely be attributed
to his own hand. The figure subjects are in the manner of
Cipriani and may well have been executed by him. The
allegory in the centre differs considerably as between No. 18
and No. 19, and still more from the example at the Soane
Museum, which is followed in the engraving. It is scarcely
necessary to say that the allegories celebrated the Peace and
the Nation's Victories as well as the King's birthday.

DAVID ALLAN (1744–1796)

These ten drawings by David Allan were acquired by the
Prince Regent from Colnaghi on 23rd March 1812 for
30 gns. (Archives Invoice 27835, which gives details).
Lot 49 on the second day of the second Paul Sandby sale
on the previous March 17, consisted of 'Eleven capital
drawings by D. Allan, Views in Rome during the Carnival
with many Humourous figures', bt. Colnaghi £8 12s. od.
It is not clear what happened to the eleventh drawing;
perhaps the number was a misprint.

The nine drawings which retain their margins all bear
Colnaghi's pencil inscription: 'Original Drawing by Allan
from Mr. Sandby's Collection'.

Four of the drawings were engraved by Sandby in aquatint
in 1780, and were accompanied, according to Allan
Cunningham, *Lives*, 1846 (vi., p. 28), by a printed description. The engravings are in reverse, thus restoring the
architecture, etc., to their proper positions. The architecture
and several details shew that the remainder of the drawings
were also made for reversal. The drawings do not bear Paul
Sandby's mark. Probably they were never his property, but
were entrusted to him for engraving, and as this was never
fully carried out, were overlooked in the studio. This might
also account for the damage which they have sustained.

David Allan exhibited at the Royal Academy 1779 (No. 4)
'Five drawings representing the Amusements, Manners etc.
of the Carnival at Rome'.

21. THE OPENING OF THE CARNIVAL. The Obelisk
near the Porta del Popolo, Rome.

Pen and brown wash, some corrections in pencil, with
washed mount at foot. 14⅞ × 21 in. (36.8 × 53.4 cm.)
                                              (13351)

Three figures on the left are on two pieces of superimposed
paper, the wash a different colour. Some perspective lines
in pencil.

Inscribed by the artist on the border at foot left: 'Da. Allan
invt. et del Rome 1775', and the title, as given, on a label
stuck on within ornaments.

Engraved in reverse by Paul Sandby, 1780, in aquatint.
Though architecture, inscriptions, etc., have been drawn
for reversal, the dancers, drivers and musicians become
left-handed in the engraving. 'Barbati' on one of the
banners is replaced by 'Cavalli'. A label with 'Confetti' is
added to a basket, and more incidents are introduced in the
background.

22. THE ROMANS POLITE TO STRANGERS. Palazzo Rus-
poli al Corso Rome.

Pen and brown wash within washed mount. 15⅛ × 21⅛ in.
(38.5 × 53.8 cm.)   (13358)

Signed (cursive): D. Allan del. The title, as given, within a
pencil cartouche below.

Engraved in reverse as the preceding. The various legends in the drawing are not in reverse, but reversal is shown to be intended by the right hands used in riding, etc. There are several minor changes in the engraving, and many more onlookers placed in the windows.

23. THE HORSE RACE AT ROME DURING THE CARNIVAL. Piazza del Popolo.

Pen and brown wash over red chalk, in washed border. Considerably weakened by fading or more probably cleaning. 15⅛ × 20⅝ in. (38.3 × 52.4 cm.) (13359)

The horses in mid-distance are on a superimposed piece of paper. Signed: D. Allan Del, almost obliterated by washing. The title, as given, in open pencil on a plain cartouche.
Engraved in reverse as the preceding. In architecture, incidents and legends the artist has, in general, kept reversal in mind.

24. THE VICTOR CONDUCTED IN TRIUMPH. Piazza S. Marco.

Pen and brown wash over pencil and red chalk within washed border. The left hand bottom corner on an added piece of paper. 15⅜ × 20¾ in. (39 × 52.6 cm.) (13360)

Somewhat stained and weakened by cleaning.

Signed: D. Allan inv.; the title, as given, in open pencil without cartouche.
Engraved in reverse as the preceding.
In the incidents reversal has not been kept in mind throughout; 'Vittoria' on a banner becomes 'Victoria' in the print.

25. THE ARRIVAL OF A YOUNG TRAVELLER AND HIS SUITE during the Carnival, in Piazza de' Spagna, Rome. *Plate* 26

Pen and brown wash over pencil. Much has been washed out and redrawn largely with darker ink. 15¾ × 21¼ in. (40 × 54 cm.) (13352)

Signed: D. Allan del, almost obliterated. The title, as given, on pen in the washed mount below.
Exhib.: Spring Gardens (Humour Exhibition) 1925, No. 17.
The legends 'Caffe degli Inglesi' on the left, 'Ville de Londres' on the right are not drawn in reverse. The architecture and incidents show that reversal was kept in mind.

26. GALLANTRY & DEVOTION. Piazza dello Rotondo (Pantheon), Rome.

Pen and brown wash over red chalk and pencil, some chinese white oxydised. 15⅛ × 20⅞ in. (38.4 × 53 cm.) (13353)

Signed: D. Allan invt, the title, as given, in pen over pencil on an added slip at the foot.
The architecture and some of the actions are in reverse.

27. PIAZZA NAVONA, ROME. (With groups of priests, mountebanks and charlatans.)

Pen and brown wash, touched with white, in plain border. 14½ × 20⅝ in. (37 × 52.5 cm.) (13355)

Signed: D. Allan invt, the title 'Piazza Navona Rome' in pen over pencil.
The architecture is reversed, the gestures ambidextrous. The legends are not reversed.

28. FRENCH GAIETY AND ITALIAN MAGNIFICENCE, French Academy, Rome. *Plate* 27

Pen and brown wash over some pencil and red chalk, with details in darker ink. 15⅛ × 20⅛ in. (38.5 × 52.2 cm.) (13356)

Signed: D. Allan invt, the title, as given, in pencilled cartouche.
The legends read 'Poema heroica', 'Ce vuole L'Ingenuita et Modestia La Natura et L'Antico', 'De Piles, Du Fresnay, Art of Limning'.
The incidents are clearly drawn for reversal.
In 1775 the French Academy was in the Palazzo Mancini.

29. PIAZZA MONTANARA AT THE THEATRE OF MARCELLUS, ROME *Plate* 28

Pen and brown wash, over pencil, many corrections in stronger ink. 14¼ × 20⅞ in. (36.1 × 53.1 cm.) (13354)

Signed: D. Allan invt, and the title as given in pencil in plain margin below.
The architecture and some incidents are in reverse.

30. THE CARNIVAL AT ROME. MUSICIANS AT THE COLUMN OF MARCUS AURELIUS IN THE CORSO *Plate* 29

Brown and grey washes over pencil and red chalk, some white (blackened). 13⅜ × 20⅜ in. (34 × 51.7 cm.) (13357)

The drawing has been cut close and has suffered considerably from washing and discoloration, but remains the most delicately drawn and one of the best grouped in the series. The architecture and actions are reversed, but not the inscriptions.

WILLIAM ANDERSON (1757–1837)

31. THE BATTLE OF THE NILE, August 1–3, 1798

Four drawings, uniform. Watercolour. 3½ × 10½ in. (8.9 × 26.7 cm.) (Souvenir Album VI, p. 1)

(1) The British Fleet bearing down to the enemy at anchor.
(2) South-west view at 10 p.m. on 1st August.
(3) South-west view on the 2nd August.
(4) West view of the fleet when victory was complete on 3rd August.

Except the first, these drawings agree closely with two series of prints of some three times the size (*c.* 7 × 14½ in.) published respectively in November 1799 and December 1800, and from different plates. (Cust, *Naval Prints*, 1911, Vol. I, No. 134(i) and note.) Each plate of the earlier series, published by G. Riley, 65 Old Bailey, is inscribed 'Finish'd from a Drawing in the possession of Capt. Sir T. B. Thompson by F. Chesham with aquatinta by W. Ellis'. In the later series, 'His Majesty' is substituted for 'Capt. Sir T. B. Thompson', 'painted by W. Anderson' is added after the name Ellis, and the publisher is given as Alexander Riley, 82 Pall Mall. Both sets of prints are dedicated to the King by George Riley.
A manuscript note in the Royal Library copy of Cust's *Naval Prints* states that the four drawings were presented to King George III 'by the artist George Riley'. It is not known from what this was derived by Miss Heaton-Smith, Assistant Librarian 1905–1916.
The first drawing differs considerably from the prints inasmuch as in it the *Culloden* is not shown, the brig *Mutine* is in the foreground, and the English ships sailing in to attack are viewed from the port and not the starboard quarter. Unfortunately the original sketch of this subject by Col. Walter Fawkes, who gave Anderson his information, is not among his sketches of the battle preserved in a notebook of Anderson's, as are the three others (L. Paul, *The Mariners' Mirror*, IV, p. 266). In view of this difference, that of the size and the use of the word 'painted' in the inscriptions of the 1800 series it seems probable that both prints and drawings were reduced from some common originals in oil which have now disappeared.

The subject of the second drawing was used as part of the embellishments to a portrait of Nelson published by G. Riley, 20th February 1799 (O'Donoghue, Vol. III, p. 315, No. 17). The engraving follows the drawing in making the mistake of showing the English ships with the ensign on a staff instead of at the mizzen peak. The two sets of prints published in November 1799 and December 1800 correct this mistake.

See also drawings signed by Coote Manningham (Nos. 427 to 431), which may also be by Anderson.

JOHN AUGUSTUS ATKINSON (1775–after 1831)

Several watercolours and off-prints of military scenes, some signed, in Volume IV of Military Drawings (Nos. 16515–16517, 16420–16424, 16473, pp. 56, 57, 59, 60, 61, and 77 *verso*); also a single sheet with two semi-caricature figures of soldiers on p. 144, Vol. I of the Dighton drawings.

HENEAGE FINCH, FOURTH EARL OF AYLESFORD (1751–1812)

32. VIEWS ON THE MEDWAY NEAR ROCHESTER

Plates 30 and 31

An album ($11\frac{1}{4} \times 17\frac{3}{4}$ in.—28.6 × 45.1 cm.) containing 14 sketches, in brown and grey washes with a little colour, of riverside scenes, inscribed on the first page in Queen Charlotte's handwriting, 'Views taken by the Earl of Aylesford of the Country round Rochester and given to me by Him on the 19th June 1809'. The volume is uniform, except for the absence of the coat-of-arms on the covers, with those at Packington described in the *Print Collectors' Quarterly*, Vol. XI, No. 3, October 1924, and another, once in the Benno Geiger collection, the contents of which were dispersed under the names of Francia and Edridge. Each drawing is surrounded by a washed mount. It is not clear why this volume, which is not mentioned in any of the old inventories, escaped inclusion in the sale of Queen Charlotte's personal property in 1819.

The fourth Earl, distinguished, *inter alia*, as an etcher, draughtsman and collector, was Lord of the Bedchamber 1777–1783 and Lord Steward of the Household 1804–1812. Aylesford, the then family estate, is near the Medway.

FRANCIS BARLOW, Manner of

33. A HUNTING ACCIDENT

Pencil, pen with black ink, brown wash, heightened with white. $6\frac{3}{8} \times 9\frac{1}{2}$ in. (16.1 × 24.2 cm.)   (17239)

Known traditionally as 'King Charles II hunting with the Duchess of Portsmouth', this is presumably the 'drawing King Charles with the Duchess of Portsmouth Hunting' which was bought for the Prince Regent from Colnaghi on April 26, 1813 for £1 11s. 6d. (Archives Invoice 27842). An erased and undecipherable inscription at the foot of the drawing may be Flemish.

REV. WILLIAM HENRY BARNARD

(1769–1818)

William Henry Barnard, born 1769, son of the Rev. Henry Barnard, grandson of William Barnard, Bishop of Londonderry (1697–1768). Ensign in the Fifteenth (Yorkshire East Riding) Regiment from 1785 to 1789; took Holy Orders 1793; friend and pupil of J. B. Malchair, the Oxford drawing master. Rector of Marsh Gibbon and Water Stratford, Bucks. Died 1818.

34. WINDSOR CASTLE AND SURROUNDING COUNTRY FROM ST. LEONARD'S HILL

Pen over pencil on joined paper. $3\frac{7}{8} \times 19$ in. (9.8 × 48.2 cm.)   (17560)

On the back of an account from F. Stracy, Grocer to Their Majesties, Castle St., Windsor, April, May & June 1805 to the Rev. Mr. Hays.

Inscribed: 'Windsor Castle from St. Leonard's Hill' (partly cut off).

Acquired with the two following in 1947 from Walker's Gallery from among a large series of Barnard's drawings sold at Sotheby's, January 29, 1947, Lot 44.

35. WINDSOR CASTLE FROM THE NORTH, 1805

Pen over pencil. $5\frac{7}{8} \times 12\frac{5}{8}$ in. (15 × 32 cm.)   (17561)

Inscribed: 'Windsor from Farnham July 4th (or 5th) 1805.'

36. THE SAME, FROM NEARER

Pen over pencil. $12\frac{1}{8} \times 19$ in. (30.8 × 48.4 cm.) (17562)

BERNARD BARON (*c.* 1700–1766)

37. AFTER J. ADOLPH: KING GEORGE III WHEN PRINCE OF WALES, whole length to right on rearing horse, by the seashore. The Garter ribbon on the right shoulder.

Black and red chalk and stump, squared in red. 22 × 18 in. (55.9 × 45.8 cm.)   (13249)

Identical with the line engraving of 1755 (O'Donoghue, Vol. II, p. 300, No. 4), but in reverse.

38. AFTER VANLOO: FREDERICK LEWIS, PRINCE OF WALES, whole length, to left, standing.

Sanguine. $20\frac{3}{4} \times 14\frac{5}{8}$ in. (52.7 × 37 cm.)   (13251)

Drawing for, or after, the line engraving of 1753 (O'Donogue, Vol. II, p. 257, No. 24) in the same direction.

39. AFTER VANLOO: AUGUSTA, PRINCESS OF WALES, whole length, standing, full face.

Sanguine. $20\frac{5}{8} \times 14\frac{3}{4}$ in. (52.6 × 30.2 cm.)   (13252)

A pencil inscription on the modern mount, presumably copied from the back of an old mount, reads: 'Drawn and presented to H.R.H. by B. Baron May 20th 1756. The original drawing is in the Earl of Bath's possession'.

Drawing for, or after, the line engraving of 1753 (O'Donoghue, Vol. I, p. 91, No. 11) in the same direction.

See also Nos. 362 and 363 (after Hogarth).

GEORGE BARRET (*c.* 1767–1842)

40. CLASSICAL LANDSCAPE, A CASTLE WITH A CHASM

Watercolour, almost monochrome, damaged. $6\frac{1}{2} \times 10\frac{3}{8}$ in. (17.6 × 26.3 cm.)   (13374)

41. VIEW ON THE COAST SEEN THROUGH A WINDOW

Plate 32

Watercolour; a beginning. $15\frac{3}{4} \times 10\frac{1}{4}$ in. (40 × 26 cm.)   (13371)

An early drawing, probably a view in the Isle of Wight.

42. MOUNTAIN LANDSCAPE WITH STONE FOOT-BRIDGE

Watercolour. $6\frac{1}{8} \times 8\frac{7}{8}$ in. (15.4 × 22.4 cm.)   (13372)

43. LANDSCAPE COMPOSITION, a meadow with foot-bridge over a stream.

Watercolour, unfinished. $6\frac{1}{8} \times 8\frac{3}{4}$ in. (15.4 × 22.4 cm.)   (13373)

Uniform with the preceding; they are probably both instructional drawings, for laying washes.

JOSEPH CHARLES BARROW (fl. 1790–1802)

44. WEST VIEW OF TARBERT, upon the River Shannon, in the County of Kerry, Ireland, the Seat of Sir Edward Leslie, Bart.

Watercolour, in deep black border. $14\frac{7}{8} \times 23\frac{1}{2}$ in. (37.7 × 59.6 cm.)   (17044)

Signed: J. C. Barrow 1795.

The title, as given, inscribed on the back in ink; a pencil inscription erased.

45. EAST VIEW OF TARBERT, etc.

Companion to the preceding, and uniform with it in size, border, signature, inscription and erasure.   (17045)

46. VETERINARY COLLEGE, ST. PANCRAS

Grey wash; on card, with margin. $4\frac{1}{4} \times 6$ in. (10.6 × 15.2 cm.)   (17617)

Signed in margin: Barrow Delin. Inscribed in the large Colnaghi hand at back, 'Veterinary College, Drawing, 7/6', the price almost erased.

Acquired by the Prince of Wales from Colnaghi on January 13, 1800, for 7/6 (Archives Invoice 27117).

FRANCESCO BARTOLOZZI (1725–1815)

47. DR. ARNE, half length standing to right in profile, his hands on a keyboard, on which is a lighted candle.   *Plate* 39

Pencil, an accidental rubbing of red chalk. Illegible words, in ink, on the back, stuck down. $7\frac{7}{8} \times 6$ in. (20.1 × 15.2 cm.)   (13296)

Exhib.: B.F.A.C. 1931–1932, No. 180. R.A. (British Art) 1934, No. 589 (1123).

Reprod.: *Connoisseur*, XCII, August, 1933, p. 77.

Acquired by King George IV from Colnaghi, 'Dr Arne a Drawing by Bartolozzi', on May 7, 1821, for £1 1s. (Archives Invoice 28321).

Three prints derive from this drawing:

(1) In the same direction in stipple (red, black and in colours), published May 10, 1782 by Wm. Humphrey without name of engraver and with the ambiguous inscription, 'Done from an original sketch by F. Bartolozzi' (B.M. Sat. 8240). Engraved by Gillray after Bartolozzi according to Wright-Grego, *Gillray*, p. 372, followed by Thieme Becker; by Bartolozzi after Loutherbourg according to *Library of Fine Arts*, IV (1832), p. 7.

(2) Etched, in reverse, without imprint; B.M. Sat. 8240(a), and O'Donoghue, Vol. I, p. 73, No. 4, as by W. N. Gardiner after J. Nixon, presumably following a pencil inscription on an example in Anderdon's *Collectanea* at the British Museum. Calabi No. 749 seems to confuse this with No. 1.

(3) Etching, coarsely elaborated, nearly full length to right with accessories, an organ stool, etc.; no imprint but entitled 'Harmony and Sentiment', and with four lines of verse.

A red and black chalk drawing at Cambridge is intermediate between the present drawing and the engraving (1). Certain details which are improved in it are further elaborated in the print, e.g., the instrument, left sleeve and shadow, while others, candle and buttonholes on sleeve, which it has in common with the pencil drawing, are absent from the print. These careless omissions together with the improvement may confirm the attribution of the engraving to Gillray.

Fig. 5. Engraving after P. L. Ghezzi: Filippo San Felice (cf. Cat. No. 47)

Though no doubt a portrait of Arne, the drawing seems to have been inspired by the caricature by Ghezzi of Filippo San Felice (Vatican Library, Ottabuoni MSS 3115) engraved in 1758 by Martin Tusscher as title page or frontispiece to a collection of six caricatures (*Figure* 5).

48. THE IMPRISONMENT OF MARIE ANTOINETTE

Black and red chalk. $6\frac{5}{8} \times 22$ in. (42.4 × 55.8 cm.)   (13305)

Two figures lightly repeated below.

The remains of an old pencil inscription, 'Original by Bartolozzi', at foot of drawing.

Except the heads and certain details, as weak and mechanical in execution as it is in invention.

Presumably the 'Drawing of the Queen of France forced into Prison' by Bartolozzi, bought by the Prince of Wales from Colnaghi on January 17, 1803 for £4 4s. (Archives Invoice 27216).

49. AN ENGLISH OFFICER (? GENERAL HUTCHINSON), head and shoulders, facing half right, his right hand on the hilt of his sword.

Black and red chalk. $13\frac{3}{8} \times 9\frac{3}{4}$ in. (34 × 24.8 cm.)   (13303)

Inscribed in pencil in the margin below the drawing, 'F. Bartolozzi R.A. Fecit' in the Colnaghi hand.

'A Drawing of a Port. of Genl. Hutchinson by Bartolozzi' was bought by the Prince of Wales from Colnaghi on July 23, 1803, for £4 4s. (Archives Invoice 27239), and is assumed to be this drawing. It may be a replica of the 'crayon drawing in the possession of the Earl of Donoughmore' from which Goss engraved the mezzotint portrait of Lord Hutchinson (1757–1832), published June 1, 1802 (O'Donoghue, Vol. II, p. 71, No. 3).

50. CIPRIANI PAINTING

Pencil. $7\frac{7}{8} \times 5\frac{7}{8}$ in. (20 × 14.8 cm.)   (13295)

Reprod.: *Connoisseur* XCII, August, 1933, p. 76.

See on No. 125.

51. ITALIAN PEASANT DANCE

Pencil and watercolour. $14 \times 16\frac{7}{8}$ in. (35.5 × 42.6 cm.)

    (13306)

Inscribed in the large Colnaghi hand 'Original by F. Bartolozzi R.A.'

Probably the 'Drawing of Rural Dancing by Bartolozzi', bought on August 18th 1803 by the Prince of Wales for £5 5s. with the following two drawings and No. 105 (Bunbury, *q.v.*) (Archives Invoice 27421).

52. ANGELICA AND MEDOR

Black pencil and red chalk. $13\frac{1}{2} \times 9\frac{1}{8}$ in. (34.4 × 23.1 cm.)

    (13301)

Probably the drawing by Bartolozzi with this title but reading 'Medora', bought by the Prince of Wales for £4 4s., with the preceding.

53. MRS. BILLINGTON, bust facing half right.

Red chalk, a little black; an erased pencil inscription at foot. $6\frac{5}{8} \times 5\frac{1}{8}$ in. (17 × 13 cm.)   (13299)

Presumably the 'drawing of Mrs. Billington' bought by the Prince of Wales for 10/6 with the preceding, etc.; the name is on the present (modern) mount.

54. A ROMAN LADY WITH A BASKET OF FLOWERS

Red and black chalk on toned paper. $10\frac{1}{2} \times 6\frac{7}{8}$ in. (29 × 17.2 cm.)   (13298)

55. LADY DIANA BEAUCLERK, head and shoulders, facing three-quarters right.

Black and red chalks. Feigned oval, $9\frac{1}{4} \times 7\frac{5}{8}$ in. (23.6 × 19.3 cm.)   (13302)

Seems to bear no resemblance to the portrait by Reynolds of 1764–1765 at Caen Wood of Lady Diana Beauclerk (1734–1808).

56. ST. MATTHEW AND THE ANGEL (after Guercino).

Red chalk. $10\frac{7}{8} \times 15\frac{3}{4}$ in. (27.8 × 40 cm.)   (2516)

Entered in the George III catalogue (Inventory 'A,' p. 62) among the drawings by Guercino as by Bartolozzi 'from one at Bologna that the family could not then dispose of'. Engraved by Bartolozzi. Calabi No. 2146.

57. CUPID ASLEEP (after Guido)

Red chalk. $11\frac{3}{8} \times 13\frac{7}{8}$ in. (29 × 35.9 cm.)   (13300)

BARTOLOZZI, ascribed to

58. TWO YOUNG GIRLS, half length standing.

Coloured crayons. Oval, $5\frac{3}{4} \times 4\frac{5}{8}$ in. (13.5 × 11.8 cm.)

    (13297)

Would appear to be subsequent to 1802, the date of Bartolozzi's leaving England.

MARY BEALE (1632–1697)

59. A LEATHER-WORKER (?), seated to left with a board on his knee and a knife in his left hand.

Red chalk. $9\frac{7}{8} \times 7\frac{7}{8}$ in. (25 × 19.8 cm.)   (13375)

The letter 'B' in pencil in top left corner.

Exhib.: B.F.A.C. 1938, No. 52, together with another example (from the collection of Sir Robert Witt, having '50' in top left corner) so similar even in details which would *prima facie* appear accidental as to suggest that both are copies from some lost original or, judging from the knife in the left hand, that both have been worked up upon offsets from a lost original.

After LADY DIANA BEAUCLERK (1734–1808)

60. GEORGIANA SPENCER, DUCHESS OF DEVONSHIRE, half length, facing left, seated at window, a book in her left hand.

Watercolour, mainly brown, on old washed mount. $6\frac{1}{2} \times 7$ in. (15.8 × 17.6 cm.)   (13567)

Inscribed in pencil on the old mount in the large Colnaghi hand, 'Lady Georgina (*sic*) Spencer Duchess of Devonshire Drawn by Lady Diana Beauclerk'. Acquired by the Prince Regent with this title from Colnaghi on August 6, 1819, for £5 5s. (Archives Invoice 28219).

The general clumsiness of the drawing and its differences from the engravings by Bartolozzi and others, viz., the tree with branches instead of foliage only, the hand half concealed within the open book, the absence of the pillar on the right, all indicate a copy rather than the original drawing.

Georgiana (Spencer), 1757–1806, first wife of the 5th Duke of Devonshire.

LOUIS BÉLANGER (1736–1816)

61. THE REBUILDING OF CARLTON HOUSE

Pencil, pen and watercolour within washed and ruled border. A rough scale at foot. $12\frac{1}{4} \times 17\frac{1}{4}$ in. (31.8 × 44.3 cm.)   (13030)

Recognized by Mr. H. Phillips as almost identical with a drawing in the Crace Collection at the British Museum (L.B. 5, reproduced *Survey of London*, Vol. 20, pl. 56) which is described by William Capon as a copy made by him from a drawing by L. Bélanger of 1790. The present drawing had already been judged to be by a French hand, and may safely be regarded, if not as the drawing copied by Capon, as either the sketch by Bélanger upon which it was based or as an unfinished replica. The distant view of Westminster over the housetops was misunderstood by Capon.

Other drawings of English scenes by L. Bélanger in the Royal Library are *Catalogue of French Drawings*, Nos. 309 and 310. No. 309 was engraved, circular, by L. Guyot in 1792. It was bought by the Prince of Wales from Colnaghi on October 31, 1808, for £2 2s. (Archives Invoice 27743).

JOHN HODGES BENWELL (1764–1785)

62. A COURT CANDIDATE IN DISTRESS. (The Westminster Election, 1784.)

Pen and black ink over slight pencil within ruled border. $10 \times 13\frac{1}{8}$ in. (25.2 × 33.5 cm.)   (17649)

Signed in capitals J. H. BENWELL fecit, and inscribed with the title as given and a wrong date, 1782. 1/6 in red chalk on the back. No legends.

Engraved, in reverse, anonymously, April 20, 1784; an impression at the Guildhall is described by Mrs. George, B.M. Sat. VI, p. 104.

Fig. 6. Blake: The spirit of a just man newly departed
(Cat. No. 64)

Fig. 7. Blake: Joseph discovering himself (Cat. No. 65)

WILLIAM BLAKE (1757–1827)

63. THE ASSUMPTION   *Frontispiece*

Pen and watercolour over pencil. 15⅞ × 10⅜ in. (40.2 × 26.7 cm.)   (13379)

Signed: W.B. inv. 1806, at foot.
Colls.: Butts, Fuller, Richard Fisher.
Lit.: Gilchrist (1880), ii, 244, No. 220.
Exhib.: B.F.A.C. 1876, No. 99 (Fisher); B.F.A.C. 1927, No. 36, with reproduction; R.A. (British Art), 1934, No. 707 (1304); British Council, 1947, Paris, etc.

64. 'THE SPIRIT OF A JUST MAN NEWLY DEPARTED APPEARING TO HIS MOURNING FAMILY'   *Figure* 6

Pen and grey wash. 13 × 19 in. (33 × 48.3 cm.) (13598)
The title, as given, inscribed at foot.

65. *Recto:* JOSEPH DISCOVERING HIMSELF; THE BRETHREN ALARMED   *Figure* 7

Verso: BENJAMIN ACCEPTED AS A HOSTAGE
                                                   Figure 8

Pen and grey wash. 13¼ × 17⅞ in. (33.5 × 45.5 cm.)
                                                   (13599)

The subjects communicated by Mr. Geoffrey Keynes as identified by Mr. Joseph Wicksteed.

66. 'HELL BENEATH IS MOVED FOR THEE, TO MEET THEE AT THY COMING – ISAIAH' (xiv. 9)   *Figure* 9

Pen and grey wash on toned paper. 14⅞ × 17 in. (36 × 43.2 cm.)   (13600)

The title, as given, at foot right, in pen, as on No. 64.
These three drawings were identified by Mr. Geoffrey Keynes in April, 1942, as together forming Lot 166 in the Frederick Tatham sale at Sotheby's, April 29, 1862. They were then bought by Richard Fisher for 10/- and no doubt reached the Royal Library with No. 63.

JOHN BOADEN (1839)

67. THE EMPEROR ALEXANDER I OF RUSSIA, bust, profile to left.

Pencil. 7¼ × 5¼ in. (18.3 × 13.3 cm.)   (14209)

Signed: Drawn by John Boaden 1814.

Engraved by C. Picart, 1814.

Perhaps the 'Drawing Profile Empr. Alexand' bought by the Prince Regent, October 3, 1814, from Colnaghi for £4 4s. (Archives Invoice 28023).

Fig. 8. Blake: Benjamin accepted as a hostage (Cat. No. 65 *v.*)

Fig. 9. Blake: 'Hell beneath is moved for thee' (Cat. No. 66)

68. MISS BOADEN, half length, full face.
Black, brown and red chalk. 16⅞ × 12½ in. (42.6 × 31.7 cm.)   (13382)
Signed: Drawn by John Boaden, Jan. (or June ?) 1810.

69. PORTRAIT OF A LADY IN COURT DRESS, half length, head inclined to left.
Black chalk, some touches of white. 16½ × 12⅛ in. (42.5 × 30.8 cm.)   (13380)
Signed: John Boaden delt. 1818.

70. THE SAME, dress and ornaments altered.
Black chalk, heightened with white. 13⅞ × 11¼ in. (35 × 28.7 cm.)   (13381)
Signature and date as on the preceding.
Queen Victoria at the age of 14 recorded in her Diary (February 1, 1833) her admiration for Boaden's 'Amy Robsart' at the British Institution.

LOUIS PHILIPPE BOITARD (fl. c. 1738–1760)

71. A TAILOR'S SHOP. A fitting in the foreground; beyond, the workers sitting cross-legged on a window-counter. Ornamental frame with cartouche.   *Plate 33*
Pencil, pen, brown and grey wash. 8⅛ × 11¾ in. (20.7 × 29.6 cm.)   (13279)
The inscription 'Gravelot', in brown ink, smudged, seems to be an early attempt at a 'signature'.
Drawing for the engraving, in reverse, by Bickham after Boitard, 'The Merchant Taylors', of June 29, 1749. (Kindly communicated by Mr. H. Phillips.)

ROBERT BOWYER (1758–1834). See on No. 716.
(Anon.)

CHARLOTTE BOYLE (1769–1831),
LADY HENRY FITZGERALD,
BARONESS DE ROS

72. CLASSICAL LANDSCAPE COMPOSITION with temple and river, and maidens bringing offerings to a statue of Pomona.   *Figure 10*
Gouache. 22⅛ × 33¼ in. (56.3 × 84.2 cm.)   (17614)
Signed: Charlotte Henry Fitzgerald 1801.
Purchased by H.M. Queen Mary in 1934 at the sale of the effects of Sir Augustus Fitz-George. Formerly the property of H.R.H. George, Duke of Cambridge.

FIG. 10. Charlotte Boyle (Baroness de Ros): Classical Landscape (Cat. No. 72)

Charlotte, daughter of Hon. Robert Boyle (later Boyle-Walsingham, brother of the Earl of Shannon), and of Charlotte Hanbury-Williams (d. 1790), married Lord Henry Fitzgerald, third son of the 1st Duke of Leinster, 1791; claimed and obtained the Barony of Ros in her own right in 1806; died 1831. Her mother, Mrs. Walsingham, the famous 'blue-stocking', had a residence in Windsor Castle for 15 years to 1783 (E. and F. Anson, *Mary Hamilton*, 1925, p. 138), and was 'esteemed by the judges to be the first lady Painter' (*ibid.*, p. 218). According to the same letter-writer the daughter 'is at the age of 14 the most accomplished young Person I ever met with. She is Mistress of Music, & Painting, models in a surprising manner, knows perfectly Modern and Ancient History, French, Italian, Geography, Mathematics, Astronomy, the English Classics, is learning Spanish & Latin, &c. &c.' It is good to know that two days later Miss Boyle 'joined me in the Garden and shewed me her birds, & the nests she had found'. A portrait of the writer by Miss Boyle when 12 years old, made in 1781 at Windsor Castle, is reproduced with these letters.

JOHN BOYNE (c. 1750–1810)

73. SPECIMENS BEFORE A MANAGER
Pencil, pen and watercolour, on washed mount, similar to No. 74. 18 × 14½ in. (46 × 35.7 cm.)   (17651)
Exhib.: B.F.A.C. 1931/32, No. 89.
Signed twice at foot, 'Boyne delt', left; and 'Boyne Int et delt', right. The title, as given, in pencil on the mount. £2 2s. 0d. in pencil on the back.
Acquired by the Prince Regent from Colnaghi, August 16, 1813, for £2 2s. (Archives Invoice 27939), title as given.

74. TRAVELLERS ARRIVING AT AN INN
Pen and watercolour on washed mount, uniform with the preceding. 17¾ × 14½ in. (45.2 × 37 cm.)   (17652)
Signed: J. Boyne delt.

75. VENUS ATTIRED BY THE GRACES
Pen and watercolour with lined and washed mount (in one piece). 17¾ × 14⅛ in. (45.2 × 36 cm.)   (17653)
Signed: J. Boyne Int et delt. The title, as given, in pencil in the Colnaghi hand at foot. £2 2s. 0d. at back in pencil.

76. A MATRON OF ROME BLESSING HER SON on the Morn he attended Augustus as a Volunteer from the Gates of the Capitol to the Temple of Paul.
Pen and watercolour, unmounted. 11¾ × 8⅞ in. (30 × 22.7 cm.)   (17654)
The title, as given, in pencil at top; below, also in pencil, 'My son thy plight I ever shall deplore, Return Victorious or Return no more,' the latter over an erasure, both in the artist's hand.

77. MISS GEORGE AND MR. EDWIN in the Characters of Wawsky & Trudge in 'Inkle and Yarico'.
Pen and watercolour. 7⅞ × 5¼ in. (20 × 13.2 cm.) (17655)
Inscribed by the artist in ink on the back with the title, as given, and 'Drawn by J. Boyne'; both repeated on the front in pencil.
Colman's opera 'Incle and Yarico' was produced at the Haymarket, August 4, 1787.

78. EDWIN THE ACTOR, HOLDING A SWORD IN BOTH HANDS

Pencil, pen and watercolour, on lined and washed card. 7⅞ × 5¼ in. (20 × 13.5 cm.)   (17656)

Without signature or title but clearly by the same hand and after the same model as No. 77.

79. LOVERS VOWS

Pencil, watercolour and some gouache; on the reverse a careful pencil tracing incised with stylus. 7¾ × 5⅛ in. (19.8 × 13 cm.)   (17657)

The title in pencil, apparently in Boyne's hand, at foot over an erasure which seems to read 'Publish tomorrow'.

JOHN BOYNE, manner of

80. A BOY, HEAD IN PROFILE

Pen and watercolour. 3⅞ × 3⅛ in. (9.9 × 7.8 cm.) (17658)

MICHEL VINCENT BRANDOIN (1733-1807)

81. THE YOUNG POLITICIAN (C. J. Fox).

Pen and watercolour, washed mount, uniform with the following five. 8⅝ × 7⅜ in. (22 × 18.2 cm.)   (13259)

An anonymous engraving, published by H. Bryer c. 1771 (B.M. Sat. V. 4892), reproduces the drawing exactly with all the legends.

82. THE HAIRDRESSER

Pen and watercolour, washed mount, uniform with the preceding. 8¾ × 7⅜ in. (22.1 × 18.5 cm.)   (13258)

Akin to the anonymous caricature 'Ridiculous Taste', published July 15, 1771, by M. Darly (B.M. Sat. IV, 4628).

83. THE PATRIOTIC PAINTER. LESSONS WITHOUT ENTRANCE sn. (Painter walking to left, carrying on his right shoulder easel, from which bottles brushes, etc., are suspended, and in his left hand portfolio, palette, and mahlstick. Cocked hat and sword.

Pen and grey wash, on the same elaborate washed mount as the preceding. 8¾ × 6¼ in. (22.2 × 16 cm.)   (17661)

The title as given, inscribed below and above in pencil. '7/6' in red chalk on back of mount.

Exhib.: B.F.A.C. 1931/32, No. 192, where it was wrongly connected with B.M. Sat. IV., 4520.

The style of this and the following three drawings, hitherto anonymous, and the mounting, connect them conclusively with the preceding.

84. A PIRATE, looking to right and brandishing a pistol in his right hand.

Pen and grey wash, mounted and priced as the preceding. 8¾ × 6¼ in. (22.2 × 16 cm.)   (17662)

85. A MACARONI QUIZZING, moving to right, holding glass to his left eye, sword suspended on his right.

Watercolour, mounted and priced as the preceding. 6½ × 4⅜ in. (16.7 × 11.2 cm.)   (17663)

86. AN OLD WARRIOR, STANDING, holding in his left hand a long cane, a patch over right eye, right sleeve empty.

Watercolour, mounted and priced as the preceding. 6½ × 4⅜ in. (16.7 × 11.2 cm.)   (17664)

C. BRAUNS (1810)

87. Three views of Oatlands, the river front. Watercolour, with coloured margin.   (17962A, B, C)

A VIEW OF OATLANDS HOUSE. 18⅜ × 35 in. (46.5 × 89 cm.) 'Peinted (*sic*) by C. Brauns, 1810.'

VIEW OF OATLANDS. 18⅜ × 33¼ in. (46.7 × 84.3 cm.) 'p. by C. Brauns 1810.'

VIEW OF OATLANDS. 18⅜ × 33⅛ in. (46.7 × 84.2 cm.) 'drawn by C. Brauns 1810.'

These three large drawings, all showing the gothicized front of the house presumably as rebuilt by the Duke of York after the fire of 1792, are in the primitive manner of crude Continental souvenirs. The artist is, deservedly, unrecorded.

GABRIEL BRAY (fl. 1778-1785)

88. A REGATTA AT SPITHEAD, JUNE 23, 1773

Watercolour on two pieces of paper. 21 × 58¾ in. (50.3 × 148 cm.)   (17010)

Signed: G. Bray, and inscribed 'Spithead 23 June 1773 G. Bray Delint.' on the back of the drawing in ink. 'Inventory A', p. 159 (1816), transferred (1840) to p. 145.

CHARLES BRETHERTON (c. 1760-1783)

89. GIRL HOLDING A BIRD TO HER BOSOM, AMONG TREES

Pencil, pen and watercolour. Circular, diam. c. 13¼ in. (34 cm.)   (17666A)

90. THREE GIRLS AT A RUIN

Pencil, pen and watercolour. Circular, diam c. 10⅞ in. (27.7 cm.). A similar figure in pencil on the reverse.
(17666B)

91. A GIRL SEATED, OVERLOOKING THE SEA

Pencil, pen and watercolour. Circular, diam. 8⅞ in. (22.7 cm.)   (17666C)

These three drawings are accompanied by a hand-coloured etching, similar in character and signed at top: 'Bretherton Junr inv: et fecit'.

JAMES BRETHERTON (fl. 1770-1781)

92. THOMAS ALLEN (1542-1632,) bust facing half right.

Pencil. 4¼ × 3⅛ in. (11 × 8 cm.)   (17667)

Inscribed on the back: 'Tho. Allen'.

Engraved in reverse by J. Bretherton from a portrait at Trinity College, Oxford.

RICHARD BROMPTON (1734-1783), After. (? by J. Saunders, exh. 1778-1808.)

93. KING GEORGE IV WHEN A BOY, IN GARTER ROBES

Pencil and pen with brown wash, touches of red. Squared and incised in places. 20¼ × 14⅝ in. (51.8 × 37.1 cm.)
(13924)

Engraver's drawing; so far as finished, faithfully followed in the mezzotint by J. Saunders after Richard Brompton, published 1774 (O'Donoghue, Vol. II, p. 310, No. 6; C.S. No. 5).

JAMES BRUCE OF KINNAIRD (1730–1794) OR LUIGI BALUGANI (1737–1770)

94. THE ANTIQUITIES OF AFRICA COLLECTED IN SEVERAL JOURNEYS THROUGH THE TWO MAURETANIAE AFRICA PROPER NUMIDIA GAETULIA AND LYBIA

Plates 35–38

Two folio volumes uniformly bound, perhaps in the East, in red morocco heavily stamped in the centre with large Oriental tools. Volume I contains forty-four pages of drawings (25 × 18½ in.—63.5 × 47 cm.) with title pages to each of the six sections, two of them with ornaments. Volume II contains forty-three pages of drawings with six unornamented title pages. Each volume has a general title page with the title as given above.

Each section contains one or more large views of the antiquities with figures and landscape backgrounds. They measure *c.* 12 × 16 in. (30 × 40 cm.), and are very carefully executed in pen and grey wash, with ruler. These are followed, in a manner adopted from Robert Wood's *Ruins of Palmyra*, 1753, by a ground plan, reconstructed elevation and several sheets of architectural ornaments. Bruce in his manuscripts quoted by Playfair, *Travels in the Footsteps of Bruce*, 1877, p. 5, says that six such subsidiary plates may be computed to each view.

Apart from the title pages to the sections and scales (in feet and inches) to the details, the drawings are not lettered in any way. The monuments represented in Volume I are Carthage, three views: an aqueduct, baths and (?) ancient cisterns; Uthina (Udena); Thignica (Ain Tunga); Suffetula (Sbeitla), five views of four different buildings; Thunodrunum. There is also a section with two sheets of the medals of Carthage and an ornamented title page.

Volume II has Diana Veteranorum (Zana); Lambesa; Thamugadi (Timgad), two views: the Arch of the Gods and the Capitol; Tipasa, two views: the Arch of Caracalla and the Temple of Jupiter; Thisdrus (El Djem) two views, the exterior of the amphitheatre and the interior (unfinished); and, on loose unbound sheets, Ptolometa (Tolmetta). Besides the two volumes the Library contains, unbound, 14 views of Palmyra (11610–11623) and four of Baalbec (11624–11627), each measuring *c.* 16¾ × 24¾ in., in the same style as the preceding and on the same paper, but twice the size.

Bruce, who visited North Africa in 1765 and Palmyra and Baalbec in 1767, says in his Memoir (Playfair, *op. cit.*, p. 9) that he presented to the King two of the three large folio volumes which held his drawings. This is stated by Murray (*Life and Writings of James Bruce*, 1808, p. 115) to have occurred after a visit to the King on Bruce's return to England in 1774, and to have been in fulfilment of a promise made before he went abroad. Bruce himself refers to this visit and speaks of the third volume as remaining in his own custody because not finished when he gave the others to the King. He also mentions explicitly that he showed his views of Palmyra upon the largest Imperial paper to the King, but his enumeration of them as thirteen and of those of Baalbec as two does not agree with the number of unbound drawings now in the Royal Library.

According to an anecdote related by Mr. Petre to Philip Bliss (1787–1857) and subsequently corroborated by Barnard, Royal Librarian from 1774 to 1830, himself, the King secreted the drawings which he had accepted from Bruce when the traveller's character and veracity became questioned. Later, when Bruce had regained credit, search was made for the drawings, which was only ended when the King, in one of his 'short and partial suspensions from his sad calamity', sent for Barnard and told him where to find

them. (*Oxford Bibliographical Society Proceedings and Papers*, Vol. III, p. 231; kindly communicated by Mr. O. G. S. Crawford). The first mention of the drawings in the inventories is a memorandum by Glover, dated August 26, 1828 (Inventory 'A', p. 172), saying that they, with other prints and drawings, were taken from the Library at Buckingham House by command of His Majesty, and with the exception of the large drawings, had been placed in 'Press E'.

The two volumes were exhibited by Woodward (Royal Librarian, 1860–1869) to the Society of Antiquaries on March 27, 1862, but they could not be found in the Royal Library when sought for by Playfair, who, however, in the course of his search discovered and identified the 18 drawings of Palmyra and Baalbec. Thieme-Becker (*s.v.* Balugani) erroneously refers to 'four volumes in the Londoner Royal Library'.

A large number of other sketches and drawings was examined by Playfair among the Thurlow papers. These unfortunately are said on enquiry to exist no longer, thus meeting the fate which Playfair anticipated for them if they remained in private possession.

The authorship of these drawings, with all Bruce's activities, has been hotly debated ever since his return to this country. He, while not denying that he received assistance, claimed that he had himself made all the drawings with the aid of a *camera obscura*, and he consistently belittled the share of the Italian draughtsman, Luigi Balugani, whom he carried with him on his travels and who died in Abyssinia in 1770. He expresses himself indeed in his memoirs as if Balugani was limited to drawing foliage and ornaments in sculpture. In support of this contention Lord Mendip told Lord Colchester that Bruce had shewn him 'six sketches of buildings and landscapes which the King when he bought the rest desired Bruce to finish; and that Bruce took them to Scotland, and upon his return shewed them to Lord Mendip finished in the same exquisite style as the rest'. (*Diary and Correspondence of Charles Albert, Lord Colchester*, 1861, Vol. I, pp. 163, 164, entry of December 2, 1798. Kindly communicated by Mr. C. F. Bell.) Moreover, when the Thurlow drawings were shewn at the Institute of British Architects and the Graphic Society in May 1837, and with them drawings claimed by Bruce to have been made by him at Paestum before he met Balugani, competent judges were satisfied that these and '*the greater part, and best, of those of the African cities*' were by the same hand. It is impossible to doubt that the drawings in the Royal Collection are by one hand only, and that the hand, thoroughly experienced in the Italian tradition, of the figures and foliage. The preliminary sketches in the Thurlow collection without the figures and *staffage*, reproduced by Playfair and regarded by him as the 'best', also appear to be by this hand, with one marked exception (Plate VIII), and that collection may well have contained work by both hands, just as it also contained drawings in watercolour and gouache.

For a full account of Bruce during his stay at Bologna on his return through Italy, and the definite accusations made against him for his treatment of Balugani, see Emilio Chiovenda in *Atti della Reale Accademia d'Italia*, Rendiconti della Classe di Scienze Naturali &c.; serie settima, Vol. II, fasc. 7, Decembre, 1940, also E. Panzacchi in *Vita Italiana*, 1896–7.

ADAM BUCK (exh. 1795–1833)

95. FREDERICK, DUKE OF YORK, 1812. Full length profile to left, carrying his hat and stick in his right hand; Windsor Castle in the distance.

Watercolour. 16⅛ × 12 in. (40.9 × 30.5 cm.)   (13937)

Signed: Adam Buck 1812 London.

A drawing of the Duke of York by Adam Buck was exhibited at the Royal Academy 1812, No. 442.
Presented to the Royal Library by H.M. Queen Mary in 1923.

ADAM BUCK, Ascribed to

96. PRINCESS CHARLOTTE, full length standing, profile to left, in a formal garden.
Pencil and watercolour with some body-colour. $11\frac{3}{8} \times 8\frac{1}{2}$ in. (29 × 21.5 cm.) (13936)
Presented to the Royal Library by H.M. Queen Mary, 1924.
Reprod.: *Connoisseur*, XCII, August 1933, p. 81.
Subject and artist are both problematical.

SAMUEL AND NATHANIEL BUCK (fl. 1730–1755)

97. WINDSOR CASTLE AND TOWN, LOOKING SOUTH
Pen and grey wash within lined border with space at foot for the dedication, etc., left empty save for 'Berks' in pen under the drawing on the extreme right. 'Windsor Castle' at top. $7\frac{1}{4} \times 14\frac{3}{4}$ in. (18.5 × 37.5 cm.) (17369)
Almost identical with the engraving of 1733 in Buck's *Antiquities* and inferior in execution.

JOHN BUCKLER (1770–1851) AND JOHN CHESSEL BUCKLER (1793–1894)

98. SOUTH VIEW OF WINDSOR CASTLE, 1813
Watercolour. $11\frac{1}{4} \times 18\frac{3}{8}$ in. (28.8 × 46.8 cm.) (17406)
Signed on mount: J. Buckler 1813.
Acquired 1934 from the J. Lister Parker Collection.

99. SOUTH-EAST VIEW OF WINDSOR CASTLE, 1813
Watercolour: $11\frac{1}{8} \times 17\frac{1}{2}$ in. (28.3 × 44.3 cm.) (17405)
Signed: J. Buckler 1813.
Acquired 1934 from the J. Lister Parker Collection.

100. FROGMORE, 1813
Watercolour. $7\frac{1}{4} \times 11$ in. (18.5 × 28 cm.) (17407)
Signed: J. Buckler 1813 at foot right in margin.
From the same series as the two preceding, but acquired earlier. See also No. 637.
The following drawings, signed 'J. Buckler' and dated, except as stated, are also in the Library. All were acquired before 1915.
Warwick Castle from the meadows, 1808. 'From Dugdale's Warwickshire.'
Ragley, seat of the Marquis of Hertford. The Hall. 1814.
Gate House, Bolton Abbey, 1816.
South East View of Stede Chapel, near Ribchester. J. C. Buckler, 1817.
'Hall of the Ancient Mansion at Chiselhurst, Kent, belonging to the Rt. Hon. Lord Viscount Sidney. Pulled down April, 1822.'
Gateway at Orchardleigh, Somerset, the seat of Thomas Champneys, Esq., Not signed, not dated.
Unidentified gabled house. Signed: J. C. Buckler Junr. 1811.

J. BULMAN (fl. 1760)

101. THE ENGLISH BEAU FROM PARIS. A middle-aged man preening himself before a mirror, a valet taking snuff and a maid at open door right laughing.

Pen and grey wash in imitation of a print. $10\frac{3}{8} \times 9$ in. (26.3 × 23 cm.) (within border). On the reverse a monochrome sketch of a landscape with ruin. (17650)
Signed: J. Bulman inv. et del: with the title, as given. 4/– on back.
Topographical drawings by Bulman are in the King's Maps at the British Museum.

HENRY WILLIAM BUNBURY (1750–1811)

102. THE COUNTRY CLUB   *Plate* 34
Pen and watercolour. $14\frac{3}{4} \times 20\frac{7}{8}$ in. (37.5 × 53 cm.) (17670)
Inscribed in the Colnaghi hand 'Original Drawing by Bunbury Esqre', the price £7 7s. od. at back.
Engraved by Dickinson, June 26, 1788 (B.M. Sat. VI, No. 7452).
Exhib.: B.F.A.C. 1931/32 No. 189.
Presumably the 'Drawing of the Country Club by Bunbury Esqr.' acquired by the Prince of Wales from Colnaghi, January 7, 1803, for £7 7s. od. (Archives Invoice 27209), with 'a Drawing of the City Fowlers by Do' at £2 12s. 6d., which may be a misdescription of the following.

103. A FAMILY GROUP
Pencil and watercolour. $15\frac{3}{4} \times 23\frac{1}{8}$ in. (40 × 60 cm.) (17671)
Inscribed on the old mount in the large Colnaghi hand: 'Original Drawing by Bunbury'.

104. HOW TO EXPRESS ASTONISHMENT
Pencil, buff paper. $8\frac{5}{8} \times 6\frac{1}{2}$ in. (22.1 × 16.4 cm.) (17672)
Inscribed in pencil below, with the title as given: 'Original Sketch by Mr. Bunbury' above.

105. FALSTAFF PLAYING THE PRINCE
Pencil, pen and watercolour. $13\frac{7}{8} \times 18\frac{1}{4}$ in. (35.4 × 46.4 cm.) (13307)
Inscribed in the large Colnaghi hand: 'Original by Bartolozzi R.A.'
Engraved by T. Macklin after H. Bunbury, T. Macklin Execut March 21, 1798 (or 1796).
Presumably 'A drawing of Sir John Falstaff by Bartolozzi' bought by the Prince of Wales from Colnaghi on August 18, 1803, for £6 6s. (Archives Invoice 27241), together with Nos. 51–53 (Bartolozzi).

106. ALL FOURS. An elderly and a very bored young man at cards.
Pencil and watercolour in feigned oval. $12\frac{5}{8} \times 16\frac{3}{8}$ in. (32.2 × 41.8 cm.) (17673)
Inscribed with the title as given in ink and 'Drawing. Original Bunbury', in pencil, in the large Colnaghi hand on the mount; '21/–' on back.
Engraved in reverse by J. R. Smith, March 14, 1783 (B.M. Sat. V, No. 6341).
Acquired by the Prince Regent from Colnaghi on July 6, 1812, for £1 1s. (Archives Invoice 27877).

107. AN OLD WOMAN CLOTHED IN GREY (apparently an aged mother upbraiding a repentant daughter far advanced in child).
Watercolour over light pencil in false circle. $14\frac{7}{8} \times 13\frac{1}{4}$ in. (38 × 33.5 cm.) (17674)

The title, as given, written below, with brush.
Signature or inscription 'Bunbury' in pen, partly cut into.
Acquired by the Prince Regent from Colnaghi on May 10, 1814, for 15/– (Archives Invoice 27995).

108. HOW TO MAKE THE MOST OF A HORSE
Pencil and brown wash, roughly incised, on washed mount. 8⅝ × 6¾ in. (22 × 17.2 cm.)   (17675)
Inscribed in the Colnaghi hand: 'Original Drawing by Bunbury'.

Engraved by Dickinson, 1791, for Bunbury's *Academy for Grown Horsemen . . . by Geoffrey Gambado Esqre.*

H. W. BUNBURY, Manner of

109. JOHN GILPIN'S RIDE
Pencil, pen and watercolour, cut to oval. c. 12¼ × 15⅞ in. (32 × 40.5 cm.)   (17676)
The horse roughly sketched on the reverse.

WILLIAM CAPON (1757–1827), after William Oram

110. COPY OF THE CEILING DECORATION FOR THE THEATRE IN GREAT ALIFF ST., GOODMAN'S FIELDS, BY WILLIAM ORAM; from a sketch made in 1786.
Watercolour. 6⅛ × 9⅞ in. (15.5 × 25 cm.)   (17124)
Copy or inferior replica of a drawing inscribed and signed by W. Capon, 1802, at the British Museum (Garrick Topography Volume, Burney Collection), and engraved by L. Stow as Plate 191, Vol. II, of Wilkinson's *Londina Illustrata*, 1820.

ALFRED EDWARD CHALON, R.A. (1781–1866)

111. THE DUCHESS OF KENT, 1837. Full length, seated in a garden.
Watercolour. Top corners cut. 17¾ × 12⅜ in. (44.9 × 31.4 cm.)   (13245)
Signed in gold: A. E. Chalon, R.A. 1837.
Lithographed (in colour) by R. J. Lane in 1838 (O'Donoghue, Vol. IV, p. 373, No. 3).
Bought by H.M. Queen Mary, September, 1935, from Walker's Galleries, and presented by her to the Royal Library.
In 1838 Chalon exhibited a portrait of the Duchess of Kent in the Royal Academy, No. 623.
Chalon was Painter in Watercolours to Queen Victoria.

112. PRINCESS VICTORIA OF SAXE-COBURG (1822–1857), three-quarter length, nearly full face, standing to right at a console, caressing a dog.
Watercolour. Octagonal, 18½ × 13⅝ in. (46.9 × 34.7 cm.)   (13247)
Signed in gold along the right lower shorter side: 'A. E. Chalon R.A. &c. 1839'.
Formerly No. 667 in the Inventory of Pictures (Lord Chamberlain's Dept.). Transferred to the Royal Library in April 1930.
The princess, a cousin of the Prince Consort and Queen Victoria, married Louis Duc de Nemours in 1840. She arrived in England on June 3, 1839.

113. PRINCE AUGUSTUS OF SAXE-COBURG (1818–1881), AND COUNT ALEXANDER MENSDORF, full length, in foreign uniforms; a groom holding two horses in a landscape background.
Watercolour. 34 × 25¾ in. (85.2 × 65.4 cm.).
Signed in gold at foot left: A. E. Chalon R.A. &c. 1839.
Inventory of Pictures, Lord Chamberlain's Department, No. 668.
Prince Augustus of Saxe-Coburg and Count Alexander Mensdorf were first cousins of each other and of Queen Victoria and the Prince Consort.

114. PRINCE LEOPOLD OF SAXE-COBURG (1824–1884), 1839, full length, in uniform; the Marble Arch and the front of Buckingham Palace in the background.
Watercolour. 21 × 15½ in. (53.3 × 39.4 cm.).
Signed at foot, left, in gilt: A. E. Chalon R.A. &c. 1839.
Inventory of Pictures, Lord Chamberlain's Department, No. 669.
These four cousins of Queen Victoria paid a visit to England from June to September, 1839. On June 10 Queen Victoria mentions in her Diary that all four were being painted by Chalon.

115. PORTRAIT OF A YOUNG WOMAN wearing coral ornaments, a feather in her hair.
Watercolour. 9 × 8⅛ in. (22.8 × 20.5 cm.)   (13246)
Signed: A. E. Chalon R.A., the initials in monogram.
Formerly No. 2195 in the Inventory of Pictures (Lord Chamberlain's Department). Transferred to the Royal Library, April, 1930.

SIR WILLIAM CHAMBERS (1726–1796) AND G. B. CIPRIANI

116. DESIGN FOR THE FIGURES OF THE FRONT PART OF THE ROYAL COACH   *Plate* 41
Fine pen with brown ink and grey wash. 13¾ × 9½ in. (35 × 24 cm.)   (14000)
Inscribed, above: 'The Fore part of the First Coach'.
A drawing, 'The King's State Coach by Sir William Chambers the figures by Cipriani—fine—£4.4.', was bought by the Prince Regent from Colnaghi on June 12, 1811 (Archives Invoice 27638), but this, the following drawing, and a third (13998), in purple wash, perhaps Italian, were given to the Royal Library, with a printed description of the State Coach, by J. L. Douthwaite, Esq., Librarian at the Guildhall, in November, 1937. See also Nos. 123 and 124.
The State Coach finished in 1762 and still in existence was designed by Sir William Chambers, the paintings by Cipriani. The Tritons in the front support the driver's seat and are supposed to be drawing the coach by the cables over their shoulders. This corresponds with the present drawing, whereas, in the back part, the intention of the following drawing has not been carried out. Though no doubt Sir William Chambers was rightly credited with the general designs, these detailed drawings may well be the work of Cipriani.
'There is come forth a new state coach, which has cost 8,000*l*. It is a beautiful object, though crowded with improprieties. Its supports are tritons, not very well adapted to land-carriage; and formed of palm-trees, which are as little aquatic as tritons are terrestrial.' (Walpole to Sir Horace Mann, November 30, 1762.)

117. THE KING'S STATE COACH: THE HINDER PART

Fine pen with brown ink, grey wash; cut irregularly at the foot. $16\frac{3}{8} \times 11$ in. (41.5×28 cm.) (13999)

Companion to the preceding, but the two chief figures in the design were not carried out.

PRINCE CHARLES EDWARD (1720–1788)

118. AFTER MARATTA: ST. JEROME IN ECSTASY

Red chalk, within border with inscription below. $7\frac{1}{2} \times 6$ in. (19×15.5 cm.) (17627)

Signed: Carlo P. and inscribed EX DONO EIUSDEM CAROLI PRINCIPIS WALLIAE FILII JACOBI III. BRITANNIAE REGIS AN. 1733.

A manuscript note on the back reads: This Drawing was done by The Prince, just turn'd of 12 years of age, without his Drawing Master Pompeo or any body else ever touching or putting an hand to it, as was known at the time to the whole Family. His Royal Highness made a present of it to Cardinal Imperiali, who put the Inscription below it, & esteeming it so much kept it with his Jewels. After The Cardinals death, it was carryed amongst his most valuable things by The Prince Francavilla his heir into a remote part of the Kingdom of Naples, & by the means of Cardl. Spinelli it was recoverd from thence in the year 1744 by me

James Edgar

The drawing was presented to H.M. King George V in 1916 by Mr Charles ffoulkes, Curator of the Armouries at the Tower, according to whom it had been given to his great-grandfather Sir Robert Strange by Andrew Lumisden, his brother-in-law and successor to James Edgar as Private Secretary to Charles Edward. According to this account Andrew Lumisden received it as a gift from Cardinal Francavilla.

The Young Pretender's proficiency in music and drawing is mentioned in the *Letters from a young Painter Abroad to his Friends in England* (by James Russel), ed. ii, 1750, Vol. I, pp. 77 and 281.

JEAN BAPTISTE CLAUDE CHATELAIN (1710–1771)

119. FLAT LANDSCAPE WITH TREES *Plate* 43

Black chalk and pencil, touches of red (accidental?), $7\frac{5}{8} \times 11\frac{7}{8}$ in. (19.5×30.5 cm.) (6649)

Inscribed in border below drawing, partly cut off: D Cha D Chat delain 1746.

A good example of a known, but rare type of drawing by J. B. C. Chatelain, to whom the inscription seems to relate. Originally included in the second of two volumes entitled 'Italian Flemish & Dutch Landscapes' (George III Inventory 'A', pp. 121 and 122, where J. H. Glover, Royal Librarian, attributed this drawing to Chatelain).

MRS. CHENEY. *See under* Sir William Gell (p. 52).

GIOVANNI BATTISTA CIPRIANI (1727–1785)

120. DESIGN FOR THE MONUMENT OF KING GEORGE III IN THE COURTYARD OF SOMERSET HOUSE *Plate* 42

Pen, grey and blue wash. $23\frac{5}{8} \times 17\frac{3}{8}$ in. (59.6×44.1 cm.) (13248)

Inscribed 'Cipriani' in ink under border at foot.

Purchased by the Prince Regent from Colnaghi for £10 10s. on June 12, 1811, as 'Monument erected in honor of his Majesty at Somerset House—by J. B. Cipriani—very fine.' (Archives Invoice 27638).

This design, altered from a fountain, is closely followed in the monument by Bacon. It has not elsewhere been credited to Cipriani. On the contrary, J. T. Smith (*Nollekens*, Vol. II, p. 176), while inveighing against Barretti for giving in his *Guide to the Royal Academy* the entire credit to the sculptors for their carvings on the fronts of Somerset House, and asserting that they were all executed from finished designs by Cipriani, makes an express exception for Bacon's bronze statue of King George III and the figure of Thames below it. The drawing is more in the manner of Cipriani than of Bacon, but so many of the finished drawings by both of them would appear to have been worked up by 'ghosts' that any definite judgment is difficult.

121. DESIGN FOR A MEDALLION; the head of King George III; the garden front of Old Somerset House on the reverse, both within wreaths on a feigned plaque.

Black chalk. Pen and grey and brown washes, on washed mount. $3\frac{3}{8} \times 6\frac{1}{8}$ in. (8.5×15.3 cm.) (13291)

On the obverse of the medallion, in pencil: 'GEORGIUS III D.G. MAGN. BRIT. FR. et HIB. Rex'; on the reverse, 'ACADEM: INSTIT: A°. MDCCLXVIII'.

Engraved by Bartolozzi as the headpiece to the dedication by Sir William Chambers of his *Dissertation on Oriental Gardening*, 1772 (O'Donoghue, II, p. 302, No. 42; Calabi, No. 2415).

Purchased by the Prince Regent from Colnaghi on June 12, 1811, for £3 3s. as 'A Drawing, Medal for the Royal Academy by Cipriani—fine' (Archives Invoice 27638). No such medal is known at the Royal Academy.

122. CROWNING A THERM, with a seated Muse and sketching cupids; a feigned plaque.

Pen, grey and brown washes, on washed mount. $5 \times 6\frac{1}{4}$ in. (12.9×16 cm.) (13292)

Acquired by the Prince Regent from Colnaghi for £3 3s. at the same time as No. 121 as 'A Drawing, vignette of Sir W. Chambers Oriental Gardening'. It was engraved by Bartolozzi as the vignette on the title page of the book (Calabi No. 1693).

123. DESIGNS FOR THE DECORATION OF THE ROYAL STATE COACH (see also Nos. 116 and 117 ante)

Allegorical figures, Mars, Minerva and Mercury upholding a Royal crown; two female figures, one holding a column, the other a mirror.

Pencil, pen and grey and brown washes. $7\frac{3}{8} \times 11\frac{3}{4}$ in. (18.7×29.8 cm.) (17969)

On the reverse: a pen sketch of the side of a coach with four decorated panels, and two sketches, of Neptune or the River Thames, with a nereid, in pen over pencil.

Under the rapid sketch of a coach on the reverse the artist has written 'giunzione dei fiumi'—'americha' as though referring to the left hand side panel, and 'Citta di Londra' for the other.

A group of Minerva and Mars holding the crown occurs on the centre panel on the near side of the Royal coach, but its decoration does not contain any themes which correspond with the words written on the reverse of the sketch. Tritons and nereids occur in the back panel of the coach, but without close resemblance to the figures in the sketch. This and the following sketch must therefore represent a very early stage of the design.

Presented to the Royal Library, with No. 124, by Professor Anthony Blunt, Keeper of the King's Pictures, in March, 1946.

124. ALLEGORICAL FEMALE FIGURES, ONE WITH A CORNUCOPIA, SUPPORTING AN EMPTY ESCUTCHEON

Black chalk and pen. $6\frac{1}{4} \times 8\frac{3}{4}$ in. (16 × 22.4 cm.) (17970)

These two standing figures bear some resemblance to, and possess some of the same attributes as, the female figures on the door panel on the off side of the Royal Coach, where however there is no escutcheon. See on No. 123.

125. BARTOLOZZI ASLEEP IN A CHAIR   *Plate* 40

Pencil. Same paper as No. 50. $7\frac{7}{8} \times 6\frac{1}{8}$ in. (20 × 15.3 cm.) (13294)

'2 Drawing[s]—Portraits of Cipriani and Bartolozzi by themselves' were bought by the Prince of Wales from Colnaghi on September 22, 1809, for £3 3s. (Archives Invoice 27825).

Reprod.: *Connoisseur* XCII, August, 1933, p. 76.

A self-portrait by Bartolozzi at Lisbon 'Album Cifka' (Catalogue 1948, No. 36) in black and red chalk, inscribed 'se ipsum fecit', seems to show the same features, though at a much more advanced age.

126. THE TOILET OF VENUS

Black and red chalk with a little wash, in feigned oval; on washed mount. $8\frac{3}{4} \times 7\frac{7}{8}$ in. (22.2 × 18.2 cm.) (13293)

A drawing by Cipriani, 'Venus Bathing', and a 'Ditto, Venus from the Bath', were purchased by the Prince of Wales from Colnaghi on January 10, 1800, for £3 3s. and 10/6 respectively (Archives Invoice 27114); but it would not be safe to identify this drawing with either of these because the latter, to which it more nearly corresponds, was not definitely entered as by Cipriani. Moreover, 'A Drawing, Venus at her Toilet', artist unnamed, was bought by the Prince Regent from Colnaghi on October 14, 1811, together with a 'Mars and Venus', for £6 6s. (Archives Invoice 27657).

127. 'FREDERICK, DUKE OF YORK' (1763–1827), bust, profile to left, hair in a queue.

Red and black chalk, cut to oval. $3\frac{1}{8} \times 2\frac{5}{8}$ in. (8.1 × 6.7 cm.) (17964)

Inscribed on the back in a contemporary hand, in pencil, 'by Cipriani'. On a piece of stamp paper at the back of the frame, in a Victorian hand, 'Duke of York by Cipriani'. Accepting the authorship, the identification of the sitter cannot be correct. He wears no orders and is clearly more than 22, which was the age of the Prince when Cipriani died.

JOHN COLLET (*c.* 1725–1780)

128. A SQUALL. The bearskin has been blown from a tall soldier upon the head of an ensign whose hat is on the ground.

Watercolour. $6\frac{3}{4} \times 6\frac{1}{8}$ in. (17.2 × 15.5 cm.) (13624)

Signed: Collet.

Exhib.: Spring Gardens (Humour Exhibition), 1925, No. 8.

'A Drawing by Collet [and] Two Ditto of french Soldiers' were bought by the Prince of Wales on March 6, 1800, from Colnaghi for 15s. each. (Archives Invoice 27138).

Fig. 11. Collet: Kitchen Scene (Cat. No. 129)

129. KITCHEN SCENE. The man pleading with a seated girl who caresses a cat on the table.   *Figure* 11

Watercolour. $4\frac{1}{2} \times 4\frac{3}{4}$ in. (11.5 × 11.8 cm.) (13625)

Remains of signature, Collet, number '572'.

Exhib.: Spring Gardens (Humour Exhibition), 1925, No. 11.

130. KITCHEN SCENE. A wooden-legged soldier kisses a maidservant, while the mother sleeps in a chair.

Watercolour. $6\frac{7}{8} \times 6$ in. (18.5 × 15.4 cm.) (13626)

Signed: Collet.

131. 'NEAR WINDSOR THE KEEPER'S HOUSE'

Watercolour on washed mount. $5\frac{1}{4} \times 7\frac{1}{4}$ in. (13.4 × 18.5 cm.) (17460)

Inscribed with title, as given, in pencil on the back.

Hitherto anonymous.

132. CITIZEN SOLDIERS   *Figure* 12

Pen, grey wash, a little colour. $5 \times 6\frac{1}{2}$ in. (12.6 × 16.3 cm.) (17646)

Carefully drawn with strong outlines, somewhat in the manner of Collet. The cockades worn in the hats were probably intended to be coloured. The costume is too late to associate the drawing with an interesting group of caricatures connected with the 1745 rebellion which bore the name A. Sabbatini in the Arthur Kay Collection (Christies' April 9, 1943).

SAMUEL COOPER (1609–1672)

133. KING CHARLES II, head in profile to R.   *Plate* I

Red and black chalk on brown paper (faded). $6\frac{7}{8} \times 5\frac{1}{2}$ in. (17.8 × 14 cm.) (14040)

Colls.: Richardson (father and son) with marks Lugt 2184 and 2170.

Exhib.: B.F.A.C. 1938, No. 58.

Fig. 12. Manner of Collet: Citizen Soldiers (Cat. No. 132)

Reprod.: *Connoisseur*, XCII (1933), pp. 75 and 127.
Lit.: Goulding, *Walpole Annual*, Vol. IV (1914–1915), p. 23.
A note written by the younger Richardson on a label at the back of the mount reads: 'This Drawing is the portrait of K. Charles II^d for his Inauguration Medal; & for which he sate (as I have heard my Father say) the very same day that He made his Publick Entry, through London; to Loose no time in making the Dye.' This probably refers to two medals by John Roettier of 1661. Evelyn wrote in his Diary, January 10, 1662: 'Being called into His M's Closet where Mr. Cooper ye rare limner, was crayoning of the King's face and head to make the stamps for the new milled money now contriving I had the honour to hold the candle whilst it was doing, he choosing the night and candlelight for the better finding out of shadows.'
Another label with a transcript of Richardson's note, adds that the drawing was presented to King George III on May 29, the anniversary of the Restoration, by 'his dutiful Son George P.'
Inventory 'A', p. 151 (1816), mentions this drawing with the inscription. Its absence, with others, is noted in 1841, and for many years, until recently, it hung framed in the Royal Library.

134. THE SAME, in the same materials but with traces of white also.
4⅞ × 4⅝ in. (12.6 × 11.7 cm.)   (14039)
It bears a mark in ink (Lugt 1753) which, recorded on one drawing at Christ Church (Bell, *Christ Church Drawings*, 1914, p. 17), is regarded as a variant of Sir Peter Lely's; and another, also in ink, an italic W or JW, which is unknown to Lugt. Apparently a copy, not a tracing, from the preceding, it may owe its look of greater finish merely to its not having suffered through exposure to the light. Provenance unknown.

JOHN SINGLETON COPLEY (1737–1815),
Attributed to

135. A MAN WRITING, seated half right at a table, the features not indicated.
Black and white chalk on blue paper. On the *verso*, a rough sketch of a left hand. 8⅞ × 7½ in. (22.5 × 19 cm.) (13603)
The attribution to Copley (made anonymously on the present mount) is conjectural only.

J. S. COPLEY, After

136. THE THREE YOUNGEST DAUGHTERS OF KING GEORGE III. The Princesses Mary, Amelia and Sophia.
Pen and grey wash over pencil. 9¾ × 7⅝ in. (24.7 × 19.1 cm.)   (14225)
Purchased 1932 from Mr. Randall Davies, who was not prepared to affirm its authenticity.
A spirited sketch from the painting of 1785 in the Royal Collection (Cust, p. 37), or the engraving by Bartolozzi of February 1, 1792, after it (O'Donoghue, Vol. V, p. 37, No. 1).

RICHARD CORBOULD (1757–1831)

137. FREDERICK, DUKE OF YORK, full length, looking to left, wearing ribbon of the Garter.
Pen and wash with wash border. 8 × 5 in. (20.2 × 12.7 cm.)   (13893)
Similar to the engraving by A. W. Warren for Lyttelton's *History of England*, 1803 (O'Donoghue, Vol. II, p. 253, No. 14). The stance and details are similar, but in the engraving he wears a hat, there is a background of hills and camp, and the features are different. The face in the drawing would seem to follow the print by Scott after Lawrence (O.D., Vol. II, p. 254, No. 32).

W. H. CORNWALL (fl. 1817)

138. WINDSOR CASTLE FROM A FIELD NEAR THE INFANTRY BARRACKS
Pencil, grey and blue wash. 9 × 15½ in. (23 × 39.5 cm.)   (17371)
Signed: W. H. C., April 29, 1817, in ink and inscribed in pencil with the title, as given, both on the back.
A volume of similar sketches—much in the manner of James Bourne—is in the Eton College Library, where the artist's name is given in full.

139. WINDSOR CASTLE: GATEWAY AND PART OF ST. GEORGE'S CHAPEL
Pencil, grey and blue washes. 11⅛ × 15½ in. (28 × 39.3 cm.)   (17372)
Signed: W. H. C., April 10, 1817, and inscribed with the title, as given, in ink on the back. Uniform with the preceding.

140. WINDSOR CASTLE FROM BROCAS CLUMP
Pen and watercolour. 6⅜ × 8¼ in. (16.3 × 21 cm.) (17553)
Inscribed in pencil at foot, June 10, 1822, and on the back, in ink, signed with the initials.

HENDRIK DE CORT (1742–1810)

141. WINDSOR CASTLE FROM THE NORTH
Pencil, pen, grey and brown washes, torn and mended, a perpendicular fold in centre. On Whatman paper. 19⅞ × 26⅝ in. (50.3 × 67.5 cm.)   (14587)
Apparently inscribed by the artist 'Windsor Castle' at the back (hidden by a mend), and in the large Colnaghi hand in the sky 'Windsor from the North'.
Formerly regarded as by Paul Sandby (see *Sandby*, No. 63), and possibly based on a drawing by him or his aquatint of January 1, 1777. An oil painting by de Cort clearly based on this drawing appears to have been in the London market. (Photograph in the Royal Library, Windsor, General Views, Vol. 2.)

142. WINDSOR CASTLE FROM CRANBOURNE LODGE

Pencil, grey and brown washes, on thick paper, slightly toned. Perpendicular fold in centre. 18⅞ × 25⅜ in. (48 × 63.5 cm.) (14611)

Inscribed by the artist in pencil on the back, 'Windsor Forest near Craenbury Lodge'; and in the largest Colnaghi hand in the sky, 'Windsor Forest from Cranbourne Lodge'. Formerly attributed to Paul Sandby. (See *Sandby Catalogue*, p. 56.)

143. WINDSOR CASTLE: THE ROUND TOWER, FROM THE QUADRANGLE looking West, and showing the Tennis-court building in the moat.

Pencil, with grey and brown washes. 13⅛ × 17⅝ in. (33.5 × 44.1 cm.) (14985)

Inscribed at the back by the artist in pencil, 'Berckshire the Tower at Windsor', in an ornamental hand.
The Tennis-court Building is still shewn in Pyne's *Royal Residences*, 1819, Vol. I, p. 82.

144. WINDSOR CASTLE: MAIDS OF HONOUR TOWER, and the exterior of the Castle to the west.

Pencil, two pages of sketch book, unstitched (J. Buttershaw paper), corners cut. 9⅛ × 17⅞ in. (23.1 × 37.9 cm.) (17500)

Inscribed at the back 'Windsor' in de Cort's hand and 'Windsor Castle' in another hand, both in pencil.

145. IN FROGMORE GARDENS

Pencil. 10⅞ × 18½ in. (27.5 × 46.7 cm.) (17527)

Inscribed with the title, as given, in pencil at the back in de Cort's hand; and in pencil in a modern hand, 'nr. Frogmore', at foot right, on the front.

Five pencil drawings of Frogmore (17522–17526) and one of Westminster Hall (17156), all similarly inscribed on the front, have been grouped with this, but are clearly by an English early 19th-century hand. One of them is on paper watermarked 1794.

146. IN KEW GARDENS

Pencil, pen and grey wash. 9½ × 26⅜ in. (24.2 × 67.1 cm.) (14983)

Signed and inscribed by the artist on the back, 'In Kew Gardens 1791 H d C'; and, on the front, at the top, centre, in the Colnaghi hand, 'Kew Gardens'.
Two leaves of a sketchbook, unstitched. Showing the palace on the left with the Greek summerhouse slightly to the right of it, and a Chinese summerhouse on a bridge over water which extends the whole length of the drawing, on the right. The buildings are shewn from the same point of view as in the engraving, Canot after Woollet (1763) 'View of the Palace from the South Side of the Lake'.

147. THE SAME, the Greek summerhouse on the left.

Pencil and wash on toned Whatman paper from the same sketchbook. 9½ × 13⅛ in. (24.2 × 33.4 cm.) (14984)

Fig. 13. Hendrik de Cort: Knole, the Aviary (Cat. No. 148)

Inscribed on the back in pencil by the artist, 'In Kew Gardens', and, also in pencil on the front in the sky in a large Colnaghi hand, 'Kew Gardens'.

148. KNOLE: THE AVIARY *Figure* 13
Pencil, pen and grey wash, on Whatman paper. 13⅛ × 19½ in. (33.7 × 49.6 cm.) (17963)
Inscribed at the back by the artist in his ornamental hand, 'Kent—Knole the Duke of Dorset's—the Birds House'; and in another hand, 'the Aviary'. A small architectural detail in pencil at the back.

149. AVIARY AT NEW TIMBER IN SUSSEX
Pencil, grey and brown washes. 16⅓ × 24⅞ in. (42 × 63 cm.) (13314)
See *Catalogue of Flemish Drawings*, No. 210.
The names of the artist and place now on the mount were presumably based on inscriptions at the back which are no longer visible.

RICHARD COSWAY, R.A. (1742–1821)

150. MARIA, DUCHESS OF GLOUCESTER, WITH HER DAUGHTER PRINCESS SOPHIA MATILDA AND PRINCESS MARY, LATER HER DAUGHTER-IN-LAW *Plate* 23
Pencil with slight colour in the faces. 11⅜ × 8¾ in. (30 × 22 cm.) (17032)
Exhib.: R.A. 1934, No. 635 (1167), Pl. CLII.
Reprod.: Williamson, *R. and M. Cosway*, 1897, opp. p. 1 (as ladies unknown).
'G' within a wreath on a pilaster behind the central figure. Maria (Walpole) Duchess of Gloucester (1739–1807);— married (1) James, 2nd Earl Waldegrave; (2) William Henry, Duke of Gloucester.
Princess Mary, 4th daughter of King George III, married William Frederick, 2nd Duke of Gloucester, in 1816.
Princess Sophia Matilda of Gloucester, 1773–1844.

151. CAROLINE, PRINCESS OF WALES, AND PRINCESS CHARLOTTE; full length, on balustrade.
Pencil and colour wash on lined mount. 9 × 5⅝ in. (23 × 14.2 cm.) (17033)
Inscribed: 'R. Cosway R.A. pinxit' . . . 'fecit 1798' in pencil on the mount, both almost erased and most probably modern.
No. 2029 in the Lord Chamberlain's Department inventory, with a transcript of a note at the back of the then frame, 'Princess of Wales and Princess Charlotte. Given by the Princess of Wales to Lady Willoughby d'Eresby. Drawn by Cosway'. Transferred to the Royal Library between 1883 and 1887.
Exhib.: Grafton Gallery (Fair Children), 1895, No. 289.

152. ELIZABETH LADY CRAVEN (MARGRAVINE OF ANSPACH) in the character of Elia in her own comedy, 'The Miniature Picture'. Full length looking left, her right arm extended, holding (?) a handkerchief. In male costume with wig, bands and gown.
Pencil, the face in watercolour. 8 × 5¼ in. (20.5 × 13.5 cm.) (13408)
Reprod.: *Connoisseur*, XCII, August, 1933, p. 79.
Perhaps the 'Margravine of Anspach, a drawing by Cosway', acquired by King George IV from Colnaghi, May 24, 1821, for £1 11s. 6d. (Archives Invoice 28325). The title, as given above, on the modern mount. For the play, *cf.* Toynbee: H. Walpole, *Letters*, Vol. XI (to Mason), pp. 178–180.

R. COSWAY, Attributed to

153. WILLIAM, DUKE OF CLARENCE, half length, nearly full face, in Garter Robes.
Pencil and watercolour. Oval (framed as a miniature). 3½ × 2⅝ in. (8.8 × 7 cm.) (17098)
Inscribed on the back in ink: H.R.H. The D. of Clarence [K. Will: IV] R. Cosway pinx., and numbered in pencil '190'.

FRANCIS COTES (c. 1725–1770), After

154. QUEEN CHARLOTTE, WHOLE LENGTH, SEATED, WITH THE PRINCESS ROYAL ASLEEP ON HER KNEE and the Duchess of Ancaster to left, after the painting in the Royal Collection (Collins Baker, p. 65).
Watercolour and pen over pencil. 9½ × 7½ in. (24 × 19 cm.) (13934)
This drawing would appear to have been concocted in the 19th century from the painting by Cotes in the Royal Collection, which does not contain the Duchess of Ancaster, or from the engraving by Ryland after it of July 31, 1770 (O'Donoghue, Vol. I, p. 409, No. 6). A drawing in the British Museum (L.B. 3, reproduced by S. Sitwell, *Conversation Pieces*, pl. 95) is similar to the present drawing and seems scarcely more plausible.

DAVID COX (1783–1859), Manner of

155. FOREST SCENE WITH WINDSOR CASTLE IN THE DISTANCE
Brush with brown wash over black chalk, on brown paper. 5¼ × 8⅞ in. (13 × 22.4 cm.) (17442)
Acquired since 1915.

ALEXANDER COZENS (c. 1717–1786)
156. HERNE'S OAK
Pen and watercolour (in lined mount). 11⅝ × 7 in. (29.5 × 17.9 cm.) (17551)
Signed on the mount: Alexr. Cozens.
Inscribed in pencil on the mount, in the artist's hand: 'An exact drawing of Hern's Oak in Windsor Park, mention'd in Shakespear's Merry Wives of Windsor'. Numbered at back '129'.
Presented by E. Horsman Coles, Esq., C.B., in 1946.
The tree, consisting of the trunk and one limb, is already dead. It is apparently the same as that shown on p. 54, and in the woodcut after a drawing by Stark on p. 31, of W. Perry, *A treatise on the identity of Herne's Oak*, 1867.

157. AFTER MARCO RICCI: ITALIAN LANDSCAPE COMPOSITION
Pen and grey wash on brown toned tracing paper, joined horizontally. 14½ × 21¼ in. (37 × 54.2 cm.) (17354)
The word 'right' in pencil in the left hand bottom corner.
Copy or tracing from Marco Ricci, No. 01155 in the Royal Library.
Exhib.: Sheffield and Tate Gallery, 1946, No. 1.
This drawing was found in Queen Charlotte's Portfolio of drawings by the Princes and Princesses (see on No. 6). Since, unlike other drawings which have found their way into that portfolio, it bears no indication which would connect it with the Royal Princes, there seems no reason why it should have been placed there, unless it had been somehow connected with their instruction. On grounds of style it may safely be given to Alexander Cozens, their instructor at least from 1778 to his death.

JOHN ROBERT COZENS (1752–1797)

158. AN ENGLISH COUNTRY HOUSE IN A PARK
Plate 44

Watercolour. 6⅞ × 9¼ in. (17.6 × 23.4 cm.)   (17051)
Inscribed on the old washed mount, Cozens junr.
From the Duke of Connaught's collection at Bagshot, 1942.
Bell and Girtin, *Walpole Society*, Vol. XXIII, *Supplement*,
p. 12, No. 448. Unusual in subject, size and state of preserva-
tion, the drawing exhibits John Cozens' subtlety and deli-
cacy as exercised on a commonplace English scene. It should
be compared with Constable's famous 'Malvern Hall'.

J. R. COZENS, After

159. WINDSOR CASTLE FROM SNOW HILL

Watercolour. 11½ × 16¾ in. (29 × 42.2 cm.)   (14750)
Purchased Christie's, March 23, 1928, Lot 11 (as by
Turner).
Reproduced, as by Turner, *Connoisseur*, XCIII, September,
1933, p. 149 (Cundall), with a suggestion by Mr. A. J.
Finberg (probably made on the strength of a photograph
and in mockery) that it was by James Bourne.
A copy, conceivably by Girtin, of a landscape by J. R.
Cozens, of which a large version from the William Smith
Collection is in the possession of Mr. and Mrs. Cowan
(*ibid.*, No. 447).

WILLIAM MARSHALL CRAIG
(Exhib. from 1788, d. 1828), Attributed to

160. PRINCESS MARY (?), daughter of King George III.

Grey wash. Oval with ornaments below and royal coronet
above. 7⅞ × 4¾ in. (19.9 × 11.9 cm.)   (13894)
Given by Dr. Williamson, July, 1920, as a portrait by
W. M. Craig of Princess Elizabeth.
Several portraits of the Royal Princesses, deriving directly
and indirectly from Beechey, appeared in the magazines of
the period. The present drawing corresponds exactly in its
ornaments to the portrait of Princess Elizabeth engraved
by Scriven after Beechey for the *Belle Assemblée* (August 1,
1806, and later issues), but the head is totally different and
bears more resemblance to the portraits of Princess Mary
and Princess Sophia. Such versions of Royal Portraits are
the merest journalistic productions and are of no icono-
graphic value. (*Cf.* also *Lady's Monthly Museum*, 1806.

ROBERT CRONE (d. 1779)

161. CLASSICAL LANDSCAPE
Plate 45

Black and white chalk, (?) grey washes on blue prepared
paper, discoloured. 11½ × 16¾ in. (29.2 × 42.3 cm.)
(6650)
Mentioned in George III Inventory 'A', pp. 121 and 122
(see on No. 119), where J. H. Glover attributed it to
'Crone or Wilson'.
In the manner of his master Wilson, but more detailed in
treatment and broken up in composition. E. Edwards'
statement that a few examples of Crone's rare landscapes
are in the Royal Collection has been exaggerated by later
writers and may itself have had no other basis than some
casual mention of this drawing. No painting by Crone is
recorded as being in the Royal Collection.

W. DALE (1756)

162. AFTER J. ADOLPHE: GEORGE PRINCE OF WALES, AFTERWARDS KING GEORGE III, ON HORSEBACK, etc.

Black wash, imitation mezzotint, on vellum. 22⅜ × 17¾ in.
(57 × 45.2 cm.)   (13250)
Signed in lower border: W. Dale fecit 1756.
For the print by Baron after Adolphe, of which this is a
copy, see No. 37.

RICHARD DALTON, F.S.A. (*c.* 1715–1791)

Appointed Librarian to King George III in 1760; Antiquarian and Keeper of the Medals in 1774 and Surveyor
of the King's Pictures in 1778.
There are references in letters of 1741 from the Countess of
Pomfret to the Countess of Hertford (Duchess of Somerset)
to the drawings made by him in Rome, including some of
statues drawn in red chalk for Lord Brooke. These are
described as early drawings, superseded by improved drawings in black and white on blue paper (*Correspondence*, 1805,
iii, pp. 102 and 110).
In 1749 he travelled in Greece, Turkey and Egypt with
Lord Charlemont. In 1758 he revisited Italy, and frequently
later in order to purchase works of art for King George III.
A list of his disbursements for their Majesties on one of the
later occasions is in the Royal Archives (Document
15602–3).

163. DRAWINGS FROM ANTIQUE STATUES

All red chalk, about 20 × 13 in. (51 × 33 cm.) (17337–49)
Numbers 1–8 were engraved, generally in reverse, in 'A
Collection of Twenty Antique Statues Drawn after the
Originals in Italy by Richard Dalton Esq. and engraved
by Ravenet, Grignion, Wagner, Baron, &c.' John Boydell,
1770. All are signed or initialled except Nos. 1, 7, 8, 11,
and 13, and dated 1741, except Nos. 6 and 10, which are
dated 1742.
(*Cf.* also Vertue III, p. 142, for Dalton's prints of 1748.)
Nothing is known of their history before they were acquired
in 1946 from Calmann. Three retain the canvas on which
they were backed before insertion in a book, and others
show marks of the same treatment.

(1) The Fighting Gladiator (Pl. 3). Not signed.   (17345)
(2) Flora in the Farnese Palace (Pl. 4, in reverse). Signed
and dated 1741.   (17341)
(3) A Muse in the Capitol (Pl. 6, in reverse.) Initialled,
1741.   (17342)
(4) Hercules Farnese. (Pl. 7, in reverse.) Signed, 1741.
(17337)
(5) Apollo Belvedere. (Pl. 9.) Signed, 1741.   (17339)
(6) Apollo in the Villa Medici. (Pl. 13, in reverse.) Signed,
1742.   (17343)
(7) Venus of Medici. (Pl. 16, in reverse.) Not signed.
(17348)
(8) The Sleeping Hermaphrodite in the Villa Borghese.
(Pl. 20.) Not signed.   (17349)
(9) Apollo Belvedere. A different view from No. 5. Signed,
1741.   (17338)
(10) Ganymede. Signed, 1742.   (17344)
(11) Demeter. Not signed.   (17346)
(12) A Vestal. Signed, 1741.   (17340)
(13) Apollo and Daphne by Bernini. Not signed. (17347)

164. VIEWS IN THE MEDITERRANEAN AND EGYPT

(1) A Harbour scene. Pen and watercolour. $12\frac{1}{4} \times 19\frac{3}{4}$ in. (31.1×50.2 cm.). Numbered '1' at back of the mount. (17359)

(2) The Piraeus; the Acropolis in the background. Pen and watercolour. $12\frac{1}{4} \times 20$ in. (31.1×50.8 cm.). Numbered '2'. (17358)

(3) A roadstead with shipping. Pen and watercolour. $12\frac{1}{4} \times 19\frac{3}{4}$ in. (31.1×50.2 cm.) Numbered '3'. (17360)

(4) A rocky valley overlooking a harbour; goatherds and shipping. Pen and watercolour. $12\frac{1}{4} \times 19\frac{7}{8}$ in. (31.1×50.5 cm.). Numbered '4'. (17364)

(5) Two women in (?) Greek Islands costume in a landscape. Pen and watercolour. $12\frac{1}{8} \times 19\frac{7}{8}$ in. (30.8×50.5 cm.). Numbered '8'. (17362)

(6) A woman in (?) Greek Islands costume, back and front views. An Icon on the wall. Pen and watercolour. $12\frac{1}{8} \times 19\frac{7}{8}$ in. (30.8×50.5 cm.). Numbered '8'. (17363)

(7) Dancing girls of Egypt. Pen and watercolour. $18 \times 27\frac{1}{8}$ in. (45.7×68.9 cm.). Numbered '1'. (17356)

(8) Ethiopians on floats coming down the Nile. Pen and watercolour. $17\frac{3}{4} \times 27\frac{1}{4}$ in. (45.1×69.2 cm.) Numbered '2'. (17357)

(9) Fortifications on a cliff. Pen and watercolour. $10\frac{3}{4} \times 13\frac{3}{8}$ in. (27.3×34 cm.) Numbered '1'. (17361)

(10) The same. Numbered '1'. (17361A)

(11) Mograbins or African Merchants, a mixture of Moors and Arabs. Pen and watercolour. $10\frac{1}{4} \times 12\frac{7}{8}$ in. (26×32.7 cm.). Numbered '2'. (17355)

(12) The same. Numbered '2'. (17355A)

Nos. 7, 8, and 10 are engraved as Plates XIII, XIV, and X of the *Antiquities and Views in Greece and Egypt . . . from drawings made on the spot A.D.* 1749, by Richard Dalton Esq. Surveyor of His Majesty's Pictures . . . 1791, Plate XIII being much altered, Plates X and XIV closely followed but in reverse.
George III Inventory 'A', p. 159, mentions eight drawings of Egypt, etc., by Mr. Dalton, against which J. H. Glover has written under date November 24, 1840, that there were then only six of these drawings, 'numbers 5 and 6 being missing', but adding four small drawings by Dalton and two large drawings by him with the titles of Nos. 7 and 8. These two are mentioned in an earlier entry, p. 158.
All the drawings are uniformly mounted on ivory cards with gilt ruled and washed borders. The numbering at the back of the mounts is also uniform.

GEORGE DANCE, R.A. (1741–1825)

165. REVD. —. POTE, quarter length, seated, profile to left.
Pencil and slight wash. $10\frac{3}{8} \times 7\frac{1}{2}$ in. (25.5×19 cm.) (13412)

Signed: May 11th 1793. Geo. Dance.

The sitter's name, without Christian name, in open letters on the old washed mount. Presumably Revd. Joseph Pote, rector of St. George's, Southwark, and prebendary of Lichfield Cathedral (*c.* 1738–1797).

166. PORTRAIT OF A LADY (? MRS. SIDDONS), half length, seated, profile to left.

Pencil and slight pink wash on washed mount. $13\frac{5}{8} \times 10\frac{3}{8}$ in. (34.9×26.6 cm.) (13413)

Signed: Sept. 29th 1793. Geo Dance, the name almost cut away, at foot left, and again 'Geo. Dance' at foot right.

167. DR. PATRICK RUSSELL, M.D., quarter length, seated, profile to left.

Pencil with slight wash on washed mount. $10\frac{1}{8} \times 7\frac{1}{2}$ in. (25.7×19.4 cm.) (13411)

Signed: March 23rd 1794 Geo: Dance.

The sitter's name on the washed mount.
Etched, soft ground, in reverse, by W. Daniell and published 1802.

GEORGE DANCE, Manner of

168. A MAN CARRYING AN EMPTY SACK AND READING A PAPER

Pen and grey wash, on Whatman paper, 1794. $10\frac{3}{8} \times 7\frac{5}{8}$ in. (26.4×19.5 cm.) (17647)
Inscribed '5/–' at back.

169. 'GEORGE STUBBS IN THE ACT OF ETCHING' *Figure* 14

Pencil. $7\frac{1}{2} \times 6$ in. (19.1×15.3 cm.) (14203)

Fig. 14. G. Dance (?): Portrait of George Stubbs (Cat. No. 169)

The title may have been copied from an inscription on the back. The head resembles the engraved portrait of Stubbs after Falconet (O'Donoghue, Vol. IV, p. 215, No. 2), and to a less extent the soft-ground etching after Dance (*ibid.*, No. 1), to whom the drawing might possibly be attributed,

Fig. 15. N. Dance: A Levée (Cat. No. 170)

or to his brother Nathaniel. A larger drawing of a head with similar features and in much the same position, which is in the collection of the writer, has also been conjecturally attributed to one of the Dances.

NATHANIEL DANCE, R.A. (1735–1811)

170. A LEVÉE   *Figure* 15

Pencil, pen, brown and grey washes. Oval, $10\frac{1}{2} \times 8\frac{5}{8}$ in. (26 × 22 cm.)   (17648)
Lightly blacked for tracing on the back and inscribed '4/–'.

THOMAS DANIELL, R.A. (1749–1840),
Attributed to,
Or WILLIAM DANIELL

171. AN INDIAN VILLAGE SCENE: peasants with a horse below a building with trees.
Black chalk. $7\frac{3}{8} \times 9$ in. (18.8 × 23 cm.)   (12872)
Hitherto anonymous and among the Dutch drawings.

WILLIAM DANIELL, R.A. (1769–1837)

172. MUNKERNEKA GAUT, BENARES
Watercolour, over pencil. $4\frac{3}{8} \times 6\frac{7}{8}$ in. (11.1 × 17.6 cm.)   (14230)

Presented by H.M. Queen Mary, 1933.

GIOVANNI DAVID (1743–1790)   *Figures* 16 *and* 17

173. The Library possesses two sketch books, each with about ninety views in pencil, pen and grey wash, with occasional colour, of Turin, France, England and Belgium, September, 1785, to October, 1786, of which four are of Windsor Castle. The books are 7 × 10 in., bound in boards, with the sketches on one side of the page only, except towards the end of the second volume. The first volume is inscribed by the artist: 'Disegni di Giovanni David Genovese, fatti nei suoi Viaggi in Francia, Inghilterra && (*sic*) dall' mese di 7bre 1785 a tutto Ottobre 1786'. Most of the views are carefully dated and inscribed with Italian approximations to the place names which are as fantastic as the delineations themselves. Several of the French views are of considerable interest. Besides Windsor, which was visited on June 4, the artist sketched in London from May 24 to 28, Richmond and Hampton Court on June 3, and Dover on June 23 and 24, 1786. There are no sketches from October 15, 1785, to February 12, 1786, both in Paris. Apparently acquired since 1915.

GEORGE DAWE, R.A. (1781–1829)

174. PRINCESS CHARLOTTE AND PRINCE LEOPOLD IN THEIR BOX AT COVENT GARDEN   *Figure* 18
Pencil. $9\frac{1}{8} \times 11\frac{1}{2}$ in. (23.2 × 29.3 cm.)   (13892)
Engraved by W. T. Fry, with the omission of the moustache and other slight modifications (O'Donoghue, Vol. I, p. 416, No. 47). A coloured impression in the Royal Library (No. 13996) bears a forged signature, 'H. Edridge'.

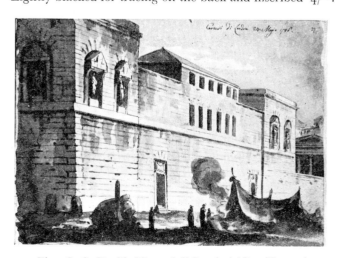

Fig. 16. G. David: 'Carceri di Londra' (Cat. No. 173)

Fig. 17. G. David: In Hampton Court (Cat. No. 173)

Fig. 18. Dawe: Princess Charlotte and Prince Leopold
(Cat. No. 174)

EDWARD DAYES (1763–1804)

175. THE LANDING OF BRITISH TROOPS AT ABOUKIR
BAY

Black chalk and watercolour, unfinished. 16 × 29⅛ in.
(40.5 × 74 cm.)   (16598)
Acquired, with the title as given and the artist's name, by
the Prince of Wales from Colnaghi on June 20, 1804, for
£2 12s. 6d. (Archives Invoices 27266).

E. DAYES, Ascribed to

176. RICHMOND, FROM BELOW THE BRIDGE

Watercolour, squared in pencil, mostly erased, on washed
mount. 8⅞ × 15⅛ in. (22.6 × 38.4 cm.)   (17054)
Inscribed on the mount, in the Colnaghi hand, 'Richmond',
'Original by Dayes'.
Acquired by the Prince of Wales from Colnaghi on July 18,
1808, for £3 3s. (Archives Invoices 27465).
If by Dayes, unusually hard and mechanical; perhaps from
his workshop.

177. KING GEORGE III, full length, standing, profile to
left wearing Star and Ribbon of the Garter. Right arm,
holding hat, extended.

Grey monochrome. 7½ × 5¼ in. (19.1 × 13.5 cm.)
(13933)
Both attribution and identification doubtful. The drawing
should be compared with No. 137.

DAYES, Manner of

178. ST. GEORGE'S CHAPEL, the exterior looking East,
with the Round Tower and the houses of the Military
Knights. A Military Knight in corner, left.

Watercolour, heavily restored. False cypher of Samuel
Prout in red. 13 × 21 in. (37.5 × 53 cm.)   (17453)
Purchased 1910.

After the cutting of trees in front of the Chapel, but before
the Round Tower was raised. Costume of 1790. Figures,
etc., reminiscent of Dayes.

WILLIAM DELAMOTTE (1775–1863)

179. DRAWINGS OF VIRGINIA WATER, with title page,
dated 1836, list and map.

Pencil, c. 6 × 7¾ in. (15 × 19.5 cm.)   (17501–17513)

  (1) Stone Grotto, near Water Fall.
  (2) Cascade.
  (3) Belvidere.
  (4) Keeper's Lodge.
  (5) High Bridge.
  (6) Ruins of Columns, Arch, etc.
  (7) Ditto, another view.
  (8) Distant view of Windsor Castle, from the Ruins.
  (9) Chinese Boathouse.
 (10) Ruins.
 (11) Royal Cottage.
 (12) Chinese Pavillion.
 (13) Map of the Lake, Buildings, and Gardens, with
     Vignette.

The plan in pen, coloured, contains a pencil vignette of a
Lodge in Windsor Forest which is signed, as is the plan
itself: Wm. A. Delamotte junr. This suggests that these
elaborate drawings in the style of contemporary steel engravings are the work of a member of a younger generation,
otherwise unknown.
No. 11 is inscribed on the back in ink: 'Royal Cottage
Virginia Water the Favorite Residence of Geo: 4th.'
Erased pencil inscriptions are on the back of some of the
other drawings.

T. DESSOULAVY, *see under* Sir William Gell (p. 52)

ANTHONY THOMAS DEVIS (1729–1817)

180. REIGATE: The church in meadows at the foot of the
downs.

Pen with grey and blue wash, with border. 13½ × 18¼ in.
(34.1 × 46.3 cm.)   (14765)
The inscription 'Reygate' cut from elsewhere and placed
on the border.
Purchased 1942 from the Fine Art Society.

DENIS DIGHTON (1792–1827), Military Painter to
the Prince Regent

181. THE CORONATION OF KING GEORGE IV. The
Duke of Wellington, Henry Dymoke, the King's Champion,
and Lord Howard of Effingham, acting for the Earl
Marshal, mounted, emerging from the temporary structure.

Watercolour. 10½ × 15⅛ in. (26.6 × 38.4 cm.)   (13606)

182. THE THIRD AND LAST CHALLENGE BY THE CHAM-
PION DURING KING GEORGE IV'S CORONATION BANQUET
IN WESTMINSTER HALL, 1821   *Plate* 48

Watercolour. 16¾ × 21½ in. (42.4 × 55 cm.)   (13630)
Signed: Denis Dighton Military Painter to His Majesty.

The modern mount is inscribed: 'Taken from the Lord
Chamberlain's Box No. 1, between the 1st and 2nd Courses
July 19th.'

Military Drawings, Volumes I, II, and XI, contain a large
series of watercolours, military scenes, exercises, etc., signed
by this artist.

Fig. 19. Robert Dighton: Sir John Lade, Bt. (Cat. No. 185)

Fig. 20. Richard Dighton: The Duchess of Cambridge
(Cat. No. 185)

R. DIGHTON, Junr.

Drawings of English Army Officers signed 'R. Dighton Junr' are in Military Drawings, Volume V. See also on No. 185 below.

RICHARD DIGHTON (1795–1880) *see* No. 185 below.

ROBERT DIGHTON (1752–1814)

183. AN ELECTION SCENE IN COVENT GARDEN, 1784: the candidates, Fox, Hood, and Wray, addressing the mob from the steps of St. Paul's on the left.   *Plate* 47

Watercolour in washed border. $14\frac{7}{8} \times 17\frac{3}{8}$ in. (37.5×44.3 cm.)   (13416)

Signed: R. Dighton del.

Blue ribbons in hats bear the three candidates' names.

Exhib.: B.F.A.C. 1931/32, No. 92; Edinburgh (King's Pictures), 1947, No. 122.

Probably the drawing acquired by the Prince Regent from Colnaghi on April 8, 1816, for £5 5s. as 'a drawing, Election at Covent Garden, by Dighton' (Archives Invoice 28092).

Dighton exhibited at the Royal Academy, 1785, a 'View of Covent Garden during the Election 1784; a tinted sketch', perhaps this drawing.

Dighton also made drawings of two other elections at Covent Garden. That of 1788, when Lord Hood and Lord John Townshend were candidates, is the subject of the drawing at one time in the possession of Mr. Ralph Edwards (*cf.* B.M. Sat., Vol. VI, p. 515), and reproduced in *The Times* of March 18, 1931, etc., where it was wrongly described as the election of 1784, and the present drawing as for the election of 1796. The drawing of the election of 1796 was exhibited at Messrs. Spink's gallery in 1948. An etched

coloured version of it was rightly relegated among the prints in the Royal Library, although the price marked at the back shews it to have been acquired by the Prince of Wales from Colnaghi for £15 15s. on May 22, 1809, as 'a drawing of the Hustings of Covent Garden on the election of Mr. Fox, Sir Al. Gardner containing many remarkable characters. Delineated by Dighton, a very interesting and curious drawing' (Archives Invoice 27809). This print differs in many respects both from Messrs. Spink's drawing and from the published print (B.M. Sat. 8815) by M. N. Bate after R. Dighton, which is clearly from another plate.

184. THE PRINCE OF WALES (KING GEORGE IV) on a white horse, in profile to left, wearing a green coat.

Pen and watercolour. (sight) $24 \times 19\frac{1}{4}$ in. (61×49 cm.)   (17637)

Signed and dated: Dighton 1804.

Presented 1927 by Mr. Oswald T. Falk.

185. PORTRAIT SKETCHES

Invoices in the Royal Archives specify numerous purchases from 1802 to 1826 from the Dightons, of sketches of public characters, sometimes named, at one guinea each. There are also from 1814 occasional purchases both of prints and drawings of public characters from Messrs. Colnaghi. In March, 1802 (Archives Invoice 26809), five named sketches are invoiced as from R. Dighton Junior, and in 1805 (Archives Invoice 27320) 'nine small figures by Master Dighton' are included at one guinea. In April of the same year (Archives Invoice 27321) four military drawings by R. Dighton Junior are specified. The invoices of March, 1802, and April, 1805, are docketed 'Robert Dighton Junr.', and one at least of the Military drawings corresponds with

Fig. 21. Richard Dighton: Mrs. Fry reading to the Prisoners
(Cat. No. 185)

the latter invoice and is signed Robert Dighton Junr. Two other military drawings and one character drawing (Vol. I, p. 27) are signed Robert Dighton Junior, and others of each class are signed R. Dighton Junr. The dates are 1805, 1806 and 1808. Thirty-two prints in the Royal Collection, signed Dighton Junior or R. Dighton Junr. bear dates from 1800 to 1806. One, undated, is signed Robert Dighton Junior. Further, one of the drawings in the Royal Library (Vol. I, p. 38) signed Dighton 1803, and invoiced 1806 (26838), is inscribed 'Dighton Junior H.R.H. Prince of Wales' Volunteers', and seems to show a private of at least 17 years of age. It would therefore appear that Dighton had an unrecorded eldest son named Robert who died young (about 1808). Denis Dighton is said to have been born in 1792 and received a commission in the 90th (Perthshire Volunteers) Regiment in 1811. Richard Dighton, said to have been born in 1795, seems not to have signed and dated prints before 1816, and if his date of birth is rightly given as 1795, can scarcely have invoiced and given receipts for drawings and prints by 1802. The earlier invoice seems to be receipted R. J. Dighton Junr., the second initial does not occur anywhere else.

The portrait sketches by the Dightons and some subject drawings have been pasted in two large volumes, in each of which an alphabetical order has been more or less followed. The intention evidently was to separate the drawings by Richard from those of his father and to confine the first volume to the latter. Since however several drawings by R. Dighton Jnr. and Richard have been included in the first volume and, moreover, alphabetical order has not been strictly followed, it has appeared more convenient to catalogue the whole series in one list, now given for convenience of reference as an Appendix on p. 118.

A third volume contains seventeen named and five unnamed portrait sketches of men in costume of the Victorian period by Richard Dighton, and two more drawings of a still later period, c. 1860–70, are in Queen Alexandra's scrapbook. Strictly speaking, the younger Dightons fall outside the scope of this catalogue, but they are included in it because of the overlap of their drawings with their father's.

Some imitations and copies of the Dightons' figures are in a recently formed album called 'Caricature Portrait Drawings 1780–1800'.

ROBERT DIGHTON, Manner of

186. THE ROYAL FAMILY, c. 1787, Windsor Castle in the distance.

Pen and grey wash. 6⅝ × 9¾ in. (16.8 × 24.6 cm.) (13935)

Clearly a fantastic composition, showing every member of the Royal Family with Princess Amelia (b. 1783) about four years of age, possibly intended less for a caricature than it actually is. Perhaps for a cheap print or illustration.

L. DOUGLAS (c. 1770)

187. 'THE SPLENITIVE ENGLISHMAN TRAVELLING IN GERMANY'

Black chalk on brown paper. 8⅛ × 12½ in. (20.5 × 32 cm.) (17665)

Signed: L. Douglas inv. in border, with the title as given.

In border also: ' "Maul and Drink Gilt" This must be wrote on the paper under the Chaise'. '2' (i.e. 2/–) on the back.

Engraved. The copy at the British Museum (B.M. Sat., IV, 4733) has the name of the artist erased, and was attributed by F. G. Stephens to Bunbury. Another example shows that the erased name was L. Douglas as on the drawing. The print has a further legend on a paper in the postillion's pocket.

JOHN DOWNMAN, A.R.A. (1750–1824)

188. EDWARD, DUKE OF KENT (1767–1820), half length, profile to left, wearing full dress Windsor uniform with the ribbon and star of the Order of St. Patrick.   *Plate* 4

Black chalk and watercolour, oval. 7⅜ × 6 in. (19.5 × 15.2 cm.) (17019)

The date 1785 in pencil is a later addition, but is appropriate if the order worn is correctly identified. The Duke was nominated the first Knight on the foundation of the Order of St. Patrick in 1783.

Exhib.: R.A. 1934, No. 655 (857), repr. in catalogue, CLIII.

189. EDWARD RANDLES, THE BLIND HARPER OF WREXHAM, AND HIS DAUGHTER ELIZABETH, THE MUSICAL PRODIGY   *Figure* 22

Watercolour. 25¼ × 18 in. (64 × 45.5 cm.) (17022)

Signed in pencil at foot right: 'Jno. Downman 1807'. The pianoforte inscribed 'Micheau fecit'.

Coll.: Sir E. Boehm (name on a label at back of old frame). W. Milbank (Sale Christie's, December 20, 1889, bt. Shepherd); Mrs. A. M. Salomons (sale Sotheby, February 2, 1933, Lot 209, called 'Queen Charlotte as a child seated at the Piano', 'by Micheau'. Bought for the Royal Library).

Studies for both figures are at the British Museum (*B.M. Quarterly*, Vol. XIV, No. 3, p. 63).

For Elizabeth Randles (1800–1829) and her father see Farington, *Diary* (ed. Grieg, Vol. II, p. 125 and note), and R. M. Clay, *Country Life*, July, 1948 (with reproduction).

Fig. 22. Downman: Edward Randles and his daughter Elizabeth (Cat. No. 189)

190. A NAVAL OFFICER, PERHAPS THE DUKE OF CLARENCE, afterwards King William IV, half length, three-quarter face to right. Blue uniform with yellow facings, no orders.

Black chalk and watercolour, oval. 7⅞ × 6⅜ in. (20 × 16.3 cm.)   (17020)

Signed: J. Downman pt. 1785.

Exhib.: R.A. 1934, No. 656 (858).

191. A GENTLEMAN, CALLED LIEUT. ISAAC SCHOMBERG, H.M.S. *Pegasus*.

Black chalk and watercolour, oval; the eye discoloured. 7⅞ × 6⅜ in. (19.7 × 16.2 cm.)   (17021)

SIR WILLIAM DRUMMOND
(? 1770–1828) *see under* Sir William Gell (p. 52)

AUGUSTUS EARLE (exhibited 1806–1838)

192. THE RUINS OF LEBIDA (LEPTIS MAGNA)
Figure 23

Watercolour. 13¾ × 21⅜ in. (34.8 × 54.2 cm.)   (17055)
Presented by Sir B. B. Bloomfield, November, 1816 (pencil inscription on mount). A letter from the artist, 66, Warren Street, Fitzroy Square, undated, preserved with the drawing, states that the sketch was made in the company of Capt. Smyth and the Consul General, Colonel Warrington. It was from Leptis that the ruins at Virginia Water were brought and erected in 1827.

Fig. 23. Earle: The ruins of Leptis Magna (Cat. No. 192)

JOHANNES ECKSTEIN (fl. 1770–1802)

193. PUNCH AND JUDY SHOW   *Plate* 50

Pen and watercolours. 14 × 17½ in. (36 × 44.8 cm.)
(13313)

Signed: Eckstein 1798, label at back as on the following.
Purchased by the Prince of Wales from Colnaghi with
No. 194 as 'Two Drawings by Eckstein of Punch and
Dromadary' for £8 8s. on April, 16, 1800 (Archives
Invoice 27145). Presumably these were the two drawings
exhibited by Eckstein at the Royal Academy 1799 as 'Punch
(468) and 'The Camel' (610). They were engraved (in
reverse) by Eckstein with aquatint by C. F. Stadler.

194. THE CAMEL AT EXETER CHANGE   *Plate* 49

Pen and watercolour. 14¼ × 17⅝ in. (35.6 × 44.5 cm.)
(13312)

Signed: Eckstein, and inscribed PIDDOK. EXETER CHANGE.
LOND. 1798. A label at the back gives the address Eckstein 35
(or 55), Grays Inn Lane.
See on No. 193.

195. THE FORTUNE-TELLER OR 'POOR HOLMS'

An old man in dressing gown, peacock fan in his right hand,
addressing four young women, one of whom holds a paper
headed 'Potion'. On a chair a Bible lies open at 'Isaiah'.
In a niche behind, wooden figures.

Pen and watercolour. 12⅝ × 10¾ in. (32 × 27.4 cm.)
(17236)

Signed: Eckstein 1798.

Presumably the drawing exhibited by Eckstein at the Royal
Academy, 1799 (with Nos. 193 and 194), as 'A Fortune-
teller' (No. 417). A note on the modern mount states that
'Poor Holms' was written on the back of the drawing. This
connects with the purchase by the Prince of Wales from
Colnaghi on December 26, 1799, of '1 Drawing Poor Olms'
for £5 5s. (Archives Invoice 27699), both equally unintelligible.

196. MOCK ASTRONOMERS, A CARICATURE. A group
of men with telescopes, etc., outside an inn observing the
reflection of the inn-sign (The Sun) in a punch-bowl.

Pen and watercolours. 10⅜ × 8 in. (26.5 × 20.4 cm.)
(17237)

Signed: Eckstein.

'A drawing by Hickstein' was bought by the Prince of
Wales from Colnaghi on January 14, 1800, for £1 11s. 6d.
(Archives Invoice 27119).

Seven watercolours of military scenes, two with signatures,
are in Military Drawings, Vol. IV (Nos. 16486–16492).

HENRY EDRIDGE (1769–1821)

197. KING GEORGE III, full length, standing, facing half
left, right hand with hat resting on his cane, left hand on
sword hilt. He wears Windsor uniform with the star and
ribbon of the Order, and the Garter on his knee. Background: the Round and Edward III Towers, Windsor
Castle.   *Plate* 11

Pencil and slight wash, torn and mended. 12¾ × 9⅛ in.
(32.2 × 23.2 cm.)   (13864)

Signed: H. Edridge, January, 1803, at foot left.

Engraved by A. Cardon, 1812 (O'Donoghue, Vol. II,
p. 234, No. 53).
A 'Portrait of his late Majesty a drawing by Edridge' was
acquired by King George IV from Colnaghi, September 5,
1821, for £16 16s. (Archives Invoice 28338). There were
also portraits by Edridge of the King, Queen, the Princesses
(omitting the Princess Royal), the Dowager Princess of
Orange and four others hanging in the Yellow Bed-room at
the Queen's House, Frogmore (Pyne, *Royal Residences*, 1817,
p. 20).
Reprod.: *Connoisseur*, August, 1933, XCII, p. 80.
Edridge exhibited portraits of the King at the R.A., 1803,
(No. 427, with the Queen) and 1821, 'his late Majesty King
George the Third in the year 1802' (No. 490).
Farington, in January, 1803 (Grieg, Vol. II, p. 74),
mentions that Edridge had been at Windsor for seven weeks

making portraits of the royal family. The King had sat on the last three days before he left for London. (See also July 4, 1803, Grieg, Vol. II, p. 118).

198. QUEEN CHARLOTTE, full length, seated under a tree, facing half right, holding fan and wearing a portrait-miniature on a necklace. Background: Frogmore House and lake. *Plate* 10

Pencil and slight wash. $12\frac{3}{4} \times 9$ in. (32.5×22.9 cm.)
(13865)

Signed: Edridge 1803, at foot left.

A portrait of the Queen by Edridge was acquired with No. 197 at the same price.
Reprod.: *Connoisseur*, XCII, August, 1933, p. 80.
Edridge exhibited portraits of the Queen at the Royal Academy, 1803 (No. 427, with the King) and 1815 (No. 435).

199. THE SAME

Exact duplicate of No. 198, but much rubbed or injured in cleaning. (17323)

Signed: 'H. Edridge 1804', at foot left.

Removed in 1945 with No. 221 from the Queen's Sitting-room at Windsor, for which they had apparently been acquired with Nos. 207 and 210.

200. THE (?) PRINCESS ROYAL, full length, facing half left, seated on a sofa, holding an open book face downwards on her knee. Landscape through window.

Pencil and slight wash, touches of white, rubbed and damaged. $13\frac{1}{2} \times 9\frac{1}{2}$ in. (34.3×24.1 cm.) (13868)

Signed: H. Edridge, May, 1805 (or 1806).

Presented to the Royal Library by H.M. Queen Mary in March, 1917, with Nos. 223 and 224.
Charlotte Augusta Matilda, Princess Royal (1766–1828), married in 1796 Frederick, afterwards King of Wurtemberg. The identification of the sitter is very doubtful. No portrait of the Princess by Edridge was exhibited at the Royal Academy, nor was she in England in 1805 or 1806.

201. EDWARD, DUKE OF KENT, full length, standing, facing right. Background: Gibraltar. *Plate* 21

Pencil, grey and blue washes on toned paper. $12\frac{1}{8} \times 9\frac{1}{2}$ in. (32.8×23 cm.) (13851)

Signed: Edridge 1802 at foot left.

No. 1026 (with photograph taken in 1872) in the Inventory of Pictures, Windsor (Lord Chamberlain's Department); transferred to the Royal Library, April, 1924.
Edridge exhibited a portrait of the Duke of Kent at the Royal Academy in 1816 (No. 418).
Edward, Duke of Kent (1767–1820), fourth son of King George III, father of Queen Victoria.

202. THE SAME

Close replica of the preceding, with no blue wash and little pencil work in the background, but faded and damaged. The signature and date are the same. $13 \times 9\frac{1}{8}$ in. (33×23.5 cm.) (13850)

203. PRINCESS AUGUSTA, full length seated, looking half left, wearing anchor locket, a book in her hand. Background: Frogmore and a Gothic porch.

Pencil and light wash on toned or discoloured paper. $12\frac{3}{4} \times 9$ in. (32.2×23 cm.) (13860)

Signed: Edridge 1802, at foot right.

A portrait of Princess Augusta by Edridge was acquired by King George IV on July 23, 1821, from Colnaghi for £16 16s. with Nos. 209 and 217 (Archives Invoice 28337). See also on No. 197. Edridge exhibited portraits of Princess Augusta at the Royal Academy in 1806 (No. 603) and 1815 (No. 427).
The anchor locket shewn in these four portraits may relate to the Princess' love of the sea and devotion to her brother William, Duke of Kent, the sailor and future King William IV (*cf.* D. M. Stuart, *The Daughters of George III*, 1939, p. 82, etc.).
On June 20, 1802, Farington notes that Lysons on return from Windsor told him that Edridge was there making drawings of the princesses, 'but is obliged to wait their time and has them not to sit more than an hour in a day' (unpublished).
Augusta Sophia (1768–1840), second daughter of King George III.

204. PRINCESS AUGUSTA (2)

An exact replica of the preceding save that the arms are folded and the book is placed, open, on the cloak which is differently thrown over the seat.

$12\frac{5}{8} \times 8\frac{7}{8}$ in. (32×22.6 cm.) (13861)

Noted on the mount as given by H.M. Queen Mary (see on No. 211).

205. PRINCESS AUGUSTA (3), seated to right, three-quarter face to right, wearing anchor locket, holding book. Windsor Castle, the south-east corner, in background to right.

Pencil and watercolour. $12\frac{3}{4} \times 8$ in. (32.5×23 cm.)
(17577)

Acquired from Walker's Galleries in June, 1947.

206. PRINCESS AUGUSTA (4), full length, standing, facing right, wearing anchor locket. Background: Weymouth Bay with shipping. *Plate* 12

Pencil and slight wash. $12\frac{5}{8} \times 8\frac{7}{8}$ in. (32.1×22.1 cm.)
(13854)

Signed: Edridge 1802, at foot left.

Reprod.: *Connoisseur*, XCII, August, 1933, p. 80.

207. PRINCESS AUGUSTA (5), full length, seated, under tree, facing half right, cameo in bandeau. Background: Frogmore, Gothic summer-house.

Pencil and slight wash, the cheeks highly coloured. $12\frac{5}{8} \times 8\frac{7}{8}$ in. (32×22.6 cm.) (14248)

Presented by H.M. Queen Mary with No. 210, *q.v.* Mounted and inscribed in the Royal Library with Nos. 199, 210 and 221. The identification of the sitter is not certain. The summer-house as in No. 209. See also No. 230.

208. PRINCESS AUGUSTA (6), head only, facing three-quarter left, with turban and aigrette.

Pencil and watercolour. $5\frac{5}{8} \times 3\frac{5}{8}$ in. (14.2×9.3 cm.)
(13987)

Presented to H.M. Queen Mary by Messrs. Colnaghi in May, 1931, with Nos. 212, 213 and 226, and by her to the Royal Library.

209. PRINCESS ELIZABETH, full length, seated on a rustic stone seat, looking to right. Background: the Frogmore lake and Gothic summer-house.

Pencil, with slight wash. 12¾ × 8⅞ in. (32.2 × 22.5 cm.)

Signed: Edridge 1802, at foot left.   (13853)

A portrait of Princess Elizabeth by Edridge was acquired with Nos. 203 and 217 from Colnaghi on July 23, 1821, for £16 16s. (Archives Invoice 28337). See also on No. 197.
Edridge exhibited portraits of Princess Elizabeth at the R.A. in 1806 (No. 609) and 1815 (No. 439).
None of these drawings is identical with the portrait of the Princess engraved by S. W. Reynolds after Edridge and published by Harding in 1831 (O'Donoghue, Vol. II, p. 157, No. 5).
The Gothic summer-house at Frogmore is identical with that shewn on No. 207. See also No. 230.
Princess Elizabeth (1770–1840), third daughter of King George III, married in 1818 Frederick, Landgrave of Hesse-Homburg.

210. PRINCESS ELIZABETH (2), full length, facing front, seated at escritoire, cutting paper. Landscape background.
                                        Plate 14

Pencil and slight wash. 12⅝ × 8⅞ in. (32.1 × 22.4 cm.)
                                        (14247)

Signed: Edridge 1804 (almost erased) at foot left.

Stated to have been presented to Lady Cathcart in 1804. Purchased at Robinson & Fishers, November 14, 1940, and given to the collection by H.M. Queen Mary, 1940, with No. 207.
Several examples of the Princess' skill in cut paper work are in the Royal Library (*cf.* Nevill Jackson, *Silhouette*, 1938, pl. 47). For her drawings see D. M. Stuart, *op. cit.*, p. 151.

211. PRINCESS ELIZABETH (3) as on the preceding, but with pen or brush in her hand, resting her head on her left hand and looking up. No bandeau in hair.

Pencil and slight wash. 12⅝ × 8¾ in. (32 × 22.2 cm.)
                                        (13867)

Signed: Edridge 1804, at foot left.

Presented by H.M. Queen Mary.

212. PRINCESS ELIZABETH (4), half length, standing facing half right, wearing bandeau and feather.
Pencil and wash (head only). 6⅞ × 4½ in. (17.4 × 11.8 cm.)
                                        (13985)
Inscribed in pencil, 'Princess Elizabeth'.
Presented to H.M. Queen Mary by Messrs. Colnaghi in May, 1931, and by her to the Royal Library. See on No. 208.

213. PRINCESS ELIZABETH (5), bust, full face.
Pencil and wash. 6 × 4½ in. (15.4 × 11.6 cm.)   (13986)
Inscribed in pencil (erroneously), 'Princess Mary afterwards Duchess of Gloucester', in the same hand as on the other drawings presented at the same time (see on No. 208).

214. ERNEST, DUKE OF CUMBERLAND, full length standing, facing half left, in Windsor uniform with Garter and Star. Windsor Castle background.   *Plate* 19
Pencil and slight wash. 12¾ × 9 in. (32.3 × 22.8 cm.)
                                        (13852)

Signed: Edridge 1802, at foot left.
Exhib.: R.A. 1934, No. 730 (1141).
Ernest, Duke of Cumberland (1771–1851), fifth son of King George III, afterwards King of Hanover.

215. AUGUSTUS FREDERICK, DUKE OF SUSSEX, full length standing, facing half right, wearing uniform with kilt, Garter and Star. Distant view of Windsor Castle.
                                        Plate 20
Pencil and slight wash. 15¾ × 11½ in. (40 × 29.9 cm.)
                                        (13869)

Signed: H. Edridge, Jany. 1806, at foot left.
Exhib.: Edinburgh, 1947 (King's Pictures), No. 116.
Edridge exhibited a portrait of the Duke of Sussex in the Uniform of the Loyal North Britons at the R.A. in 1806 (No. 604).
Augustus Frederick, Duke of Sussex (1773–1843), sixth son of King George III.

216. ADOLPHUS FREDERICK, DUKE OF CAMBRIDGE, full length standing, facing half right, in uniform, wearing the Star of the Garter. Windsor Castle background, looking down Castle Hill.   *Plate* 18
Pencil and wash, discoloured through exposure. 13 × 9¼ in. (33.4 × 23.5 cm.)   (14246)
Signed: Edridge 1802, at foot left.
Acquired from Colnaghi, November 26, 1821, for £16 16s. with No. 220 or 221 (Archives Invoice 28340).
Adolphus Frederick, Duke of Cambridge (1774–1850), seventh son of King George III.

217. PRINCESS MARY, full length standing, facing half right. Background: Queen's Lodge, the towers of Windsor Castle rising behind.
Pencil and slight wash on toned paper. 12⅝ × 8⅞ in. (32.1 × 22.7 cm.)   (13862)

Signed: H. Edridge 1802, at foot left.

A portrait of the Duchess of Gloucester was acquired from Colnaghi for £16 16s. on July 23, 1821, with Nos. 203 and 209 (Archives Invoice 28337). See also on No. 197.
Edridge exhibited portraits of Princess Mary at the Royal Academy in 1806 (No. 602) and 1815 (No. 440).
Princess Mary (1776–1857), fourth daughter of King George III, married 1816 her cousin William Frederick, Duke of Gloucester.

218. PRINCESS MARY (2), full length standing, facing to left, right hand on balustrade. Towers of Windsor Castle in the background.
Pencil, grey wash and some red. 12¾ × 9 in. (32.3 × 22.6 cm.)   (13858)

Signed: Edridge 1802, at foot left.
See on the preceding.

219. PRINCESS MARY (3), full length standing, facing three-quarter left. View from the west end of the North Terrace overlooking the river.   *Plate* 13
Pencil, grey wash, some pink and blue. 12¾ × 8⅞ in. (32.2 × 22.6 cm.)   (13859)
The figure only, half length, engraved in soft ground, by M. A. Bourlier, 1806 (O'Donoghue, Vol. III, p. 201, No. 15).

Signed: Edridge 1802, at foot left.

Presented by H.M. Queen Mary.

220. PRINCESS SOPHIA (1), full length, standing to right, facing half right, leaning on the plinth of a balustrade. Background: Windsor Park. *Plate* 22

Pencil, grey wash, blue and some pink. $12\frac{3}{8} \times 8\frac{5}{8}$ in. (31.5 × 21.5 cm.) (13857)

Signed: Edridge Apr. 1802, at foot right.

Exhib.: R.A. 1934, No. 731 (1148), Pl. CLXIII (as Princess Mary).

Reprod.: *Connoisseur*, XCII, 1933, p. 80.

A portrait of Princess Sophia was acquired from Colnaghi on November 26, 1821, for £16 16s. (with No. 216) (Archives Invoice 28340). See also on No. 197.

Edridge exhibited a portrait of Princess Sophia at the R.A. in 1806 (No. 605).

Princess Sophia (1777–1848), fifth daughter of King George III.

221. PRINCESS SOPHIA (2). The same.

Pencil and slight wash on toned or discoloured paper. $12\frac{3}{4} \times 8\frac{7}{8}$ in. (32.5 × 22.5 cm.) (17324)

The signature, 'Edridge 1802' at foot left, has faded almost to illegibility.

See on No. 199.

222. PRINCESS SOPHIA (3), half length, full face, with spectacles. *Plate* 15

Pencil and watercolour. Oval, framed as a miniature, $4\frac{1}{8} \times 3\frac{1}{4}$ in. (10.3 × 8 cm.) (17099)

Conjecturally attributed to Edridge, but certainly a portrait of Princess Sophia.

223. PRINCESS SOPHIA (4), head and shoulders, facing half left, leaning on her right hand.

Pencil and watercolour. $5\frac{3}{8} \times 4\frac{1}{2}$ in. (13.5 × 11.6 cm.) (13855)

Presented to the Royal Library by H.M. Queen Mary in March, 1917, with Nos. 200 and 224.

224. PRINCESS SOPHIA (?) (5), head only, facing left.

Pencil. $5\frac{3}{8} \times 4\frac{5}{8}$ in. (13.7 × 11.7 cm.) (13856)

See on the preceding, No. 223. Possibly a study, left uncoloured as unsuccessful.

225. PRINCESS AMELIA, full length, full face, standing to left, holding a book on an oval writing desk. Background: Windsor Castle, the south front. *Plate* 16

Pencil and slight wash on toned paper. $12\frac{5}{8} \times 8\frac{7}{8}$ in. (32 × 22.4 cm.) (13866)

Signed: Edridge 1804, at foot left.

Edridge exhibited a portrait of Princess Amelia at the Royal Academy, 1806 (No. 608). See also on No. 197.

Presented by H.M. Queen Mary, March, 1925.

Princess Amelia (1783–1810), sixth and youngest daughter of King George III.

226. PRINCESS AMELIA (2), bust, full face, wearing hat and feathers. *Plate* 17

Pencil and watercolour. $5\frac{1}{2} \times 4$ in. (13.9 × 10.2 cm.) (13988)

Inscribed 'Princess Sophia' in the same hand as Nos. 208 *q.v.*, 212 and 213.

In spite of the pencilled inscription on this drawing, the identification of the sitter here and in No. 225 as Princess Amelia is based on the engraving by Agar after Mee (O'Donoghue, Vol. I, p. 43, No. 5).

227. FREDERICA SOPHIA WILHELMINA, PRINCESS OF ORANGE (1752–1820), full length, standing, facing half right, looking to front, left hand resting on table.

Pencil and slight wash on toned paper. $12\frac{3}{4} \times 8\frac{7}{8}$ in. (32.1 × 22.7 cm.) (13863)

Signed: Edridge 1802, at foot left.

Frederica, sister of Frederick William II King of Prussia, married William V, Prince of Orange. Correspondence in the Royal Archives indicates that she visited Windsor and London in the summer of 1802.

For her portrait by Edridge at Frogmore, see on No. 197.

228. THE FIRST MARQUESS WELLESLEY, three-quarter length, seated, facing front, left hand on table; wearing a star.

Pencil on buff paper. $7\frac{1}{4} \times 5\frac{1}{4}$ in. (18.4 × 13.3 cm.) (13849)

Signed: Edridge 1797, at foot left. See on No. 229.

Richard Wellesley (1760–1842), K.G., Governor-General of India.

229. HYACINTHE GABRIELLE ROLAND, MARCHIONESS WELLESLEY, full length, facing half left, background of trees.

Pencil on buff paper. $10\frac{3}{8} \times 6\frac{7}{8}$ in. (26.5 × 17.5 cm.) (13848)

Signed: Edridge 1796, in ink, at foot right.

Bought with the preceding, October 3, 1924, from Mrs. Morrison. The placing of the signatures shews that the drawings have not been cut down and were not pendants.

Hyacinthe Gabrielle Roland, of Paris, first wife (*m.* 1794) of the preceding (*d.* 1816).

230. THE GOTHIC SUMMER-HOUSE, FROGMORE, 1802

Pencil. $8\frac{3}{8} \times 11\frac{5}{8}$ in. (21.2 × 29.5 cm.) (17645)

Inscribed by the artist: 'Frogmore, June 1802'.

Acquired from the collection of E. Horsman Coles, C.B., in November, 1949.

No doubt drawn during the visit of the artist to Windsor in June, 1802, for the purpose of making portraits of the Princesses, and probably used for the background of Nos. 209 of 1802 and 207.

231. WINDSOR CASTLE FROM THE NORTH, below Romney Island.

Pencil; damaged. $9\frac{1}{4} \times 13\frac{5}{8}$ in. (23.6 × 34.7 cm.) (17380)

Inscribed: Edridge, in pen at foot right.

232. QUAI DES TUILERIES AND PONT ROYAL, PARIS, 1817

Pencil. $7 \times 16\frac{1}{2}$ in. (17.9 × 42.8 cm.) (13385)

Inscribed by the artist: October 11, 1817 (partly cut off).

Exhib.: Paris (English Life), 1948, No. 575.

For Edridge's visit to Paris in September and October, 1817, see Farington, *Diary* (unpubd.), Nov. 13, 1817. He was there again in 1819 with Sir George Beaumont (*ibid.* June 2, 1819). Pencil sketch books dating from both visits are at the British Museum, and there is a drawing of the Pont Neuf, 1817, at the Victoria and Albert Museum (E.5643—1910).

233. MONTMARTRE: THE MILLS. 1817

Pencil. $7 \times 16\frac{3}{4}$ in. (17.7×42.7 cm.) (13386)

Inscribed by the artist: From Montmartre, October 20.

From the same sketch book as the preceding.

Exhib.: Paris (English Life), 1948, No. 574.

SAMUEL EVANS OF ETON (d. 1835)

234. THE TOWN HALL, WINDSOR

Watercolour, somewhat faded, in lined border. $6\frac{1}{8} \times 8\frac{1}{4}$ in. (15.6×21 cm.) (17529)

A coloured etching of the same subject, similar in style and treatment, in the Royal Library, is inscribed: 'Drawn Etched and Published by S. Evans, Eton' (the word 'etched' erased). These four drawings, roughly coloured, would appear to have formed a set, or part of a set, repeated for sale as souvenirs of the town. Other examples exist.

Evans was drawing master at Eton about 1798 and until 1818.

235. OLD WINDSOR PARISH CHURCH

Watercolour in lined border. $6\frac{1}{8} \times 8\frac{3}{8}$ in. (15.5×21.2 cm.) (17530)

Shewing the church before it was pulled down and rebuilt in 1820.

236. THE CHARITY SCHOOL, ST. ALBANS STREET, WINDSOR

Watercolour in lined border. $6\frac{3}{8} \times 8\frac{1}{4}$ in. (15.9×21 cm.) (17531)

237. THE ENGINE HOUSE

Watercolour in lined border. $6\frac{1}{2} \times 8\frac{1}{2}$ in. (16.5×21.7 cm.) (17532)

S. EVANS, Manner of

238. THE WOODEN BRIDGE, WINDSOR, AND THE ETON BANK

Watercolour, faded. $8 \times 11\frac{1}{4}$ in. (20×28.5 cm.) (17420)

Conjecturally attributed to S. Evans.

239. WINDSOR: THE NORTH-WEST END OF THE CASTLE AND THE TOWN

Watercolour, a little pen. $8\frac{1}{8} \times 11\frac{3}{4}$ in. (20.5×29.8 cm.) (17379)

The pencilled attribution to Havell on the back, presumably the vendor's, carries no conviction. Undistinguished but well preserved, it may have come from the hand of S. Evans, an assistant or a pupil.

JOHN FABER THE ELDER (1650/60–1721)

For two portraits on vellum (Charles I, 1691, and John Calvin, 1697), see L. van Puyvelde, *Dutch Drawings at Windsor Castle*, Nos. 121 (as of 1693) and 122.

240. JOHN DUKE OF MARLBOROUGH, bust in armour, nearly full face.

Plumbago on vellum. Oval, $5\frac{1}{8} \times 4\frac{1}{8}$ in. (13×10.5 cm.) (17576)

Signed: J. Faber, 1708.

Purchased by King Edward VII, November, 1906.

An inscription on the back of the frame besides a number '79' and 'John D. of Marlburgh' reads: 'This picture being valued at 40 (?) £ if I dye let it be given to my brother E . . . Watts who knows how to esteem so exquisitely fine a piece. Aprill 1715 J.W.'. 'To my Dear Brother E.W. to whom I had bequeathed it a year ago. Apll 12th 1716.'

JOHN FABER JUNIOR (*c.* 1684–1756), Attributed to

241. KING JAMES II AS DUKE OF YORK, full length, standing, full face, in Garter Robes, holding plumed hat in his left hand, right hand on hip.

Red and black chalk. $17\frac{1}{8} \times 10\frac{3}{8}$ in. (43.2×26.3 cm.) (14043)

This has been regarded as the engraver's drawing for the anonymous mezzotint, three-quarter length only, in reverse, which Challoner-Smith (IV, p. 1693, No. 55) attributes to John Faber Junior. The head, however, is by no means identical with that in the mezzotint, and resembles more closely that in the mezzotint portrait of James II by Smith after Kneller (Challoner-Smith, Vol. III, p. 1184, No. 143), and is in the same direction. Further, the mezzotint by Faber is so close to the mezzotint by Beckett after the portrait of Henry, First Duke of Grafton, by T. Hawker at Euston (O'Donoghue, Vol. II, p. 362, No. 1; the portrait reproduced by Collins-Baker, *Lely and the Stuart Portrait Painters*, 1912, Vol. I, p. 180), as to suggest that Beckett's plate was cut down for it with the necessary alterations of the head. If that were the case there would be no need for an intermediate drawing. Moreover, the drawing differs from the painting by Hawker and both mezzotints in details, e.g. the base of the column, the plinth, the landscape, and the foot of the curtain. Probably the drawing was made for an engraving which was never published, from a portrait of the King which may have been the prototype, *inter alia*, of the Hawker picture.

JOHANN LUDWIG FAESCH (or FESCH) (1738–1778)

242. GARRICK IN THE CHARACTER OF 'RANGE'

Watercolour on vellum. $3\frac{1}{8} \times 8\frac{1}{2}$ in. (?) (7.9×6.4 cm.) (13609)

Uniform with drawings of Garrick, etc., some signed 'Fesch pinxt', at the British Museum (1931–5–9–250–255).

A drawing 'Garrick in the Character of Range', was acquired by the Prince Regent from Colnaghi on July 8, 1816, for £1 1s. (Archives Invoice 28113).

JOSEPH FARINGTON, R.A. (1747–1821)

243. WINDSOR CASTLE AND TOWN FROM THE NORTH-WEST *Plate* 52

Pencil and grey wash, minute pen touches with brown ink. Squared and pricked. $11\frac{3}{4} \times 18\frac{1}{2}$ in. (30.1×47 cm.) (13639)

Inscribed 'Br' at foot, in pencil.

Etched by Farington, no date; aquatint by Stadler, June 1, 1793, but not used for Boydell's *Thames* (1794–1796).

244. WINDSOR FROM CLEWER FIELDS, Nov. 3 [1793].

Pencil and fine pen; traces of squaring and pricking. $8\frac{1}{4} \times 12\frac{3}{8}$ in. (20.5×31.5 cm.) (13638)

Inscribed: 'West View Novr. 3rd' with topographical and colour notes on the drawing. Foreground unfinished. 'Br' at foot right, in pencil.

Identical with the aquatint by J. C. Stadler for Boydell's *Thames* with date of publication, June 1, 1793.

Farington in his (unpublished) *Diary* writes as follows: 'Sunday Novr. 3rd (1793). A beautiful day. Left Henley and returned to Windsor by Braywick. Near Clewer I stopped the Chaise, and made a sketch of Windsor Castle which makes a more beautiful assemblage from this point than from any I have hitherto discovered. What part of the town is seen in this view very happily mixes with the nobler objects and gives additional importance by the contrast of sizes and forms; while the colour of the Brick, which is lowered in its tone by weather and time, and many white buildings interspersed, add greatly to the richness of the colouring and to the spirit of the general effect. No water is seen in this view.' In spite of the stated date of publication, the *Diary* shows Farington still working on this plate, with others, on December 24, 1793. He handed it in 'to Mr. Stadler to be bit in' on the 31st, and finished washing the outlines on January 17, 1794.

245. WINDSOR BRIDGE FROM THE ETON SIDE, August 25, 1790.

Pencil and reed pen with brown ink and grey wash. Faintly squared and pricked. $10\frac{1}{8} \times 15\frac{1}{8}$ in. (25.9×38.5 cm.)
(13637)

Inscribed in pen: 'August 25th. 90.' at foot, left.
Etched by Farington, January 2, 1792; aquatint by Stadler, June, 1793, for Boydell's *Thames*.

246. WINDSOR CASTLE FROM ETON PLAYING FIELDS, ANOTHER VIEW

Pencil and reed pen with brown ink, ruled borders. $12\frac{7}{8} \times 13\frac{5}{8}$ in. (32.8×35.8 cm.)
(13642)
Inscribed with many colour notes, etc., in pencil.

247. WINDSOR CASTLE FROM ETON PLAYING FIELDS, A NEARER VIEW   *Plate* 53

Pencil, reed pen with brown ink, brown and grey washes. $11\frac{1}{4} \times 10$ in. (28.7×25.4 cm.)
(13635)
Inscribed 'Br' in pencil at foot, centre. See on No. 248.

248. ETON MEADOWS. WINDSOR CASTLE IN THE DISTANCE

Pencil, reed pen with brown ink, grey wash. $13\frac{1}{4} \times 10$ in. (33.9×25.3 cm.)
(13421)
Inscribed in pencil and repeated in pen 'August 23rd'. 'Br', at foot right, in pencil.
Similar to the preceding and dating probably from the 1790 visit (see No. 245).

249. WINDSOR CASTLE FROM ETON PLAYING FIELDS

Pencil, reed pen with brown ink, grey, blue and yellow wash. Figures and cows superimposed in pencil. $12\frac{1}{8} \times 9\frac{5}{8}$ in. (30.8×24.2 cm.)
(13636)
Signed: Jos: Farington, in pen at foot, right. 'Br' at foot right, in pencil.

250. WINDSOR CASTLE FROM ETON

Pencil, fine pen with brown ink, the boat an afterthought in pencil. $8\frac{1}{4} \times 8\frac{5}{8}$ in. (20.9×22.1 cm.)
(13634)
Inscribed 'Br' at foot right, in pencil.

251. WINDSOR FROM ETON MEADOWS   *Plate* 54

Pencil, reed pen with brown ink, grey wash. $13\frac{3}{8} \times 11$ in. (34×28.1 cm.)
(13420)

Signed: Jos. Farington, in pen in the foreground.
Reprod.: *Connoisseur*, XCII, September, 1933, p. 147.

252. WINDSOR CASTLE AND TOWN FROM THE ETON PLAYING FIELDS

Pencil, traces of squaring. $10\frac{1}{2} \times 19\frac{1}{4}$ in. (26.5×49 cm.)
(13640)

Inscribed 'Br' at foot, in pencil.

253. WINDSOR CASTLE FROM ETON PLAYING FIELDS, ANOTHER VIEW

Pencil and reed pen with brown ink. $12 \times 14\frac{3}{8}$ in. (30.6×36.7 cm.)
(13641)

254. WINDSOR CASTLE FROM THE GREAT PARK

Pencil, pen with brown ink and grey washes, brown ruled border. $13\frac{1}{8} \times 19\frac{3}{4}$ in. (33×50 cm.)
(13644)
Inscribed in pencil with the title 'Br' at foot in pencil, 'Dist' also in pencil above the horizon.
Horizontal and perpendicular lines, pricked.

255. WINDSOR CASTLE AND TOWN FROM ST. LEONARD'S HILL   *Plate* 51

Pencil, fine pen, grey and blue washes. $12\frac{1}{2} \times 19$ in. (31.7×48.3 cm.)
(13643)
Dated 'Oct. 9th' at foot.
Connected with the aquatint dated June 1, 1793.

256. WINDSOR FROM LORD SHULDHAM'S, Oct. 31, 1793.

Pencil and fine pen. $12\frac{1}{4} \times 19\frac{3}{8}$ in. (31.3×49.1 cm.)
(13645)

Inscribed with the title as given, 'Octr. 31', and numbered '21' at foot right. Pencil notes.
Farington mentions his making a drawing from this point in his (unpublished) *Diary* for October 31, 1793: 'Ankerwyke, Lord Shuldhams, a large white House in the gothic taste, is situated near the end of the Hill on which we stood and with the line of ground steeply sloping from it, makes up the composition of this landscape of which I made a drawing. In the middle ground below, Beaumont Lodge, the House of Mr. Griffith is seen. A little beyond is Old Windsor but covered with trees.'

257. VIEW FROM THE NORTH TERRACE, LOOKING OVER ETON

Pencil, some traces of squaring, pricked. Unfinished. $7\frac{1}{2} \times 15\frac{3}{4}$ in. (19.2×40.1 cm.)
(13632)

258. WEST VIEW FROM WINDSOR TERRACE

Pencil. Squared and pricked. $8 \times 11\frac{7}{8}$ in. (20.4×30.2 cm.)
(13633)
Inscribed 'from Dr. Duval's. Oct. 4th'. 'Br' at foot right in pencil.

259. NEAR TAPLOW, Oct. 1, 1804.

Pencil on brown grey paper, touches of white in the sky squared. $10\frac{1}{4} \times 17\frac{1}{2}$ in. (26×44.6 cm.)
(17546)
Signed: Jos Farington, right, and dated Octr. 1. 1804, left, in pencil at foot; 'at Taplow' apparently in Farington's hand on the old mount.
Acquired from the Fine Art Society, 1946, No. 146.

JOSEPH FARINGTON AND MARY SMIRKE

260. WORCESTER BRIDGE
Plate 55

Pencil and watercolour, on washed mount. 8¾ × 12½ in. (22.2 × 32.7 cm.) (17179)

Coll.: J. Leslie Wright.

Exhib.: Leamington, etc., 1938; Fine Art Society, 1942, No. 38, whence it was acquired for the Royal Library.

Inscribed on the mount (now cut off and pasted at the back): 'Jos. Farrington April 14. 1821. supposed to be the last Drawings he made. J. Booth. made by Sir G. P. Turner Express Order.'

Farington's unpublished *Diary*, January 29 to April 16, 1821, describes the negotiations for these two drawings, commissioned through Booth the bookseller by Sir Gregory Page Turner, and largely executed by Miss Smirke.

261. SHREWSBURY CASTLE

Pencil and watercolour on washed mount. 8¾ × 13¼ in. (22.2 × 33.3 cm.) (17178)

Companion to No. 260 (*q.v.*).

FARINGTON, Attributed to

262. WINDSOR CASTLE FROM THE HOME PARK, LOOKING EAST

Reed pen with brown ink, grey washes. Much rubbed down and discoloured. On a card cut down on all sides with J. Pine's engraved copy, 1733, of Magna Charta, also cut down, on the other side. The drawing may have been used as a backing for the print. 15 × 23½ in. (38 × 58.5 cm.) (17416)

The reed pen is characteristic of Farington, but is more loosely used than as a rule by him. It may be part of the beginning of a very large drawing.

Dr. JOHN FISHER (1748–1825), Bishop of Salisbury

263. THE ROUND (MILL) HOUSE, EASTBOURNE

Pencil, pen and watercolour on washed mount. 8 × 12½ in. (19.7 × 31.7 cm.) (17311)

From a volume of sketches by Dr. John Fisher sold at Hodgsons, August 24, 1944, Lot 279, together with an etching, coloured, of the same subject, which, unlike the drawing, was indexed under this title.

The Rev. John Fisher, whose friendship with King George III as well as his proficiency as a draughtsman are frequently mentioned in Fanny Burney's Diary, was appointed Preceptor to Prince Edward, afterwards Duke of Kent, in 1780. In the summer of that year the Prince with Princesses Elizabeth and Sophia stayed for a time at Eastbourne in three 'tolerable good modern buildings, agreeably situated at the seaside'. Here, at the edge of the cliff, there was a large building called the Round-House, formerly a horizontal mill for grinding corn erected by J. Gandon for the father of Mortimer the artist (*Eastbourne . . . A Descriptive Account. . . .* London, 1787, p. 18. T. Jones, *Memoirs, Walpole Society*, Vol. XXXII, p. 23). According to Chambers' *Handbook for Eastbourne*, 1882, p. 26, the Round House was pulled down in 1841. Mary Hamilton writes in a letter of July 7, 1780, from 'Sea Houses, East Bourne', that Dr. Fisher generally stays in their house after the Prince and his other tutors had left after dinner, and 'obligingly instructs the Princess in drawing'. (Anson, *Life of Mary Hamilton*, p. 95.) J. Gandon's Plans and Elevations for the Mill House at Eastbourne belonging to Mr. Mortimer were exhibited at the Society of Artists, 1773, Nos. 107 and 108.

264. THE SAME

Pen and watercolour within wide border. 18¾ × 24 in. (46.5 × 61 cm.) (14710)

This and the next drawing are mentioned in the George III Inventory 'A'. It appears on an inserted slip, as No. 16—'View (ideal?) on the Sea Coast with a circular building', without name of artist (p. 168). The writer, J. H. Glover, has also written below the drawing 'by Paul Sandby (?)', and separately 'T.S.'.

265. WINDSOR CASTLE: THE BLACK ROD, DURING THE DEMOLITION OF THE BUILDING

Pencil, pen and watercolour. 18¾ × 24 in. (46.5 × 61 cm.) (14564)

See on the preceding. This drawing is described in the George III Inventory 'A' (p. 168) as 'No. 17—an Unfinished View of part of Windsor Castle', and is inscribed by Glover in pencil, 'By Paul Sandby (?)' with a 'T.S. (?)' perhaps by another hand, and 'Yes' in pencil under the former. Though not by Paul Sandby and palpably by the same hand as the Round House at Eastbourne (No. 264), it is of considerable topographical interest for its view of the demolition in the Black Rod below the Round Tower, which is indicated in light pencil. The Maids of Honour Tower is indicated more clearly on the right. For the date of the demolition, c. 1780, see *Sandby Catalogue*, No. 39.

A similar drawing in pencil with a little pen and colour, apparently on the same paper, but still more unfinished and smaller (13½ × 20½ in., perhaps cut down), is in the Supplementary Volume of Miscellaneous Drawings, CXXIV, No. 72, of the King's Maps at the British Museum. Its subject, the South Terrace, Windsor Castle, before the 'improvements' of about 1780, was clearly not recognized. Pencil indications 'Br' for brickwork at the foot of the walls and 'Gr' for grass show that it is a sketch made on the spot.

266. A VIEW IN KEW GARDENS

Pen and watercolour, on washed mount. 10⅜ × 16¼ in. (26.3 × 41.5 cm.) (17058)

Signed in ink: J. Fisher 1782, and inscribed in pen on the back of the mount: 'A View of the Lawn taken from the Windows of the Royal Palace at Kew'. 'View in Kew Garden' is written in pencil on the mount below the drawing perhaps in a Colnaghi hand. Though more advanced in manner than the preceding drawings and coming from a different source, it is sufficiently similar in certain details to justify an attribution to the future Bishop of Salisbury who, moreover, was frequently at the Palace, rather than to another of the contemporary topographers of the same name.

Lady HENRY FITZGERALD, *see* No. 72

THOMAS FORSTER (fl. 1695–1712)

267. QUEEN ANNE, half length, nearly full face.

Plumbago on vellum. Oval, 4½ × 3½ in. (11 × 8.8 cm.) (17028)

Signed: T. Forster delin. 1704.

Acquired Christie's, May 8, 1931, Lot 19, as a portrait of Queen Caroline. Given to the Royal Library by H.M. Queen Mary. It would appear to be somewhat youthful for Queen Anne in 1704, and bears no insignia of royalty.

LAURENCE GAHAGAN (fl. 1798–1817)

268. QUEEN CHARLOTTE in her 74th year, drawn while taking the waters at Bath.

Black chalk. 7 × 5¾ in. (17.7 × 14.5 cm.)   (13891)

Signed: L. Gahagan delt, and inscribed, in ink over pencil, 'Original'.

Engraved without date or engraver's name after 'Gahagan the celebrated modeller' (a copy by Thomson, 1817). (O'Donoghue, Vol. I, p. 410, No 32.)

THOMAS GAINSBOROUGH, R.A. (1727–1788)

269. LANDSCAPE COMPOSITION   *Plate* 46

Black and white chalk on blue paper. 11 × 13¾ in. (28 × 33.7 cm.)   (13428)

A drawing by Gainsborough was bought by the Prince of Wales from Colnaghi on January 14, 1800, for £1 11s. 6d. (Archives Invoice 27119), but as this drawing has been stripped and laid down in a modern mount there is no means of identifying it with the entry. Queen Charlotte's large collection of drawings by Gainsborough was sold in June, 1819.

270. A CART AND HORSES IN A LANDSCAPE

Blue watercolour and body-colour and (?) brown 8¼ × 11¼ in. (21 × 28.8 cm.)   (13427)

Inscribed on the back: 'This Drawing was given Me by my . . . [erased] . . . It is by Gainsborough, and was purchased at his sale at Mr. Christie's April 10 1797 John Thomas [partly erased] Smith, Engraver of the Antiquities of London and its Environs. It is drawn in a very singular manner; as will appear when held up to the light.' Any effect that may have been originally intended cannot now be judged, for the drawing has suffered from staining and discoloration, more especially towards the edges, where it appears to have been once fixed down. Smith's remark about the singular manner is however quite justified since the cart-horses and figures are merely indicated by a sweep of the brush loaded with blue body-colour; the sky and distant hills on the right appear to have been more carefully treated, and the foreground more modelled in blue; but the reddish-brown stain over the whole paper appears to be accidental, as are certainly the water stains, which have left clearer outlines than those of the original drawing and may have produced the effect noted by J. T. Smith.

J. GARSIDE

Two very crude watercolours of military character, signed J. Garside in border (Nos. 16405, 16406), are in *Military Drawings*, Vol. IV (p. 53).

SIR WILLIAM GELL (1777–1836)

Several pen and ink drawings, copies from the antique, views and ornaments, by Gell, are in two volumes of a manuscript verse translation of the Odes of Horace, Books I and II, written by Sir William Drummond and dedicated and presented by him to King George IV in January, 1828, shortly before his death. The volumes are elaborately bound and encased, and ornamented throughout with drawings, either in the book itself or inset. Besides the pen and ink drawings of Sir William Gell, there is a watercolour copy from Pinelli by Sir William Drummond, who may therefore also have made some of the anonymous pen and ink ornaments which would otherwise be attributed to Gell. There is also a series of views in Greece executed after Gell's sketches by T. Dessoulavy, a fashionable topographer and drawing-master in Rome at this date, who, whether from his practice among the English or on the strength of occasional exhibits at the Royal Academy and British Institution, is entered in the dictionaries as an English artist; but, though his work is frequently met with, nothing more appears to be known of the man. A considerable number of his views in Italy in watercolour or monochrome are inset in these volumes. Of other English artists contributing to the volumes, Richard Westmacott has two pen and wash figures, 'Venus' and 'Fortune', and a well-known amateur, Mrs. Cheney, a subject drawing in pen, 'Paris and Helen'.

Miniature portraits, of King George IV after Lawrence, of Pope Leo XII, and of Cardinal della Sommaglia by Clelia Valeri, a pencil and wash drawing apparently by an Italian from Thomas Campbell's bust of Sir William Drummond, several oil miniatures by Serafino Cesaretti, a group of subject drawings by Pinelli and a very large number of pen and ink drawings from coins and ornaments by Carlo Ruspi also decorate these sumptuous volumes, which apparently formed the last act of a somewhat eccentric life.

RICHARD GIBSON (1615–1690)

271. AFTER VAN DYCK: QUEEN HENRIETTA MARIA. Head and shoulders, facing three-quarters left.

Watercolour and body-colour on vellum; some damage and discoloration. 16⅛ × 12⅛ in. (41 × 30.6 cm.). (L.C.D. Inventory, 1337).

Copy of the portrait (c. 1632) in the Royal Collection (Cust, p. 79). This drawing is included by Cust (p. 49), who gives the references to the Inventories from the time of Charles II when it was listed as in store and described as a 'limbning' with measurements 18 × 13 in. It may be identified with the 'Queene Mother in a miniature, almost as big as the life' seen by Evelyn at Whitehall on December 6, 1660.

SAWREY GILPIN, R.A. (1733–1807)

272. A SADDLE HORSE WITH GROOM IN THE LIVERY (RED WITH GREEN) OF THE DUKE OF CUMBERLAND
                                                    Plate 69

Watercolour. 14½ × 16⅞ in. (37 × 43 cm.)   (13432)

Signed: S. Gilpin 17.

A 'Portrait of a Horse by Gilpin' mentioned in Inventory 'A', p. 148 (after 1816), repeated p. 168.

Exhib.: Edinburgh 1947 (King's Pictures), No. 118.

A replica in oil, c. 31½ × 31½ in. (80 × 80 cm.), is among the pictures from Cumberland Lodge at Windsor Castle (Lord Chamberlain's Inventory, No. 2311). For Cumberland pictures, see *Country Life*, February 20, 1932.

273. Eight drawings of different types of horse, five with grooms.   *Plate* 71

Pencil, pen and grey wash, incised. c. 6 × 7 in. (15 × 17.5 cm.)

Etched with date 1760 and 1761, identical except for No. 1, in which a soldier replaces the groom. All are in reverse. Some in the early state retain the cartouche, but the reprints of different years all omit them.

The Folio catalogue of Prints and Drawings (Inventory 'B'), p. 11, has: 'Gilpin's Horses. 8 Drawings with the prints engraved from them, oblong quarto.'

(1) The Managed Horse. Engraved in reverse and numbered '1'   (13433)
(2) The Race Horse. 'No. 2'   (13437)
(3) The Hunter. 'No. 3'   (13438)
(4) The Road Horse. 'No. 4'   (13435)
(5) The Pad. 'No. 5' (originally 'No. 2')   (13436)
(6) The Coach Horse. 'No. 6'   (13434)
(7) The Dray Horse. 'No. 7'   (13439)
(8) The Cart Horse. 'No. 8'   (13440)

THOMAS GIRTIN (1775–1802)

274. BUCKINGHAM HOUSE, c. 1791

Pen and watercolour, circular, squared for enlargement.
Diameter 3⅞ in. (9.8 cm.)   (17140)

This drawing and the slightly larger engraving, dated
November, 1794, which accompanies it, have been recognized by Mr. T. Girtin as belonging to the series of circular
topographic prints which appeared in the monthly parts of
the *Elegant Repository and New Print Magazine*, and were
re-issued in Taylor's *Temple of Taste*. The topographic prints
from this publication were re-issued alone in 1826 as the
Public Edifices of the Metropolis, the dates 1794 to 1796 being
in some cases erased and 1826 substituted. In no case is the
name of the artist stated, but the original drawings for some
of them are signed by Girtin, and a working proof of this
subject at the British Museum carries indications in his
handwriting. Some of the non-topographic prints in the
Temple of Taste are dated from 1791, and some of the
descriptions which accompany the plates of the buildings
shew that the drawings were made considerably before the
dates on the prints. Some of these would therefore be
Girtin's earliest-known work, made while he was still an
apprentice to Dayes.

The drawing differs from the print in minute details. It may
be based on the sketch by Dayes used for his drawing of
1790 (V. & A., 1756–1871, engraved by Soiron in 1793,
as the *Promenade in St. James's Park*, and for his view of
Buckingham House engraved by Knight in 1799. Dayes
himself may have used the print of 1775 by Collyer after
Malton (copied by James Miller in 1796).

The whole subject will shortly be dealt with by Mr. T.
Girtin in the *Burlington Magazine*.

See also No. 159.

HENRI GRAVELOT (1699–1773)

275. KING DAVID AT HIS HARP. Frontispiece to an edition of the Psalms.   *Figure* 24

Pen with black ink, brown wash, incised and reddened at
the back. 8¼ × 6½ in. (21.1 × 16.4 cm.)   (18000)
Signed at foot: H. Gravelot inv. et delin.

In an ornamental frame, with the Royal Arms, not completed, but with a label and the crown of a Royal Prince.
The open book has on the left-hand page GRESSUS MEOS
DIRIG, and on the right SECUND ELOQUEN (?) TU (Psalm 119,
vi. 133).

Acquired from Spink in 1946.

See also No. 71 (Boitard).

JOHN ALEXANDER GRESSE (c. 1740–1794)

276. WINDSOR FROM BISHOPSGATE

Pencil, numbers indicating colours, etc., detailed at the foot
of the drawing. 8 × 12½ in. (20.2 × 31.7 cm.)   (17566)
Signed at foot right: Gresse.

Inscribed in pencil at back of mount: 'at Gresse's Sale 10
April 94'.

Acquired from the Ford Collection, with the following
drawing, Sotheby's, March 19, 1947, Lot 67.

Fig. 24. Gravelot: A Frontispiece (Cat. No. 275)

Pyne, *Royal Residences*, 1817, Frogmore, p. 12, mentions
Gresse among the instructors in drawing to the Queen and
Princesses, and states that he held this appointment from
1777 to his death. See also Angelo, *Reminiscences*, 1828, I,
p. 194, etc.

277. A COUNTRY COTTAGE AMONG POLLARDED WIL-LOWS

Pencil. 7⅝ × 10¾ in. (19.3 × 27.2 cm.)   (17567)

Mounted as a companion to the preceding and with the
same provenance noted at the back of the mount.

SIMON GRIBELIN (1661–1733)

278. THE HAMPTON COURT RAPHAEL GALLERY AND THE SEVEN CARTOONS, 1707. Drawings for the engrav-ings.

(1) Sketch and section of the gallery shewing the portico
on the ground floor in perspective and, above, the gallery
with the cartoons in position as though seen without the
exterior wall. Medallions with portraits of Raphael, lettered
'Raphael Urbinas', and of Queen Anne, lettered 'Anna
Regina', 'Semper Eadem' and 'dedicavit An: 1707', with
ornaments respectively above and below.   (17314)

(2) The Miraculous Draught.   (17315)
(3) The Charge to Peter.   (17316)
(4) The Beautiful Gate.   (17317)
(5) The Death of Ananias.   (17318)
(6) The Blinding of Elymas.   (17319)
(7) The Sacrifice at Lystra.   (17320)
(8) Paul Preaching at Athens.   (17321)

The sketch of the gallery entirely in pencil, unfinished, $7\frac{1}{8} \times 8\frac{1}{4}$ in. (18 × 21 cm.), the keypoints of the architecture pricked, within a border of about 2 mm. The copies of the cartoons in pen in two thicknesses, with red chalk and pencil indications, apparently corrections (see below); incised in places with great precision. The backs are lightly reddened, showing very clearly the outlines, etc., traced. The cartoons measure about $5\frac{3}{8} \times 7\frac{1}{3}$ in. (13.7 × 18.7 cm.) within borders of about 2 mm.

Each copy of the cartoons is initialled S.G. at the lower bottom corner. Pen notes in French at the back, unfortunately cut into on all sides, criticize points in the drawings and refer to markings by the writer upon them which seem to be those in red chalk. As the writer refers to 'Mr G' he is perhaps not the artist himself. The criticisms are very detailed and are apparently followed in the prints. The whole of the writing on each sheet has been struck through with the pen by means of single crossed lines.

The pencil drawing (1) has in the left bottom corner two drafts in pencil, both cancelled, of the inscription intended for the engraving. The lower reads: ['A prospect of the' *cancelled*] 'A View of the Carton Galery' ['of' *cancelled*] at Hampton Court ['in' *cancelled*] with the Seven Cartons drawn and engraved by Sim. Gribelin.'

The copy of the *Sacrifice at Lystra* (7) has a pointing hand and, apparently, the statue of Hermes repeated, with the stylus only, towards the top of the sheet. That of *Elymas* has a considerable addition in pencil beyond the ruled border to the right which is followed in the print, with a consequent reduction on the left.

Gribelin's engravings, as published for John Bowles, bear no date; but they are 'dedicated to Her Late Majesty' and are therefore after 1714. According to Passavant, *Raphael*, Vol. II (1870), p. 208, they were published in 1720. The cartoons are all engraved in reverse, and therefore in the direction of the tapestries, but in the sketch of the whole arrangement they have been carefully drawn in reverse in order that, when engraved, they may appear in the direction of the original cartoons and in the order in which they were placed in the Gallery.

From the Esdaile Collection (Sale June 23, 1840, Lot 872, bt. White with Lots 871 and 873 for £2). Inscribed by him with the number 294* and a reference to E. King (Sale, May 12, 1808, Lot 1407, £14 14s., bt. Thane). The drawings also bear numbers (perhaps older) on the back from 6309 to 6316. They were acquired since the date of Ruland's Catalogue (1876), and presumably between 1915 and 1926, when they were placed in Prince Albert's Raphael Collection. They bear a dealer's cypher and the price £5 5s. (now stuck down).

SAMUEL HIERONYMUS GRIMM (1733–1794)

279. 'CAPT. MILES'S REVENGE, OR THE MACARONIES DISCOMFITED BY THEIR CHAMPION'

Pen and watercolour, incised with stylus. $4\frac{3}{8} \times 7\frac{1}{8}$ in. (10.8 × 18 cm.) (13257)

Drawing for the engraving B.M. Sat. V, 5200, in reverse.

Exhib.: Spring Gardens, Humour Exhibition, 1925, No. 9; B.F.A.C. 1931–32, No. 185.

Lit.: W. H. Whitley, *Walpole Society Annual*, XIII, p. 28; R. M. Clay, *S. H. Grimm*, 1942, p. 50, with reproduction.

There are differences from the print, where the newsboys have been removed and are represented on prints on the wall.

The last of a series of brawls in which the editor of the *Morning Post*, Henry Bate, was involved. A discharged servant and hired bully of George Fitzgerald is represented as thrashing his late master and a friend in a tavern at Epsom.

280. ENCAMPMENT OF THE 2ND WEST YORKSHIRE LIGHT INFANTRY IN THE GARDENS OF OLD MONTAGUE HOUSE DURING THE GORDON RIOTS, 1780

Pen and watercolour. $19\frac{1}{2} \times 26\frac{1}{4}$ in. (49.5 × 66 cm.) (16601)

Signed: S. H. Grimm fecit 1780.

Grimm exhibited this subject at the Royal Academy, 1781 (No. 248).

Exhib.: B.F.A.C., 'Old London', 1919, No. 35, pl. xvi.

Reprod.: R. M. Clay, *S. H. Grimm*, 1942, pl. 108.

A note by Sir Richard Holmes states that this and No. 281 were bought at Christie's for £5.

281. ENCAMPMENT AT MONTAGU HOUSE: The Regiment marching into camp.

Pen and watercolour. $19\frac{7}{8} \times 26\frac{1}{2}$ in. (50.1 × 67.2 cm.) (16602)

Signed: S. H. Grimm, June, 1780.

Reprod.: Clay, *op. cit.*, pl. 1.

Grimm exhibited this subject at the Royal Academy, 1781 (No. 218).

The prelate on the steps was identified by Sir R. Holmes from a MS. note on a coloured engraving by Sandby (in the Royal Library, later framed as a drawing, *cf. Sandby Catalogue*, No. 179) of the same subject, as Dr. John Moore, Bishop of Bangor, afterwards Archbishop of Canterbury. He is not taking the salute as stated by Miss Clay, p. 59.

FRANCIS GROSE (*c.* 1731–1791), Attributed to

282. Sixteen figure notes, mounted on a sheet of paper.

Pencil and pen, some tracings (17659)

The sheet on which they are mounted has, where not covered, a sketch in pen, a harbour scene, clearly of later date, and is inscribed 'original Sketches by Captain Grosse'.

HUGH DOUGLAS HAMILTON (1739–1808)

283. KING GEORGE III, aet. 31, bust facing three-quarter right, in black, wearing no orders. *Plate* 5

Coloured chalks and gouache. Oval, *c.* $11\frac{1}{4} \times 9$ in. (28.5 × 23 cm.) (13883)

Signed, in red, in border: Hugh Ds Hamilton fect 1769.

This and the following four drawings are almost circular, in feigned fluted wooden frames (with cartouches in two cases), which have been cut to oval.

284. GEORGE, PRINCE OF WALES, aet. 7, bust facing three-quarter right, wearing the ribbon of the Garter. *Plate* 7

Coloured chalks, Oval, $11\frac{1}{4} \times 9$ in. (28.3 × 22.8 cm.) (13885)

Signed in black: . . . D. Hamilton fect. 1769.

285. FREDERICK, DUKE OF YORK, when 6 years old, bust facing three-quarters right, wearing the ribbon of the Bath. *Plate* 8

Coloured chalks. Oval, $10\frac{3}{4} \times 8\frac{3}{4}$ in. (27 × 22 cm.) (13886)

Signed: H. D. Hamilton fct 1769 June, and inscribed, Frederick Duke of York B. 1763, D. 1827, both in border below.

Reprod.: *Connoisseur*, XCII, August, 1933, p. 78.

286. WILLIAM, DUKE OF CLARENCE (1765–1837), bust facing three-quarter left.

Coloured chalks and gouache, water-stained. Oval, $11\frac{1}{8} \times 9\frac{1}{8}$ in. (28.5 × 23 cm.) (13887)

Signed: H. D. Hamilton fect. in border, below empty cartouche.

287. EDWARD, DUKE OF KENT, AS AN INFANT, bust facing three-quarter right.

Coloured chalks, water-stained and restored. Oval, $10\frac{7}{8} \times 8\frac{3}{4}$ in. (27.5 × 22 cm.) (13888)

Not signed. Inscribed on cartouche: Edward Duke of Kent B. 1767 D. 1820.

Reprod.: *Connoisseur*, XCII, *l. c.*

288. QUEEN CHARLOTTE, bust, facing three-quarter left.
Plate 6

Coloured chalks. Oval, $10\frac{1}{4} \times 8\frac{1}{8}$ in. (26 × 21 cm.) (13884)

Signed: H. D. Hamilton Delint. 1771.

From the collection of Lord Polwarth (according to a note at the back of the frame).

Presented to the Royal Library by H.M. Queen Mary.

A letter from Queen Charlotte to Lord Harcourt of March 23, 1770 (*Harcourt Papers*, Vol. VI, p. 5), reads: 'You must by this Time have formed a very bad opinion of my Promises, as well as of the performance of Hamilton the Painter. The blame cannot fall upon me, as my Orders were given even before your Departure; but I believe that the great encouragement he has met with, has made him rather neglectfull; however, this delay is fully repaired in the Drawing, as I think it even better than the Original one you saw in the Sumer last.' A miniature of the Queen by Hamilton is stated (*l. c.*) to be at Nuneham.

JOHN HARDEN (1772–1847)

289. BRATHAY HOUSE, WINDERMERE

Watercolour. $11\frac{1}{4} \times 15\frac{1}{4}$ in. (28.6 × 38.6 cm.) (14266)

A false signature in pen 'P. Sandby 1795' on drawing. At back, 'Brathay House, at the head of Windermere Lake, Langdale Pikes and Coniston Fells in the distance—this drawing is presented to Miss Learmouth as a token of affection by John Harden May 1804'.

For this amateur and his connexion with Constable, see a note by his descendants B. and N. Clay in *Country Life*, April 16, 1938.

EDWARD HARDING (1755–1840)

A series of 20 watercolour drawings, portraits of members of the Royal Family, head and shoulders only, after Beechey, Gainsborough, Lawrence, etc. Until 1939 they were contained in a book inscribed 'Drawings containing the whole of the Present Royal Family of England copied from the Original Pictures and Presented to Her Majesty by her most Dutifull and very Respectful humble servant Edward Harding, Windsor Castle November 11th 1806.'

E. Harding published in May, 1806, engravings by Bourlier, Cheesman and others after these drawings with inscriptions such as 'Beechey del.', 'Lawrence del', except in the case of 302 and 303, which read 'Gainsborough pinx'.

Where ascertainable the drawings are copies or adaptations from paintings by the artists named with the exception of the drawing of Princess Mary (No. 307), which is clearly copied from Edridge (see No. 219). The print by Bourlier (O'Donoghue, Vol. III, p. 201, No. 15) gives no name of artist. In the case of No. 305, Princess Augusta, the print differs so considerably from this drawing that it must be from some other version. Where the original picture is unknown, the artists' names are inserted below, within square brackets, as given in the prints.

Edward Harding, brother of Silvester Harding, was Librarian to Queen Charlotte at Frogmore from 1803 until her death. He was employed by King George IV from his accession to 1825 and later, in arranging his volumes of prints, etc.

290. QUEEN CHARLOTTE. After Beechey (Cust, p. 34). Oval, $5\frac{3}{4} \times 4\frac{7}{8}$ in. (14.6 × 12.4 cm.) (13901)

291. KING GEORGE III. After Beechey (Lord Chamberlain's Inventory No. 2384).

Oval, $6\frac{1}{4} \times 5$ in. (15.9 × 12.7 cm.) (13902)

292. GEORGE, PRINCE OF WALES. After Beechey (Collins-Baker, p. 12).

Oval within washed and lined mount, $8\frac{3}{4} \times 7\frac{1}{4}$ in. (22.2 × 18.4 cm.) (13903)

293. CAROLINE, PRINCESS OF WALES. [After Beechey.] Oval, within washed mount, $6\frac{3}{4} \times 6$ in. (17.1 × 15.2 cm.) (13904)

294. PRINCESS CHARLOTTE. After Lawrence (Lord Chamberlain's Inventory, No. 328).

$7\frac{3}{4} \times 6\frac{3}{4}$ in. (19.7 × 17.1 cm.) (13905)

295. FREDERICK, DUKE OF YORK. [After Beechey.] Oval within washed and ruled mount, $7\frac{7}{8} \times 7$ in. (20 × 17.8 cm.) (13906)

296. FREDERICA, DUCHESS OF YORK. [After Mme. le Brun.]

Within washed and ruled mount, $7\frac{7}{8} \times 6\frac{7}{8}$ in. (20 × 17.5 cm.) (13907)

297. WILLIAM, DUKE OF CLARENCE. [After Beechey.] $6\frac{3}{8} \times 5\frac{1}{4}$ in. (16.2 × 13.3 cm.) (13908)

298. EDWARD, DUKE OF KENT. [After Muller.] Oval, within washed and lined mount, $9 \times 7\frac{3}{4}$ in. (22.9 × 19.7 cm.) (13909)

299. ERNEST, DUKE OF CUMBERLAND. [After Beechey.] Oval, $8\frac{7}{8} \times 6$ in. (20.6 × 15.2 cm.) (13910)

300. AUGUSTUS, DUKE OF SUSSEX. [After Beechey.] $6\frac{7}{8} \times 5\frac{3}{4}$ in. (17.5 × 14.6 cm.) (13911)

301. ADOLPHUS, DUKE OF CAMBRIDGE. Artist unnamed.

Oval, within lined and washed mount, $9 \times 7\frac{3}{4}$ in. (22.9 × 19.7 cm.) (13912)

302. PRINCE ALFRED. After Gainsborough (Collins-Baker, p. 138).

Oval, $6\frac{3}{8} \times 5\frac{1}{4}$ in. (16.8 × 13.3 cm.) (13913)

303. PRINCE OCTAVIUS. After Gainsborough (Collins-Baker, p. 138).
Oval, 7½ × 6⅛ in. (19.1 × 15.6 cm.) (13914)

304. CHARLOTTE, PRINCESS ROYAL. After Beechey (Collins-Baker, p. 12).
Oval, within washed mount, 8⅞ × 7⅜ in. (22.5 × 18.7 cm.) (13915)

305. PRINCESS AUGUSTA. [After Beechey.]
Oval, 5⅝ × 7⅜ in. (20.6 × 16.5 cm.) (13916)

306. PRINCESS ELIZABETH. [After Beechey.]
8⅛ × 6½ in. (20.6 × 16.5 cm.) (13917)

307. PRINCESS MARY. After Edridge. (See No. 219.)
Oval, 7½ × 5⅝ in. (19.1 × 14.3 cm.) (13918)

308. PRINCESS SOPHIA. After Beechey (Collins-Baker, p. 14).
Oval, 7⅝ × 6¼ in. (19.4 × 15.9 cm.) (13919)

309. PRINCESS AMELIA. After Beechey (Collins-Baker, p. 15).
Oval, 7⅞ × 6½ in. (20 × 16.5 cm.) (13920)

A portrait in watercolour and gum of George IV in Coronation Robes is inserted as frontispiece in the Royal Library copy of Nash and Brayley, 'Illustrations . . . Brighton', 1838 (see on No. 483).

GEORGE PERFECT HARDING (1778–1853)

310. WILLIAM, DUKE OF ZELL (1624–1705), half-length in armour, facing three-quarter right.
Watercolour in feigned oval and painted border. 6¾ × 5¾ in. (13.5 × 11 cm.) (17256)
Signed: G. P. Harding del. 1816.

A typed label at the back of the frame connects this drawing with Lot 379 of Queen Charlotte's sale of July 15, 1819 (£2 12s. 6d.). Presumably the drawing with this title acquired from Colnaghi by the Prince Regent on the 19th of the same month for £4 14s. 6d. (Archives Invoice 28216).

311. WILLIAM PENDRILL (PENDEREL) OF BOSCOBELL after a print (O'Donoghue, Vol. III, p. 444).
Pen, oval, in border. 3 × 4¼ in. (13 × 11 cm.) (17260)
Signed: G. P. Harding 1807. The border inscribed: William Pendrill of Boscobell in the County of Salop Aetatis Suae 84. Engraved 1808 without Harding's name.

312. HENRY, VISCOUNT FALKLAND. After Van Somer.
Whole length, nearly full face, standing at a table and holding a glove.
Watercolour. 13 × 7¾ in. (33 × 19.5 cm.) (17265)
Signed: G. P. Harding del. 1817.
Engraved: Ancient Historical Pictures, 1844, No. 10 (O'Donoghue, Vol. II, p. 191).

313. AN ELIZABETHAN YOUTH, half length, facing quarter left, right hand in waist belt. Black cloak, slashed white doublet.
Watercolour in painted border. 5¾ × 7¼ in. (13.7 × 10 cm.) (17246)
Signed: G. P. Harding delt. 1812.

314. JOHN HOWSON, BISHOP OF DURHAM (1628–1632)
Pen and grey wash. 4½ × 3⅜ in. (11.5 × 8.5 cm.) (13445)
Signed: GPH (in monogram) 1800.
Copy of the engraving by Martin Droeshout (O'Donoghue, Vol. II, p. 578) after a painting in Christ Church. Oxford.

A volume containing twenty-one portrait copies, of the Stuart Period, mostly signed and dated, is in the Royal Library.

G. P. HARDING, Manner of

315. SIR HENRY WOTTON (1568–1639) [after Janssens]
Half-length, facing three-quarter right, hand on books on a table.
Watercolour. 6 × 5 in. (14.7 × 12 cm.) (17266)
Engraved in Lodge's Portraits, V, p. 93, etc., 1816 (O'Donoghue, Vol. IV, p. 546). From the picture in the Bodleian Gallery.

316. COLONEL CHARLES CAVENDISH (1630–1643)
Copy of (?) Van Dyck.
Watercolours. 10¼ × 8¾ in. (26 × 22.5 cm.)
Not signed.

317. COLONEL ROBERT FIELDING, full length standing, facing three-quarter right, hands in muff.
Watercolour. 10⅝ × 7⅝ in. (20 × 20 cm.) (17257)
Inscribed: Col¹ Robt. Fielding, in margin below.
The notorious reprobate, gambler and bully (c. 1651–1712).

G. H. HARLOW, see Sir Thomas Lawrence,
Nos. 416, 417

ROBERT HAVELL (exhib. 1808–1822)

318. THE EMBARKATION OF KING GEORGE IV AT GREENWICH FOR SCOTLAND, AUGUST 10, 1822
Watercolour. 9½ × 14¾ in. (24 × 37.5 cm.)
(Souvenir Album, VI, p. 4)
Signed: R. Havell.

WILLIAM HAVELL (1782–1857)

319. WINDSOR CASTLE FROM ROMNEY ISLAND
Black chalk heightened with white on blue paper. 10⅛ × 15¾ in. (26 × 38.5 cm.) (17301)
Inscribed at top: Windsor Castle.
One of several studies in the same manner at Messrs. Agnews' in April, 1944 (No. 51).

320. ETON COLLEGE CHAPEL FROM KEATE'S LANE
Black and white chalk on blue paper. 7⅞ × 19⅞ in. (19.9 × 27.2 cm.)
Hitherto anonymous.

BENJAMIN R. HAYDON (1789–1846)

321. THE MOCK ELECTION. A copy of Haydon's 'Explanation of the Picture of the Mock Election which took place at the King's Bench Prison, July, 1827', published for the proprietor 1828, bound with 10 pages (both sides) of additional notes in Haydon's autograph and nine full-page pen sketches from heads in the picture, namely, the High Sheriff, the Lord Mayor, Staunton, Campbell, Meredith, the Head Constable, Harry Holt, the Smuggler,

Fig. 25. Heckel: Buckingham House (Cat. No. 324)

Botillon (a Canadian), each initialled B.R.H. 1828. The whole book, including the printed part, is on the same paper, Whatman Turkey Mill 1826. It is bound with the Royal Arms. Haydon on May 23, 1828 (*Life*, 1853, ii. 191), mentions its preparation in connexion with the purchase of the picture by King George IV.

JOSEPH HAYNES, *see* No. 364 (after Hogarth)

THOMAS HEARNE (1744–1817)

322. WINDSOR CASTLE: THE SOUTH FRONT, shewing the footpath to Datchet, and on the left the house which afterwards (1778) became Queen's Lodge.   *Plate* 56
Pen and watercolour, with washed mount, faded. 9 × 13¾ in. (22.5 × 33.5 cm.)   (17399)

323. Five sketches of cottages, etc., in Windsor Forest.
Pencil. *c.* 6¾ × 9 in. (16.7 × 22.5 cm.)   (17400–17404)
Inscribed in pen on the washed mounts: 'In Windsor Forest'. Hitherto anonymous.

AUGUSTIN HECKEL (*c.* 1690–1770)

324. BUCKINGHAM HOUSE AND WESTMINSTER, LOOKING SOUTH-EAST   *Figure* 25
Pencil and watercolour, damaged and discoloured. 11¼ × 17 in. (28.5 × 43.2 cm.)   (17612)
Signed and inscribed at the foot in ink: 'A view from Constitution Hill towards West Minster. A.H. 1734.'

In spite of the mistakes in date and initials, clearly the drawing from which was made the small engraving, 'A View from Constitution Hill Anno 1735', 'J.H.del' and 'Edmd. Scot Sc. 1776', published June 1, 1779, by Richard Godfrey, and reissued in Grose's *Antiquarian Repertory*, second edition, 1808, Vol. II, p. 181, where, in the text, the drawing is attributed to 'the late ingenious Mr. Hackell'.
Bought from Messrs. Colnaghi, September, 1948.

EGBERT VAN HEEMSKERCK II (d. 1744)

325. A MASQUERADE TICKET
Brush with brown wash over very slight pencil, ruled pen lines in the architecture. 7⅞ × 12⅞ in. (20 × 32.8 cm.)
(13280)

Inscribed in the margin at foot: 'Tues Aprill y 14 1724'; 'Burgundy & Champain' over one of the buffets and 'Super ready below stairs' on a placard between it and the next buffet.

See L. van Puyvelde, *Dutch Drawings at Windsor Castle*, No. 172. See also E. Croft Murray and H. Phillips in *Country Life*, Sept. 2, 1949, who discuss the drawing as an accurate representation of a masquerade in the Long Room of the King's Theatre at the Haymarket organized by J. H. Heidegger. The presence of yeomen of the guard suggests that this was a night on which Royalty attended. The placard above the buffet and the profusion of wax lights are mentioned in Mist's *Weekly Journal*, February 15, 1718. As a ball was advertised for the date written on the drawing it may have been intended for an admission ticket, such as was satirised by Hogarth in his print of 1727.

S. HEPY (?) (1811)

326. WINDSOR AND THE CASTLE FROM THE ETON BANK

Watercolour, much faded, the signature indecipherable. 18½ × 27¼ in. (47 × 69 cm.)   (17252)

ROBERT HILLS (1769–1849), Attributed to

327. TWICKENHAM FROM THE RIVER

Pen, grey and blue wash. 5 × 12¾ in. (12.7 × 32.4 cm.)
(13611)

Inscribed in a microscopic hand at the top, 'Twickenham'. This drawing of the early 19th century, with no pronounced characteristics, is placed, without conviction, under the name of Hills.

WILLIAM HOGARTH (1697–1764)

BIBLIOGRAPHY

[John Nichols, etc.]: *Biographical Anecdotes of William Hogarth*, 1781, 1782, and 1785. (Referred to as *Biogr. Anec.*, 1781, etc.)
John Ireland: *Hogarth Illustrated*, vols. 1 and 2, 1791; vol. 3, 1798. (*Hog. Illd.*)
Samuel Ireland: *Graphic Illustrations of Hogarth*, vol. 1, 1794; vol. 2, 1799. (*Graph. Illust.*)
John Nichols and George Stevens: *The Genuine Works of William Hogarth*, vols. 1 and 2, 1808–1810; vol. 3, 1817. (*Gen. Works.*)
[John Bowyer Nichols]: *Anecdotes of William Hogarth*, 1833. (*Anecd.*, 1833.)
Austin Dobson: *William Hogarth*, 1907. (*A.D.*, 1907.)
A. P. Oppé: *The Drawings of William Hogarth*, 1948. (*Phaidon.*)
R. B. Beckett: *Hogarth*, 1949. (*Beckett.*)

328. DESIGNS FOR KING'S PANTHEON

Drawings for three of the six plates, each containing four designs, in reverse, without name of artist or engraver, illustrating an edition of King's *Pantheon* (first published in 1710).

(*a*) Pen with brown ink and grey and brown washes; closely incised. 4¾ × 2¾ in. (12.2 × 7.1 cm.)   (13468)

The four ovals are inscribed on the ornamental frames 'Saturn & Cybele', 'Coelus & Terra', 'Neptune & . . . (erasure)', and 'Jupiter & Juno'. The engraving, headed 'page 1', completes the third title with 'Amphitrite'.

(*b*) Pencil, pen with brown ink and grey wash over red chalk; incised and reddened at the back. Dimensions as above.   (13470)

The ornamental frames are less complete than those of (*a*); the titles read 'Mercury', 'Venus and her attendants', 'Mars and his attendants', and 'Minerva'. The engraving is headed 'page 87', the inscriptions are the same.

(*c*) Pencil and grey wash over red chalk; incised and reddened at the back. Dimensions as above.   (13469)
The frames are still less complete, being only indicated roughly in pencil and grey wash. The inscriptions read: 'Hercules', 'Bachus and his attends', '. . . (erased) Flora', and 'Pan and his attendants'. The engraving is headed 'page 109' and retains the inscriptions with the misspelling.

A paper pasted at the back of the modern mount reads: 'about 15 years since. Sundry Drawings were put into my hands for Sale by Mr. Clee the engraver, of which these 4 are a part, with an assurance they were by Hogarth— Licester [*sic*] Square. Jno. Greenwood. 4th May 1787'. *Anecd.* 1833, p. 400, reads: 'Mr. Lee the engraver' and '4th May 1786'. The engraver Clee is not recorded, but there was a sale of the drawings and engravings belonging to Robert Clee at Langford's on January 20 and following days, 1774.

Coll.: Perhaps Samuel Ireland. In the Royal Collection before 1833.

Lit. and reprod.: *Anecd.* 1833, *loc. cit.*, Phaidon No. 1.

Closely related to the style of Thornhill, these drawings may be taken as exhibiting Hogarth's youthful manner.

The fourth drawing referred to in Greenwood's note (*supra*) is a medallion showing Minerva with the Gorgon's shield and lightning annihilating a recumbent two-headed and four-armed giant whose lower half terminates in a nine-headed hydra. It differs in scale and handling, and though it may be English there is no reason to ascribe it to Hogarth (Royal Library 13467).

329. THE LOTTERY, 1721

Pen and black ink over slight pencil, grey wash; corrections with brown ink and red chalk; incised in places with stylus. Damaged. 9 × 12¾ in. (22.9 × 32.4 cm.)   (13481)

Drawing for the engraving in reverse of 1721 (B.M. Sat. Vol. II, 1730).

Coll.: Standly.

Lit. and reprod.: *Anecd.*, 1833, p. 390. Phaidon No. 2.

The afterthoughts marked on the drawings are taken over with further modifications into the print; they are mainly directed to a more exact representation of the working of the lottery or, as in the large snail crawling on the figure of 'Sloth', to emphasizing the allegory.
The figures are conceived and drawn much in the manner of Thornhill, and are largely derivative from older art (*cf.* Antal, *Art Bulletin*, March, 1947, p. 38).

330. THE SOUTH SEA BUBBLE, 1721   *Plate* 59

Pencil, incised with stylus, rubbed and stained, the corners torn and about one-fifth on the right of the drawing cut off. 8½ × 9¾ in. (21.6 × 24.9 cm.)   (13479)

Drawing for the engraving, in reverse, of 1721 (B.M. Sat., II, No. 1722).

Coll.: Standly.

Lit. and reprod.: *Anecd.* 1833, p. 390. Phaidon No. 3. Ayrton and Denvir, *Hogarth's Drawings*, 1948, No. 1.

A view of St. Paul's is introduced into the print by enlarging the space between the buildings on either side. The 'balloons' are omitted, other figures are introduced, and that of Honesty tortured on the wheel is somewhat softened.
The torture of the wheel is, as noted by Dr. Antal, *loc. cit.*, and older writers, a reminiscence of Callot's *La Roue* (M. 665), while the merry-go-round recalls, perhaps in parody, the gibbet in the same plate. The strong pencil notation over a softer preparation and the already forcible characterization should be remarked.
A portrait of Pope was found by old writers in the small figure in the foreground picking the pocket of a large man. *Genuine Works*, ii, p. 24.

331. AN OPERA SINGER (wrongly called Farinelli)

Pen. 8⅞ × 5⅛ in. (22.6 × 13.1 cm.) (13476)

Coll.: Standly (as Senesino).

Reprod.: Etched by Richard Sawyer for Standly, no date; Vasari Soc., Second Series, XV, 1934, No. 5 (Croft-Murray). *Phaidon* No. 4.

Exhib.: R.A. British Art, 1934, 563 (1104).

Hogarth's authorship of this drawing is by no means certain and it has long been recognized that if the grounds on which it is attributed to him are accepted, the identification of the person represented as Farinelli is impossible.
The drawing is regarded as Hogarth's because it resembles the figure on the left of a print called (on the strength of several old inscriptions in pen) *Farinelli, Cuzzoni and Senesino performing in Handel's Ptolomeo* (B.M. Sat., II, No. 1768). That print was attributed to Hogarth because it is unquestionably quoted on a banner in his first dated print of 1724, the *Masquerades and Operas* or *Burlington Gate*, but it is not characteristic of Hogarth, and has been ascribed, on the strength of an inscription on one example, to Vanderbank (*Gen. Works*, II, pp. 39, 40). Whether it is by Hogarth or not, it must be anterior to 1724, and therefore, as was pointed out in *Anecd.* 1833, p. 320, neither of the male figures in it could represent Farinelli because he did not come to England until ten years later, in 1734; nor could the opera be *Ptolomeo* since its first performance was in 1728. It was accordingly there suggested, on the strength of a pen inscription on an impression of the print in the Royal Collection, that the characters are Berenstadt, Cuzzoni and Senesino and the opera *Giulio Cesare*. So far as concerns the presence of Berenstadt in the print, this is corroborated by a version in Lord Exeter's collection at Burghley which has three doggerel couplets engraved below the characters, two of them referring to Cuzzoni, and the third (below the figure on the right) to Berenstadt. These couplets are printed in *Biogr. Anecd.*, 1785, ii. p. 139, and *Genuine Works II*, pp. 39 and 40, where the version containing them is regarded as a copy, but they have been overlooked by all other writers. Another example in the British Museum has an erased inscription which shews the name Berenstadt, though in a different form. The example in Lord Exeter's collection further has the names Ptolomeo, Cleopatra and Cæsar written below the characters. Except for the position of the verses all these indications point to an identification with Berenstadt of the figure on the left previously called Farinelli and related to the present drawing. On the other hand, it has been argued by Mr. H. Beard (*Burlington Magazine*, September, 1950) that the action represented in the print occurs neither in *Ptolomeo* nor in *Giulio Cesare*, but in Act 3, Scene 4, of *Flavio* (1723), and in that case the figure on the left would not be Berenstadt but Senesino. This was anticipated by Standly, no doubt on other grounds, since this must be the drawing described in his sale as Senesino (Lot 960).
The drawing, though bearing a general similarity with the bulky character on the left-hand side of the print and shewing much the same attitude, does not emphasize any of the features there caricatured. The free and flamboyant handling is inspired by the baroque nature of the subject, and is no more characteristic of Vanderbank than it is of Hogarth. There is no underlying pencil sketch, as is usual with Hogarth and, contrary to his custom, the drawing is in the same direction as the figure in the print.

332-337. DRAWINGS FOR *HUDIBRAS*, 1726
(13459-64)

These six drawings were engraved in reverse by Hogarth for his set of twelve large illustrations to *Hudibras* which were issued in 1726. They were in the possession of Samuel Ireland, who states that he obtained three of them with other drawings by Hogarth from a Mr. Brent, 'an old gentleman who was for many years in habits of intimacy with Hogarth', and who may have been the fencing master mentioned in Jones' *Memoir* (*Walpole Society*, Vol. XXXII). This may have been about 1781. They were all reproduced in *Graph. Illustr.*, and are mentioned with another drawing for Hudibras as in Ireland's possession in successive editions of *Biogr. Anecd.* In the Royal Collection by 1833, probably bought by King George IV with the Barker Collection (see *Anecd.* 1833, p. 390, and *Phaidon*, p. 28).

332. HUDIBRAS: THE FRONTISPIECE

Pencil, with grey-black ink, brown and grey washes; incised. Some green stains as in Nos. 8 and 10 are presumably due to chemicals. 9½ × 13⅜ in. (23.9 × 33.9 cm.)
(13459)

Drawing for the engraving, in reverse, pl. 1, of the large set, 1726.

Lit. and reprod.: S. Ireland, *Graphic Illustrations*, Vol. II, p. 20, with aquatint by Rosenberg, *Anecd.* 1833, p. 391. *Phaidon* No. 5.

The portrait of Butler is alone washed in grey, it has not been incised with the stylus, nor, though it is carefully drawn, is it exactly reproduced in the print. More important, the satyr on the left is replaced in the print by figures of Britannia and a laughing faun holding a mirror to her. These figures were no doubt drawn with the pen on a superimposed piece of paper, for the end of Britannia's spear has overlapped into the present sheet just as did a hand on the altered drawing for *Beer Street* in the Pierpont Morgan Collection (*Phaidon* No. 76), either because the added paper was not large enough to contain the whole of the new portion, or to mark the precise position on the sheet. The incident in the distance (not incised), right, has also been entirely changed as described in *Anecd.* 1833, p. 391. Otherwise the print follows very closely the careful drawing which is elaborated in delicately toned modelling with the brush after the French manner. Only the garlands around the medallion portrait are left unfinished, being merely indicated with the pencil, but they too are fully incised with the stylus.

333. HUDIBRAS SALLYING FORTH

Red chalk, with touches of black, and black shading in foreground. Incised. 9½ × 13 in. (24.1 × 32.9 cm.)
(13460)

Drawing for the engraving, in reverse, pl. 2 of the large set, 1726.

Lit. and reprod.: As No. 332, the reproduction in *Graphic Illustrations* being in soft-ground etching in sanguine by Le Coeur. *Phaidon* No. 6.

In the print a house is introduced on the right as indicated in pencil on a trial proof in the Royal Library, and there are other lesser differences from the drawing. Reversal in the print has been to some extent kept in view, and since Hudibras holds his reins in his left hand in the drawing whereas Ralpho uses his right, the engraving was bound to leave one of them in the correct position.

The forms are fundamentally coarse, but the execution is neat and careful with 'tickled' hatching and shading; the foliage and landscape are especially delicate. As in the preceding, the model in the drawing would appear to have been the French manner, whereas the prints and the further drawings in the series are more Dutch in character. It is noticeable that the dog is gentle and inoffensive in the drawing, but becomes much more brutal in the print.

334. HUDIBRAS' FIRST ADVENTURE

Brush drawing in grey, no pencil visible. Incised through-out. $9\frac{1}{2} \times 13\frac{1}{4}$ in. (24.3 × 33.6 cm.) (13461)
Drawing for the engraving, in reverse, pl. 3 of the large set, 1726.
Damaged and stained before the old mounting; the mount, which is inscribed 'Willm. Hogarth delt.' in S. Ireland's handwriting, is identical with that of No. 336.
Lit. and reprod.: As No. 332, the reproduction in *Graphic Illustrations* being an aquatint by Rosenberg. *Connoisseur*, XCII, July, 1933, No. II. *Phaidon* No. 7.
By an unlucky oversight the print has a pistol in Hudibras' left hand, Hogarth having overlooked the effect of reversal which had been kept in view in the original drawing.

335. HUDIBRAS AND THE LAWYER

Pen and brown ink, brown and grey washes, over pencil indications. Some ruling in pen, incised with stylus. The bottom right hand corner, including the greater part of the dogs, is a restoration. The adjacent parts are stained in green. $9\frac{5}{8} \times 13\frac{1}{4}$ in. (24.8 × 33.7 cm.) (13462)
Drawing for the engraving, in reverse, pl. 7 of the large set, 1726.
Lit. and reprod.: As on No. 332, the aquatint by Merigot. *Connoisseur*, XCII, July, 1933, No. III. *Phaidon* No. 8.
The print shows several differences of detail, chiefly in the lawyer's throne and the women in the background.

336. HUDIBRAS: BURNING THE RUMPS AT TEMPLE BAR

Pen with brown ink, brown washes, over pencil indications. Incised with the stylus, chiefly in the upper portion where the drawing is sketchy and unfinished. Large tears before mounting (identical with No. 334) seem to show red from chalking at the back. $9\frac{3}{4} \times 8\frac{3}{8}$ in. (24.7 × 21.2 cm.)
(13463)
Drawing for the left-hand portion of the engraving, in reverse, pl. 11 of the large set, 1726.
Lit. and reprod.: As No. 334. *Phaidon* No. 9. Ayrton, *op. cit.*, No. 6.
The drawing was reproduced in *Graphic Illustrations* as complete, and was therefore stated in *Anecd.* 1833 to have been perfect when in the possession of Samuel Ireland. Since the old washed mount would appear to be his and must have been made for the drawing in its present state, it is more probable that the reproduction was made up with the help of the engraving.
The bow window with women looking out disappears from the print; otherwise the differences are only minor.

337. HUDIBRAS ENCOUNTERS THE SKIMMINGTON

Pen with brown ink over pencil and red chalk indications, grey washes in part, heightened with white on brownish paper. Incised with the stylus. Stained with green on the right where, as noticed by S. Ireland, a strip amounting to about one-seventh of the drawing has been cut off. $9\frac{3}{4} \times 17\frac{1}{8}$ in. (24.7 × 43.4 cm.) (13464)
Drawing for the engraving, in reverse, pl. 12 of the large set, 1726.

Lit. and reprod.: As on No. 332; the aquatint by Merigot. *Phaidon* No. 10.
The chief differences between the drawing and the print are on the left-hand side, where the figure of a man holding a torch has been much improved and reduced; the rider above him is entirely altered. In the centre the figure holding the shirt is changed, as are the horns above it, which become those of a cow in the print. The barn loses its two doors in the print. The greater part of the drawing is left at the stage of penwork with, in places, the first flat wash in grey; and several details of the print, as, for example, the head and shoulders of the man holding the bone and cleaver above the bagpiper, are omitted. Probably tracing or pencil work has been obliterated.

338. HUDIBRAS ENCOUNTERS THE SKIMMINGTON

Pen with brown ink and grey washes over pencil and red chalk, with some incision. Damaged, apparently from folding, and showing signs of red chalk on the back. $5 \times 8\frac{7}{8}$ in. (12.9 × 22.4 cm.) (13465)
Drawing for the engraving, in reverse, pl. 9 of the small set, 1726.
Coll.: Standly.
Lit. and reprod.: Facsimile in aquatint by Richard Sawyer for Standly; private plate. *Anecd.* 1833, p. 392. *Phaidon* No. 11.

The seventeen illustrations furnished for the small edition of *Hudibras*, 1726, largely followed those of an edition of 1709. In the print the design has been elongated with an extension of the house and several figures have been omitted, while others, including Hudibras himself, have been changed. The result is a considerable loss of vigour and concentration. The artificiality of the Callot-like shadow figures, more effective in the drawing than in the engraving, is noticeable.

339. THE BEGGARS' OPERA BURLESQUED, 1728

Pen with black ink, brown and grey washes, incised. Some touches of pencil, perhaps from tracing, under the heads in the centre; the pencil lines across the sky on each side of the gallows may be due to subsequent accident; red stains on the edges probably come from chalking at the back. $8 \times 9\frac{3}{4}$ in. (20.2 × 25.1 cm.) (13486)
Drawing for the engraving, in reverse, of *c.* 1728 (anonymous). (B.M. Sat., Vol. II, No. 1807.)
Coll.: Standly.
Lit. and reprod.: *Anecd.* 1833, p. 393. *Phaidon* No. 12. Ayrton, *op. cit.*, No. 7.
Exhib.: Spring Gardens (Humour Exhibition), 1925, No. 3. Edinburgh, 1947 (King's Pictures), No. 111.
Except for the insertion of inscriptions there are no important alterations in the print, which, however, is very considerably worked up in detail.
Both the penwork and washes are lighter, neater and prettier than in previous drawings, and are so much in the Continental manner that the print is conjecturally attributed in *Gen. Works*, ii. 68, to Gravelot or Vandergucht, the idea borrowed from Coypel in *Les Chats*, Amsterdam, 1728. Gravelot only came to England in 1732.

340. TWO PAIRS OF FIGURES CALLED 'DESIGN FOR THE HAPPY MARRIAGE' AND 'FIRST DESIGN FOR THE DOCTORS IN THE HARLOT'S PROGRESS'

Pen and brown wash over pencil indications, inscribed 'Hogarth' in a later hand. $5\frac{1}{8} \times 6\frac{7}{8}$ in. (13.2 × 17.5 cm.)
(13478)
Coll.: Standly.

Reprod.: W. J. Smith, private plates (two) for Standly destroyed 1825. (B.M. Sat., Vol. II, 1985; *cf. Anecd.* 1833, pp. 292 and 394.) *Phaidon* No. 18.

Exhib.: R.A. British Art, 1934, 564 (1120).

This drawing and the following are similar in character to the drawings at the British Museum commonly called 'Characters who frequented Button's Coffee House' (*Phaidon*, Nos. 14–17), which were said to have been acquired by S. Ireland with three of the 'Hudibras' drawings (see on Nos. 332–337). The traditional connection of the two male figures on the right with the doctors in pl. 5 of the *Harlot's Progress* is very remote, though it is possible that some memory of this gently disputing couple was in Hogarth's mind when he conceived the violently agitated pair in that scene. At any rate, he could scarcely have returned to these figures after painting the picture. The sheet may accordingly be dated well before 1731. The other two figures were regarded as connected with the projects for a series *The Happy Marriage*, but the obvious indication of an improper proposal or an intrigue which they contain seems entirely foreign to anything that is known of that series. (*Beckett*, Plates 163–168).

341. DR. MISAUBIN AND DR. WARD

Pencil, pen and brown ink, brown wash. Inscribed under the figures 'Dr. Misaubin and Dr. Ward' in a later hand. 4 × 6 in. (10.2 × 15.4 cm.)   (13472)

Coll.: Standly, according to *Anecd.* 1833, pp. 292 and 394, where this drawing appears to be confused with No. 340, and previously Baker.

Reprod.: W. J. Smith, private plate destroyed 1827, for Standly. (B.M. Sat., Vol. II, No. 1986.) Richard Sawyer, aquatint, 1828. *Phaidon* No. 19.

Exhib.: Royal Institute (English Humourists), 1889, No. 2. B.F.A.C. 1931–32, No. 74B.

This drawing is more competent than the preceding and the Button's Coffee House drawings, but it is akin to them in the soft and unbroken pen line and the careful contours. The contrast of fat and lean characters occurs in the Button's Coffee House drawings and in pl. 5 of the *Harlot's Progress*, with which the two doctors who are supposed to be represented in the present drawing are traditionally related, but it may be regarded as a commonplace.

342. HAZARD TABLE   *Figure* 26

Pen with grey ink, grey wash. 8⅞ × 12⅞ in. (22.6 × 32.6 cm.)   (13474)

Coll.: Samuel Ireland. Mentioned as in the Royal Collection, *Anecd.* 1833, p. 403.

Reprod.: *Graph. Illustr.*, ii, p. 104, aquatint by Le Coeur. *Connoisseur*, XCII, July, 1933, No. 1. *Phaidon* No. 20.

Exhib.: R.I. (English Humourists), 1889. No. 2. Spring Gardens (Humour Exhibition), 1925, No. 1.

The 'lifeless and inanimate' faces of the personages in this drawing seemed to S. Ireland inconsistent with the 'characteristic humour on which the reputation of Hogarth is so justly founded', but his doubts were probably due to his expecting from Hogarth some such violent satire against both Royalty and gaming as had become current in his day. Hogarth, however, consistently sought for Royal patronage, and the lack of animation or even of concentration of glances is a common feature in his portrait groups. Further, the figure of the prelate is entirely in his manner, and the drawing generally, while more carefully executed, is related to the preceding, and the Button's Coffee House, groups.

The subject of the drawing is by no means easy to explain, and while the drawing, especially in the figure of the prelate, cannot be regarded as French, it bears a distinct relation to a painting by Mercier lately in the possession of Messrs. Tooth, and probably once in the Northwick Collection as by Hogarth (*Figure* 27). There, too, a tutor is apparently debauching his pupils at the gaming table. A still further problem is introduced if the identification is accepted of the youth with the Garter as Frederick Prince of Wales, since the boy here would clearly appear to be under 21, whereas the Prince of Wales was born on January 20, 1706–1707, and only came to England on December 3, 1728, when he was nearly 22. According to the *Free and Impartial Reflections on the Character, Life and Death of Frederick, Prince of Wales* (Philobiblon Soc. Misc. vii, 1862–1863, p. 4): 'Of the capacity and talents of his Governors and Tutors nothing has been particularly mentioned'. If, on the other hand, the drawing could be placed after 1751, George III as Prince of Wales might be intended.

343. BOYS PEEPING AT NATURE, 1731

Pencil and grey wash, touched with pen and black ink; incised in places; additions in pencil, within ruled pencil border. 4 × 5½ in. (12.2 × 13.3 cm.)   (13497)

Drawing for the engraving (B.M. Sat., Vol. II, 1943) in reverse, used for the subscription ticket for the *Harlot's Progress*, 1731.

Fig. 26. Hogarth: The Hazard Table (Cat. No. 342)

Fig. 27. Mercier: Scene at a Gaming Table (*Cf.* Cat. No. 342)

Coll.: Standly.
Lit. and reprod.: Phaidon No. 22.
The drawing is very neatly executed with shading and hatching in fine brushwork. It is exactly followed in the print except that the wall is carried to the top of the plate, and a Latin inscription inserted. Pencil after-thoughts in the top left hand corner of the drawing, a palette and a medallion, are not carried into the print.

As is noted by Dr. Antal, *loc. cit.*, p. 39, the many-bosomed torso of Nature is taken by Hogarth from the picture by Rubens which belonged to Thornhill. It is repeated in the *Foundling Hospital Arms* (*Phaidon* No. 66). The idea of *amorini* practising with the utensils of the arts occurs so frequently that it seems idle to enquire whence Hogarth may have derived it. There are compositions of this subject in Thornhill's sketchbook at the British Museum (L.B. 68, *f.* 38). It is, however, possible that Hogarth had in mind and was actually parodying the title-page of a drawing-book after Nicolas Poussin (published by Veuve Poilly, *n.d.*, reproduced in L. Coutil, *N. Poussin*, 1904, No. 3, fig. 3), in which at least two of the figures are in similar attitudes, and the Hogarthian mind might have seen a similar indiscreet observation of a statue. The removal from later states of the print of this incident in the interest of propriety deprived, but with no great loss, his idea of all meaning. It, however, gave him an opportunity of paying homage to Thornhill by scheming out, on Thornhill's lines, a portrait head on the canvas which takes the place of the satyr.

344–348. These five drawings may be identified with almost complete certainty as Lots 134 and 135 in S. Ireland's sale of May 6, 1797, and Lots 307 and 308 of his sale of May 7, 1801. In the first sale the subjects of Nos. 344 and 345 are exactly specified, while the next lot (135) is described as 'Three sketches of Academy Figures'. In the later sale the two subjects called '*Macheath* and *Falstaff*' are described as 'Large sketches in chalk from Hogarth's Sketch Book purchased by Mr. Ireland from Mrs. Lewis', and No. 347, called 'Susannah and the Elders', is mentioned in Lot 307 among three chalk drawings 'taken from Hogarth's sketch book'. The pencil inscription on No. 346 and a reference in *Anecd.* 1833 to Hogarth's sketch book in the description of No. 347 identify them as the two other chalk drawings 'taken from the sketchbook'. The drawings were in the Royal Collection by 1833.

344. SCENE IN THE BEGGARS' OPERA, *c.* 1730   *Plate* 58
Black chalk with touches of white on the same dark blue paper as Nos. 345, 347 and 348; the outlines of the chief figures pricked; splashed with oil colour. $14\frac{5}{8} \times 19\frac{3}{8}$ in. 37.3 × 49.2 cm.)   (13487)
Coll.: S. Ireland. According to *Anecd.* 1833, p. 401 in the Royal Collection by 1833.
Exhib.: Grosvenor Gallery, 1877, No. 1007; R.I. (English Humourists), 1889, No. 2.
Lit.: Phaidon No. 23.
Sketch for the earlier version of the picture (*Beckett*, p. 39, Nos. 3 and 4), and not as suggested by S. Ireland (*Graphic Ill.*, I, p. 59) for the Duke of Leeds' (now Tate Gallery) version (*Beckett*, p. 40, No. 6). The lightly-sketched background figures differ from both versions. The drawing seems also to have been followed in an undated popular print, in reverse, by J. Simpson after Hogarth, *The Ticket for the Benefit of Mr. Walker*. The handling of the drawing is free and masterly, and it shows how closely the painter followed his original sketch—at any rate, of a scene which he had seen represented on the stage. The subsequent

alterations in the paintings are not altogether an improvement. The drawing can safely be dated between 1728, when the *Beggars' Opera* was produced, and 1731, when one of the later versions was mentioned in Hogarth's MS. as unfinished.

345. FALSTAFF EXAMINING HIS RECRUITS   *Plate* 57
Black and white chalk on the same dark blue paper as No. 344, etc. $15\frac{3}{8} \times 21\frac{1}{4}$ in. (38.9 × 54 cm.)   (13491)
Coll.: See on No. 344.
Lit.: Anecd. 1833, p. 402. *Phaidon* No. 24.
In the Royal Collection by 1833. S. Ireland does not mention this drawing, which is stated in *Anecd.* 1833, p. 402, to have been in his possession in 1782, though he reproduced (*Graph. Ill.*, II, p. 72) a 'sketch' then in the possession of Mrs. Garrick and now of Lord Iveagh (*Beckett*, Pl. 4). The picture shews all the persons in the drawing in approximately the same attitudes and arrangement except that the figures on the right are brought forward further and an additional head is inserted. None of the accessory detail is shewn in the drawing, nor is the architecture indicated, but the whole story is fully told. In handling the drawing is much swifter and less rounded than the preceding. White chalk already marks the principal lights.

346. NUDE FEMALE ACADEMY FIGURE (before 1736)
Black and white chalk within ruled lines on brown paper, rubbed and slightly stained with oil. $14\frac{5}{8} \times 11\frac{1}{4}$ in. (37.3 × 28.7 cm.)   (13482)
Inscribed within the ruled margin at foot, in almost erased pencil: 'From Hogarth's Sketch Book', and in ink, below: 'The original Sketch from the life for the principal female figure in the picture of the Pool of Bethesda at St. Bartholomew's Hospital—by William Hogarth—this figure was drawn in St. Martins lane—and given to me by Chs. Catton Esqre. Nov. 21 1794. S.I.'
Coll.: S. Ireland. See on No. 344. In the Royal Library before 1833.
Lit. and reprod.: Anecd. 1833, p. 394, which inserts (presumably from *Gen. Works*, ii, 190) into the inscription after 'St. Martins lane', '. . . and is said to have represented Nell Robinson, a celebrated courtesan'. *Phaidon* No. 25.
This figure is reproduced almost exactly in Hogarth's *Pool of Bethesda*, 1736, and differs considerably from the preliminary sketch (*Beckett*, Plates 84 and 85). Had the attitude followed more closely that of the sketch, the drawing would certainly have shown Hogarth on one of those few occasions when he, to use his own words, 'took the life for correcting the parts that I had not perfectly enough remembered when I came to put them in practice' (*Phaidon*, p. 13, note 2). As this is not the case, it is reasonable to suppose that he had recourse to an old academic study rather than that he deliberately set up the model in a less expressive attitude for use in the picture.

347. THREE FIGURES. A woman standing between a bearded sitting figure in oriental robes and an old woman. Black and white chalk on the same dark blue paper as Nos. 344 etc. $12\frac{5}{8} \times 11$ in. (32.3 × 28 cm.)   (13489)
Lit. and reprod.: Anecd. 1833, p. 402, describes this as 'a beautiful female, placed between a Jewish Elder and an old woman, "from Hogarth's sketchbook"', and in the Royal Collection. The inverted commas, together with the character of the drawing, identify it with Lot 307 in S. Ireland's Sale, 1801: 'three, Susanna and the Elders, in chalk taken from Hogarth's sketchbook' (see above on 344–348). *Phaidon* No. 27.

348. A NUDE MALE ACADEMY FIGURE HOLDING A JAVELIN

Black chalk heightened with white and touched with red, on the same dark blue paper as Nos. 344 etc. 21½ × 15¾ in. (54.5 × 40 cm.) (13488)

Lit.: Phaidon No. 28.

Presumably identical with the academical study of a whole length naked figure in chalk on blue paper in the Royal Collection mentioned in *Anecd.* 1833, p. 402, and probably one of the three drawings from Hogarth's sketchbook in S. Ireland's Sale, 1801, and the three sketches of Academy figures in his sale in 1797 (see above on Nos. 344–348).

To be compared with the drawing of a nude male Academy figure levering a rock, in the Pierpont Morgan Library (*Phaidon* No. 84).

349. DON QUIXOTE RELEASES THE GALLEY SLAVES (Book III, Chapter vii), *c.* 1738.

Pen with black ink and grey washes within a ruled border; roughly incised in places. With border 9⅜ × 7⅜ in. (23.7 × 18.9 cm.) (13471)

Drawing for the engraving, in reverse, intended for Lord Carteret's edition of *Don Quixote*, 1738, not used, but issued subsequently as the sixth of Hogarth's eight plates.

Coll.: Standly.

Lit. and reprod.: Anecd. 1833, p. 395. *Connoisseur,* XCII, July, 1933, No. IV. Phaidon No. 34.

Except for small details the print follows the drawing very closely. No regard has been paid to the need for reversal. Though coarsely washed and touched with the brush, the pen drawing is highly careful, even elegant, no doubt in emulation of Coypel's *Don Quixote.*

350. DON QUIXOTE: THE CURATE AND THE BARBER DISGUISING THEMSELVES (Book III, Chapter xiii), *c.* 1738.

Black chalk on blue paper, reinforced with pen and white chalk, in ruled border, black over red. Incised. Rubbed and stained. With border 10 × 7⅝ in. (25.4 × 19.4 cm.) (13490)

Drawing for the engraving, in reverse, intended for Lord Carteret's edition of *Don Quixote* (1738), not used, but issued subsequently as the last of Hogarth's eight plates.

Coll.: Standly.

Lit.: Anecd. 1833, p. 395. Phaidon No. 35.

An almost illegible pencil inscription in the margin at foot may read as on the print and given above.

The drawing is followed exactly, except for a few accessories, in the print. It is so much rubbed and discoloured that it is impossible to say how much of its weakness is due to Hogarth.

351. THE PROPORTIONS OF GARRICK AND QUIN, 1746
Plate 61

Pen with brown ink, closely following pencil. 8⅞ × 7¼ in. (22.6 × 18.5 cm.) (13477)

Four figures with a scale forming part of a letter on a folded sheet endorsed 'to T. H. to be left at the Post office at Norwich'. For the letter on the front page see the Plate. On the right hand inner page (having the address on the *verso*) a note, also in Hogarth's hand, reads; 'The Picture from whence the Print in question was taken, was Painted from Mr. Garrick big as the life, & was sold for two Hundred pounds on account of its Likeness, which was the reason it *was call'd Mr. Garrick in the Character of Richard the 3d*—and not any body else.'

Coll.: The reproduction of 1797 states that the letter was sent 'to a member of a Literary Society at Norwich who styled themselves the Argonauts; Nathaniel Roe, Stevenson, of Norwich, J. P. Kemble. Acquired by George IV from Colnaghi (Archives Invoice 28336) July 16, 1821, for £15 15s.

Lit. and reprod.: Engraved in facsimile, May 12, 1797, for Laurie and Whittle and by T. Cook, November 1, 1808, for *Genuine Works,* ii, 280. (B.M. Sat. 2820 and 2821.) Anecd. 1833, p. 395; Phaidon No. 39.

Exhib.: R.I. (English Humourists), 1889, No. 2. B.F.A.C. 1931–1932, No. 67.

A document of capital importance; the letter written in Hogarth's best autograph and the pen drawing in his cleanest manner. The apparently extemporized character of the penwork is belied by the first drawing in pencil.

A burlesque figure of Quin, after a print of him in the character of Coriolanus, has been found (*Anecd.,* 1833, p. 337) in Plate 1, fig, 19, of the *Analysis of Beauty.*

352. HEADPIECE TO THE 'JACOBITE'S JOURNAL,' 1747
Plate 62

Red chalk, the paper impressed with a plate-mark, folded and torn. 8¼ × 6¾ in. (21 × 17 cm.) (13457)

Drawing for the woodcut at the head of Fielding's weekly newspaper *The Jacobite's Journal,* the first number of which appeared on December 5, 1747. (B.M. Sat., Vol. III, Pt. I, No. 2893).

Coll.: Horace Walpole. Standly.

Lit. and reprod.: Anecd. 1833, p. 396; Phaidon No. 67.

Exhib.: Spring Gardens (Humour Exhibition), 1925, No. 2. Edinburgh (King's Pictures), 1947, No. 109.

In the woodcut the figure of the man on the ass is much altered and the object that he is waving made clear as a cap; the woman is made to hold her sword erect, and her banner is inscribed 'Harrington' and adorned with a rowel and fleur-de-lys; the object suspended from the halter is inscribed 'London Evening Post', and is brought nearer the open jaws of the ass whose legs are differently arranged; an elaborate vista of London replaces the faint indications of landscape. The sketch is in Hogarth's strongest extempore manner.

353. THE REWARD OF CRUELTY

The upper part mainly in pen with brown ink and some grey wash; the lower in brush, with grey; pencil indications mainly visible in the upper part, some being ruled and some apparently for alterations. Loosely incised with the stylus and stained red, especially where torn or cut through by the stylus showing that the paper had been reddened at the back. 18⅛ × 15⅛ in. (46.3 × 38.3 cm.) (13494)

Drawing for the woodcut (B.M. Sat. 3167, Vol. III, Pt. II), in reverse, by J. Bell after Hogarth, January 1, 1750 (1751), intended as the fourth plate of the series 'Stages of Cruelty', subsequently published February 1, 1751, in the form of engravings.

Coll.: S. Ireland. In the Royal Collection by 1833.

Lit. and reprod.: Anecd. 1833, p. 397; Phaidon No. 74.

The drawing was clearly made for the woodcut and not for the engraving, which carries a later date, and the full drawing for which is in the Pierpont Morgan Library (*Phaidon* No. 75). This is shown by the dimensions and by certain small details in which the engraving departs from the woodcut. The very considerable changes in the upper part in which the engraving and the drawing for it differ from the present drawing are already shewn in the woodcut, namely, the replacement of the figures in the centre and the skeleton in the niche above by the President seated on his throne and the royal arms above it. On the whole, the lower part of the woodcut follows closely upon the drawing, but aprons have been given to two of the operators, and those of the figures who are seated at the table wear mortar-boards and birettas, presumably to mark their indifference to death. Pencil indications on the right hand of the drawing suggest that the first idea may have been to insert the throne in this position.

The hatching brushwork may have been intended as a guide to the wood cutter, but it has not been consistently employed, and in some places becomes merely a wash.

Dr. Antal suggests (*Art Bulletin*, December, 1949, p. 334) that Hogarth in this design adapted the idea of Heemskerck's *Quack Physicians' Hall* without Heemskerck's animal imagery.

354. VIGNETTE FOR THE 'ANALYSIS OF BEAUTY' 1753

Red chalk; some lines incised with the stylus and ruler. $6\frac{1}{8} \times 5\frac{1}{2}$ in. (15.7 × 13.9 cm.)   (13456)

Drawing for the engraving, in reverse, on the title-page of Hogarth's *Analysis of Beauty*, 1753.

In the Royal Collection by 1833 (*Anecd.* 1833, p. 397).

Lit. and reprod.: Phaidon No. 80.

The mount is inscribed in pen at foot in S. Ireland's hand, 'Frontispiece to ye Analysis—given to me by Mrs. Hogarth. Saml. Ireland'. The engraving on the title page is of the same dimensions as the drawing, but the shading and the ring at the apex are omitted, the serpentine line is differently placed, has a snake-head and is not suspended by a ribbon as in the drawing.

The words inscribed under the drawing on the paper itself in Samuel Ireland's hand, 'Sketch of a New coinage by Hogarth 1762', cannot refer to this drawing and are inexplicable. A 'Sketch of his present Majesty, taken hastily on seeing the new coinage of 1764', was included in the list of Samuel Ireland's drawings by Hogarth given on page 67* of the *Biog. Anecd.*, 1781, etc. There was no new coinage either in 1762 or in 1764.

355. THE BRUISER, 1763

Red and black chalk, inscriptions added in ink. Much rubbed and damaged. 15 × $11\frac{1}{8}$ in. (38 × 28.2 cm.)
(13458)

Drawing for the caricature portrait of Churchill as a bear of August 1, 1763. (B.M. Sat., Vol. IV, 4084).

The pot is inscribed 'N.B.'; the knots of the club with 'Lye 1', etc.; the money box with 'Pray remember the poor'; the books with 'Subscribers to the North Briton' and 'A new way to pay old debts', and the open book under the dog with 'an (e)pistle to W. Hogarth by C. Churchill'.

Coll.: Standly.

Lit. and reprod.: Phaidon No. 96.

In its present condition the drawing is impossible to analyse satisfactorily; it may have been touched upon at a later date. The figure of the dog which did not require to be redrawn, since it was already on the plate of the *Self-Portrait* which Hogarth utilised for the caricature of Churchill, looks like an impression in red chalk from the plate. But some of the other red chalk seems to be of similar character, and this suggests that either the impression was taken at a later stage than a touched proof in the Royal Library, or perhaps that the drawing is an impression or tracing throughout from another. The head of a bear in the reverse direction, and the supposed head of Churchill, both in red and very faint black, suggest such an underlying

tracing. The letters 'N.B.' are on the tankard, not on the club as in some examples of the print. The money-box is different in form in the print, and there carries no inscription. The books under the oval, two of which are quite different from those in the *Self-Portrait*, are differently inscribed in the drawing and the caricature print. The palette remains much as in the *Self-Portrait* and the touched proof in the Royal Collection, but the Line of Beauty is in a different position. It was replaced in the caricature by a political print, containing figures for which the drawing was in a small memorandum book, now lost (*Phaidon* No. 116, Fig. 3), together with a head of a bear which differs from either of the two heads in the present drawing.

356. THE BATHOS, 1764   *Plate* 60

Pen with brown ink over red chalk and pencil indications; incised with stylus. Stained on the left. $10\frac{1}{8} \times 13$ in. (25.5 × 33.1 cm.)   (13466)

Drawing for the engraving of March 3, 1764, in reverse (B.M. Sat., Vol. IV, 4106).

Illegible inscriptions on the open book at foot left, and on the bell above, except that the word 'Well' seems to appear twice on the former and 'War' and 'God' on the latter. 'The Times' is written twice on the burning print at the foot of the gallows, 'Last Will and Testament' on the scroll held by Time, 'Nature Banckrupt' on a paper at the foot of the clock, and 'Finis' in large capitals on the smoke.

Coll.: According to *Anecd.*, 1833, p. 400, sent to France by John Greenwood in 1764, and obtained thence by Standly.

Exhib.: Grosvenor Gallery, 1877, No. 1017; Spring Gardens (Humour Exhibition), 1925, No. 4.

Lit. and reprod.: Phaidon No. 97.

The drawing is vigorous with a hatching, broken and shaky line. The differences in the print are considerable and many new details are introduced; the inscriptions are also altered in wording or position.

357. (*Ascribed to Hogarth.*) A CHELSEA PENSIONER, ETC.
Figure 28

A Chelsea Pensioner seated on a bench in seven different positions and a young man standing; a profile on another scale. A further figure almost erased.

Pencil, pen and grey wash; two figures and the profile in pencil only; a heavy grey smudge on the face and either several more smudges or a drawing on the reverse (now stuck down). Inscribed on the mount with the lot number (917) of the Standly sale in 1845. $6\frac{3}{8} \times 11\frac{3}{8}$ in. (16 × 28.8 cm.)   (13475)

Coll.: J. Richardson Junior, with mark, Lugt 2170. An unknown mark, Lugt 2852. Standly.

Lit. and reprod.: Facsimile by W. J. Smith for Standly, destroyed 1826 (private plate). *Anecd.* 1833, p. 291. *Phaidon* No. 13.

This charming sheet, consisting mainly of a study of a figure in seven different positions, seems foreign both to Hogarth's manner of drawing and to his habit of mind. The figures are sketches of attitudes and not of character and, as is shown most clearly by the two which are left in pencil, there is a closer and more careful observation of form than is customary with him. The handling is that of a virtuoso, the pencil work is precise, deliberate and accomplished, the subsequent pen work, executed with a flicking touch, falls into calligraphic loops, especially in the figure of the boy, and the washes are swift but at the same time very skilful. It is of course not impossible that Hogarth, with a 'quieter mind' than usual, spent an hour in sketching a pensioner

Fig. 28. Hogarth (*ascribed to*): A Chelsea Pensioner (Cat. No. 357)

with a wooden leg as he shifted and sprawled on a bench, but such a proceeding would be so contrary to his own account of his methods that he cannot plausibly be credited with a drawing to which nothing comparable is known from his hand. The ascription would have greater authority if it could be shewn to have been attached to the drawing while in the collection of Jonathan Richardson, but even so would not be conclusive since the two men were not friends.

A fancied likeness to Hogarth's own features in the profile at the top may have caused the attribution of the drawing to him.

358. (*Ascribed to Hogarth*) THE CALVES' HEAD CLUB, 1735
Pencil and grey wash; closely incised, within a ruled border. 7¼ × 7⅞ in. (18.3 × 20 cm.)   (13484)
Drawing for the engraving (by Vandergucht), in reverse, [1735] (B.M. Sat., Vol. III, Pt. 1, 2141 and 2142).
Inscribed in pen in the margin, at top: 'The true Effigies of the Members of the Calves'-head Club', and at foot, in S. Ireland's handwriting: 'This drawing was given to me May 9 1781 by Mr. Van der Guhct [*sic*]—(whose Father engrav'd it) as an original drawing of Hogarth's.'
Coll.: S. Ireland. Standly.
Lit. and reprod.: Anecd., 1833, p. 394. *Phaidon* No. 31(*a*); Ayrton, *op. cit.*, No. 8.
Exhib.: B.F.A.C. 1931–1932, No. 72.
The design, as well as the execution of the print, was attributed by John Ireland (*Hogarth Illustrated*, Vol. III, p. 375) to Vandergucht. A note in Horace Walpole's hand on his copy of the print, now in the B.M., repeats the statement of the inscription on the drawing. The drawing is followed closely by the print. Even more than in No. 360 (*Tartuff's Banquet*) the feeble and elegant forms throughout and the neat execution are inconsistent with Hogarth's

authorship, while the weakness in the shadowed objects in the foreground is entirely foreign to his manner.

359. (*Ascribed to Hogarth*) THE SAME: THE CALF'S HEAD ONLY
Pencil. 3½ × 4⅝ in. (9 × 11.7 cm.)   (13483)
Coll., etc.: See the preceding. *Phaidon* No. 31(*b*).
The head only, without the platter, but with the tufts of hair which appear in the print and may have been intended to increase the resemblance to Charles I.
Though stronger than the reduced version, this drawing contains nothing which definitely points to Hogarth as its author.

360. (*Ascribed to Hogarth*) TARTUFF'S BANQUET
Pencil and yellow-brown wash over red chalk indications; closely incised; within a ruled border. 7⅞ × 9⅛ in. (19.9 × 23.2 cm.) with border.   (13473)
Drawing for the anonymous engraving, in reverse, of 1736/7 entitled 'Tartuff's Banquet'. (B.M. Sat., Vol. III, Pt. 1, 2281.)
Inscribed in the margin below in pencil and in different hands 'Orator Henley' and 'by Hogarth'.
Coll.: Standly.
Lit. and reprod.: Aquatint by William J. Smith for Standly, private plate, destroyed 1827; Anecd., 1833, p. 403; A.D., 1907, p. 243; *Phaidon* No. 33; Ayrton, *op. cit.*, No. 23.
Exhib.: B.F.A.C. 1931–1932, No. 74(*a*).
The print is generally attributed to Vandergucht, and the drawing with its meticulous precision (closely followed in the incision) and attenuated forms is not characteristic of Hogarth. The older commentators disputed whether Orator Henley, or, as is more probable, Dr. Gibson, Bishop of London, was represented in the figure of Tartuff; his head

was also found by Nichols (*Gen. Works*, iii, 331) to resemble Dean Swift's.

There is no trace that the drawings 'John Dennis', 'Swearing a Bastard Child' and the 'Farmer's Return' were ever in the Royal Collection as stated in *Anecd.*, 1833, pp. 402, 394 and 399. As the two latter were lotted in the S. Ireland sale of 1801 respectively with the 'Game at Hazard' (No. 342) and 'Before' (No. 361), both of which are in the Royal Library, it may be assumed that the notes were confused. The drawing and tracing on oiled paper of 'Mr. Huggins' and 'Henry Fielding', mentioned in *Anecd.*, 1833, p. 399, as being in the Royal Collection, both appear to be tracings from prints. (See further *Phaidon*, pp. 60, 62 and 64. Austin Dobson (1907) follows *Anecd.*, 1833, on 'Dennis' and 'Huggins', but he manifestly had never seen the drawings by Hogarth in the Royal Collection).

HOGARTH, After

361. 'BEFORE'

Oil on canvas, unfinished, the figures in brown outline only over slight chalk. $14\frac{7}{8} \times 12\frac{7}{8}$ in. (38 × 32.5 cm.)   (13495)
Coll.: S. Ireland, Sale 1797, Lot 139, 'First Sketch in oil for the print of *Before*'; possibly, also Sale 1801, Lot 301, 'Two, *Before*, and *Farmer's Return*, by Hogarth,' £1 13s. In *Anecd.* 1833, p. 351, where this version is described as in the Royal Collection, '*The Farmer's Return*' is also stated, erroneously, to be in the Royal Collection (see above).
The subject was engraved in 1736, December 15, 'invented, engraved and published, by William Hogarth', with a companion 'After'. There are other versions of the pictures. The present version is identical with the supposed original of 1731 (R. B. Beckett, *Hogarth*, 1949, p. 63, pl. 33). Both differ from the print in many respects, furniture, costume, features, etc. The completion, in a smooth teaboardy manner, of all the accessories before the figures, and the mechanical outlining of the latter, apparently over a light tracing, suggest a copy by an artist who was highly competent, but not Hogarth himself.
Hogarth is said to have repented the acceptance of a commission for these two subjects, and the prints were more or less suppressed. In the 19th century this caused even the mutilation of a document referring to them. Hogarth drew up a list of the paintings ordered and unfinished in January, 1731, which was included among the manuscripts belonging to and described by John Ireland in *Hogarth Illustrated*, III, 23. The list then ended with 'Two little pictures, called Before and After for Mr. Thomson Dec. 7. 1730' and another. Neither of these items is now to be found on the list, which is in the British Museum, the paper having obviously been cut in order to remove the reference to the offending pair. This is a point of some interest, for there seems to be no reason for lengthy discussion of the problem whence Hogarth derived the idea of making series of modern subjects when this pair is seen to have preceded the *Harlot's Progress*, though the prints were later.

362. MARRIAGE À LA MODE, PLATE 2

Red chalk and wash with traces of squaring. $14\frac{1}{8} \times 18$ in. (36 × 45.8 cm.)   (13492)
Esdaile's inscription on the back.
See on the following.

363. MARRIAGE À LA MODE, PLATE 3

Red chalk, squared. 14×18 in. (35.7 × 45.8 cm.)   (13493)
Coll.: The two drawings together were Lot 768 in the sale, Sotheby's, June 16, 1825, of George Baker's collection, as Hogarth's original drawings. Bought for 16 guineas by Thane for Esdaile, they were sold separately as Lots 1291 and 1292 at his sale in 1840 for £6 15s. each to H. & G. for Standly. At Standly's sale in 1845 they were bought by Colnaghi (Lots 1136 and 1137) for 10 guineas the pair.
Lit.: *Anecd.*, 1833, p. 395, as tracings.
These very elaborate drawings are of the same size as the engravings (in reverse) by B. Baron of April 1, 1745, and were obviously made from the pictures in connection with them. The drawing for Plate 3 is much less worked up than that for Plate 2, and in the elaboration of the latter the squaring has almost disappeared, becoming only visible towards the edges. The drawings are presumably by one or other of the best artists from Paris whom Hogarth advertised as his engravers for this series, probably, though not necessarily, by B. Baron himself.

HOGARTH, After. By Joseph Haynes

364. THE AUCTION OF PICTURES

Pen. Inscribed in ink below: 'The Auction', 'Drawn by Jos^h Haynes from the orig^l. Sketch in my possession—S. Ireland'. $11 \times 14\frac{7}{8}$ in. (28 × 35.7 cm.)   (13480)
Collector's mark as on No. 365.
Presumably the drawing used by Le Coeur for the engraving illustrating the three-quarter canvas purchased from Mrs. Hogarth by Samuel Ireland and described in his *Graphic Illustrations*, Vol. II, p. 101. (*Cf.* Beckett, *op. cit.*, p. 63.)

(?) HOGARTH, After

365. JACK IN AN OFFICE, ETC.

Pen. $9\frac{1}{8} \times 9\frac{3}{8}$ in. (23.2 × 23.7 cm.)   (13485)
Drawing made for, or by, Samuel Ireland for his engraving of April 1, 1786, after a rare print doubtfully attributed to Hogarth. It is described, probably correctly, in *Anecd.*, 1833, p. 307, as a tracing, already then in the Royal Collection. It bears an unknown collector's mark which is found on Hogarth prints in the Royal Library.
Samuel Ireland's inscription under his print (which is in the same direction) 'Hogarth delt'—suggests that this or some other copy was passed off as an original drawing.

HOGARTH, After

366. FRONT-IS-PISS (A Witch on a Broomstick)

Pen and grey wash. $5\frac{13}{16} \times 3\frac{3}{8}$ in. (14.7 × 8.6 cm.)   (13496)
Col. Peart, with mark (Sale April 12, 1822, perhaps in Lot 2 on the second day with other English drawings). Standly (Sale 1845, Lot 1005, with the engraving and a copy. Bt. Colnaghi £1).
Copy of a print by F. M. L[e Cave] after Hogarth said to be of 1763, or of the etching from it by Samuel Ireland, *Graphic Illustrations*, Vol. I, p. 175 (B.M. Sat., IV, 4089).

HOGARTH, Supposed. Copy after

367. HOGARTH'S LODGING IN SOUTH LAMBETH

Watercolour over pencil. $11\frac{1}{8} \times 8\frac{7}{8}$ in. (28.2 × 22.3 cm.)   (13498)

Acquired by the Prince Regent on June 2, 1817, from Colnaghi, 'Drawing, View from Mr. Hogarth's Lodging, South Lambeth', 7s. 6d. (Archives Invoice 28152).

Two sheets, the lower of which may have come from the foot of the drawing, are now pasted on the back of the modern mount. The upper reads as follows: 'This original Picture in some degree explains the obscurity all the Biographers complain of in the Early part of the Life of Hogarth, as it fixes the Spot where he Lived or at least exercised his pencil. He here Commenc'd an Acquaintance with Mr. Tyers whose Portrait is Introduced in the Picture Who was proprietor of Vauxhall—The Portrait of the Landlord would be easy to ascertaine by a reference to the Parish Books. The House was taken down about 20 years back An Elderly Gentleman informs me ['it was' *erased*] he remembers it well & that it stood at the farthest corner of Grays Buildings South Lambeth.' This is followed by a free pencil outline of the figures in the drawing. The lower sheet has at the top a pointer with the explanation 'Mr. Jonathan Tyers proprietor of Vauxhall', and at the side 'The Sun Public House at South Lambeth—taken down about 20 years ago.' Below: 'View from Mr. Hogarth's lodgings South Lambeth from an original Painted by Mr. Hogarth about the year 1730—not engraved.' In the bottom right-hand corner of the lower strip the name J. T. Smith is written in pencil, possibly in the Librarian's or Colnaghi's hand.

Neither has the drawing any apparent connexion with Hogarth, nor is the rural or seaside view convincing as a representation of Lambeth.

HOLBECH, MARY ANN. *See* Lady Mordaunt

HENRY HOLLAND (1746?–1806), Ascribed to

368. CARLTON HOUSE: THE GRAND STAIRCASE

Pencil and wash. $14\frac{7}{8} \times 11\frac{1}{4}$ in. (37.7 × 28.8 cm.) (17144)

On the *verso:* Plan of a staircase in pencil.

Inscribed: On the front, in pencil, along the wainscot of the staircase, 'Carlton House'. On the back, in ink in an old hand, 'Staircase Carleton House', and the same words in pencil.

Acquired before 1915.

Reproduced, as by Henry Holland, plate 58, *Survey of London*, Vol. XX (1940), p. 75, n. The drawing is, however, not in his manner and is not a design, but represents the staircase as completed and furnished with the statues in their niches. It has every appearance of being a somewhat clumsy exercise in complicated perspective. The little frieze under the dome, shewn in C. Wild's view of the Staircase (Pyne, *Royal Residences*, 1819, pl. 5) is omitted from this drawing, which shows the clock supported by the figure of Time. Wild's view is of the staircase from the other side, showing the figure of Atlas under the dome.

WENCESLAUS HOLLAR (1607–1677)

369. WINDSOR CASTLE FROM THE NORTH-EAST, ETON COLLEGE IN THE DISTANCE   *Plate* 63

Pen with black ink, faint green, blue and pink washes. $4\frac{5}{8} \times 10\frac{7}{8}$ in. (11.8 × 27.5 cm.) (13263)

Inscribed 'Windsor' in sky, 'Thamesis fluvius' at foot right. Engraved, in colours, by Richard Sawyer, 1828, as in the possession of the publisher, W. B. Tiffen.

Reprod.: St. John Hope: *Windsor Castle*, 1913, pl. IV; *Connoisseur*, XCI, June, 1933, No. 1; Sprinzels, *Hollars Handzeichnungen*, 1938, No. 361, pl. 91; Urzidil, *Hollar, a Czech emigré in England*, 1942, pl. 16.

Purchased in October, 1907, with No. 373.

370. WESTMINSTER AND ST. JAMES'S PALACE

Pen with black ink, grey wash, soiled. $4\frac{1}{8} \times 11\frac{7}{8}$ in. (10 × 30.1 cm.)   (13264)

Inscribed, at foot, in brown ink: 'Westminster Abby. 2: Westminster Hall. 3: St. James's Palace. 4: Pall Mall. 5: Conduit', the numbers repeated above the buildings. Presumably Towneley Sale, May 26, 1818, Lot 98, with two prints by J. T. Smith.

Lit. and reprod.: Etched by Richard Sawyer, June 13, 1809, as an ancient drawing in the possession of John Towneley, T.B.M., F.R.S., R.A. (Wilkinson, *Londina Illustrata*, Vol. I, p. 89). *Connoisseur*, XCI, June, 1933, No. III; Sprinzels, *op. cit.*, No. 333.

There is a copy at the British Museum (Crace, Vol. XI, No. 23); another, then in the Gardner collection, is reproduced by Canon Edgar Sheppard, *Memorials of St. James's Palace*, 1894, p. 2.

371. THE THAMES FROM WESTMINSTER, THE NORTH BANK LOOKING EAST   *Plate* 64

Pen with dark brown ink over pencil, the right-hand portion unfinished. $5\frac{5}{8} \times 15\frac{3}{8}$ in. (14 × 39 cm.)   (13266)

Signed: W. Hollar, on a log, at foot left.

Exhib.: B.F.A.C. 1919, No. 6; Edinburgh 1947 (King's Pictures), No. 112.

Lit. and reprod.: A. M. Hind, *W. Hollar & his Views of London*, 1922, p. 34, note. Sprinzels, *op. cit.*, No. 332, pl. 57.

372. ARUNDEL HOUSE

Pen with black ink, the portions on each side, unfinished, in pencil. Within ruled margin. $3\frac{1}{2} \times 8\frac{5}{8}$ in. (9 × 21.8 cm.)   (13268)

Inscribed: 'Arundel House' in centre at top.

373. RICHMOND WITH THE PALACE AND A CAVALCADE.   *Plate* 65

Pen and black ink, green, blue and pink washes, within ruled margin. $3 \times 7\frac{5}{8}$ in. (7.6 × 19.5 cm.)   (13267)

Signed at foot: Wentzel Hollar delineavit 1638, and inscribed, in sky, 'Richmond'.

Reprod.: A facsimile engraving, in colour, and inscribed (in ink) 'T. Philips excudit', is in the Royal Library and has been attributed to Van der Gucht. *Cf.* Hind, *op. cit.*, p. 22, note 1, and p. 82; Sprinzels, *op. cit.*, No. 366, pl. 71; Urzidil, *Hollar*, 1942, pl. 17.

Exhib.: Edinburgh 1947 (King's Pictures), No. 114.

Acquired October 1907, with No. 369.

374. A CITY STANDING OVER WATER

Pen with black ink, blue and brown washes. $3\frac{5}{8} \times 6\frac{1}{8}$ in. (9.3 × 15.6 cm.)   (13270)

An unidentified view, apparently in the same early series as the following.

Sprinzels, *op. cit.*, No. 287, pl. 67.

375. ROEROORT (RUHRORT), the city with the junction of the Ruhr and the Rhine.   *Plate* 66

Pen and black ink, faint blue and brown washes. $3\frac{3}{4} \times 6\frac{1}{8}$ in. (9.6 × 15.5 cm.)   (13271)

Inscribed 'Roeroort' at top, centre, 'Roer fl' and 'Rhenus fl' respectively against the rivers. The landscape, left, as in the engraving, Parthey, No. 770.

Sprinzels, *op. cit.*, No. 168, pl. 49, relates this drawing to Hollar's journey north, 1633–34, and does not mention the etching.

Fig. 29. Hoppner: A lady seated, with a dog (Cat. No. 380)

376. A TRIUMPHAL ARCH WITH HISTORICAL SCENES

Pen with black ink, grey wash; incised with stylus; much damaged, the inscriptions illegible. $11\frac{1}{2} \times 7\frac{3}{4}$ in. (29.2 × 19.7 cm.) (13272)

Engraved in reverse as the title-page to Dugdale's *Monasticon*, 1655, with additional scenes and figures of saints, the inscriptions completed and differently placed, and other differences. Parthey No. 2660, who notes that this drawing with four states of the plate was acquired by the Royal Library from the Towneley Collection (*cf.* No. 370) (Sale, May 26–30, 1818, Lot 506, bt. Clark £1 2s.).
Sprinzels, *op. cit.*, No. 79, pl. 26.

W. HOLLAR, Ascribed to

377. WINDSOR CASTLE FROM THE SOUTH-EAST

Pen with brown ink, grey wash. $3\frac{3}{8} \times 15\frac{5}{8}$ in. (8.2 × 37.2 cm.) (13262)

Mutilated inscription above: 'of the Castel from the S.E.'; writing on the back (laid down).
Lit. and reprod.: Connoisseur, XCI, June, 1933, No. II; Sprinzels, *op. cit.*, No. 360, as doubtful.
Closely related to the upper of the two views of Windsor Castle in the etching 'Prospect of the Castle from the S.E.' Parthey, No. 1072, Hind, 114, but in a freer and apparently later technique than is commonly found in Hollar's work.

W. HOLLAR, After

378. LONDON FROM LAMBETH

Pen and black ink over brown. $6\frac{3}{8} \times 11\frac{1}{4}$ in. (16.3 × 28.6 cm.) (13265)

Inscribed above the near building on the right, 'Lambeth House', and over the distant building in the centre, 'Suffulke house'. Also 'W. Hollar D' at foot right, not a signature. Closely copied from the centre and right-hand portions of the drawing at the British Museum (L.B. 11, 1882-8-12-224), the hay barge, etc., brought in from further to the left, the inscriptions as nearly as possible in facsimile.

W. HOLLAR, Imitator of

379. A SEA-PORT ON A ROCKY COAST

Pen with black ink, much discoloured, with margin at foot. $3\frac{5}{8} \times 6\frac{3}{8}$ in. (9.2 × 16.2 cm.) (13269)

An illegible word, perhaps 'Alex^r.' in pen in the margin at foot.
Somewhat in the manner of the Tangier etchings but still more minute and niggling, especially in the waves.

JOHN HOPPNER (1758–1810)

380. A LADY SEATED, WITH A DOG   *Figure* 29

Pen and brown wash. $12\frac{1}{8} \times 9\frac{1}{4}$ in. (30.6 × 23.6 cm.) (13426)

Mounted under the name of Gainsborough, with whose manner it has nothing in common. Ozias Humphry has been suggested, but the drawing has sufficient similarity with some of Hoppner's to justify a tentative identification with the 'Drawing Unknown, whole length Portrait by Hoppner', bought by King George IV from Colnaghi on September 20, 1828, for £2 2s. (Archives Invoice 28376).

SAMUEL HOWITT (*c.* 1765–1822)

381. CASTLE HILL, showing the wall, etc., demolished for King George III, and on the right the end of Queen's Lodge.

Pen and watercolour with washed mount. $11\frac{1}{2} \times 16\frac{5}{8}$ in. (28.9 × 42.4 cm.) (17398)

Signed: Howitt.
Presented by H.M. Queen Mary, June, 1922.
A drawing of 'Windsor Castle by Howit' was bought by the Prince of Wales from Colnaghi on January 30, 1802, for £2 12s. 6d. (Archives Invoice 27172). For the topography, see *Sandby Catalogue*, No. 16.

382. THE QUEEN'S HOUSE, FROGMORE

Watercolour. $5\frac{1}{2} \times 8\frac{1}{8}$ in. (14 × 20.6 cm.) (17644)

Signed: Howitt, and inscribed in pencil at the top, Queen's House Frogmoor.
From the collection of E. Horsman Coles, C.B. Acquired 1949.
Drawing for the engraving 'Drawn, etched and published by S. Howitt Panton Street Haymarket, January 1st 1802'; the example in the Royal Library in aquatint with colour, has no title.
The drawing shows the house, as in the aquatint by Apostool after R. Cooper of 1793, with the portico but without the ornamental water and the wings shewn in the prints of 1819 and later.

383. 'THE PAVILION, FROGMORE'

Watercolour, some pencil in the figures. $5\frac{1}{2} \times 8\frac{3}{8}$ in. (14.2 × 21.3 cm.) (17599)

Transferred to the Royal Library from Frogmore, May, 1948, and removed from its frame, which bore a label, 'The

Pavilion, Frogmore, by P. Sandby', and another indicating its acquisition by H.M. Queen Mary as Princess of Wales. The late 18th-century pavilion shown in the drawing no longer exists. Three men standing and leaning against a tree may be intended to be wearing the Windsor uniform, blue coats with red facings. The drawing is not by Sandby, and may safely be attributed to Howitt in his earlier manner.

WILLIAM JOHN HUGGINS (1781–1845)

384. THE ISLAND OF ST. HELENA TAKEN AT 5 MILES DISTANT

Watercolour. 11⅞ × 29¾ in. (30 × 75 cm.)   (17016)
The localities named in the margin below.
Aquatinted (colour) by E. Duncan, April 20, 1832.
A 'Sketch of the Island of St. Helena' was acquired by the Prince Regent from Colnaghi on August 23, 1815, for 2s. 6d. (Archives Invoice 28076).

EDWARD HULL (fl. 1820–1840)

Two watercolours, uniforms of the Life Guards, signed, are in Military Drawings, Vol. IV, p. 84 (Nos. 16493–16494).

GILES HUSSEY (1710–1788)

385. PRINCE CHARLES EDWARD, the Young Pretender (1721–1788), bust, profile to right, within oval.

Pencil, unfinished. 9¼ × 6⅝ in. (23.3 × 17 cm.)   (17194)
Given to King George V by the Prince of Wales, 1921.
There are several other versions, one of which, in pen, in the possession of the Earl of Ilchester, is reproduced as the frontispiece of *A Jacobite Miscellany*, Roxburghe Club, 1948, and others are enumerated in Lord Stavordale's catalogue of the Pictures at Holland House, 1904, No. 222.

GILES HUSSEY, Attributed to

386. PRINCE CHARLES EDWARD, half length, profile to left, in armour, wearing the ribbon of the Garter.

Pencil and wash. Oval, 5¾ × 4⅛ in. (14.5 × 10.5 cm.)   (17195)
Presented by H.M. Queen Mary, 1935.

H. HYSING (1678–1753), After

387. KING GEORGE III when Prince George of Wales.

Gouache. 16½ × 10 in. (42 × 25 cm.)   (17259)
Copy from the mezzotint by Burford after Hysing (O'Donoghue, Vol. II, p. 299, No. 1) with additions top and bottom.
This drawing was formerly in a German Bible (1736) superbly bound for the young Prince whence it was extracted and mounted in (?) 1926. A list in the Royal Library, in Glover's handwriting, of the books belonging to Queen Charlotte mentions 'This bible belonged to George III when a boy, of whom there is a whole length drawing when about 9 or 10 years old.'

INIGO JONES, After

Four architectural drawings of Whitehall Palace (17086–17089) are discussed by Miss Margaret Whinney in *Walpole Society*, 1942–1943, Vol. XXXI, p. 48, note. One of them may be by Elias Ferris, the other three conjecturally the work of the engraver Hulsebergh. Inventory 'A', p. 169 (1816).

ANGELICA KAUFFMAN (1741–1807)

388. PHILIPPE EGALITÉ, DUKE OF ORLEANS

Pencil and grey wash. Oval, 5 × 4⅝ in. (12.7 × 11.7 cm.) on a sheet 7½ × 5¼ in. (19 × 13.5 cm.)   (13290)
Signed in pen: 'Angelica Kaufmann pinxit Roma 1783 et delin'; and inscribed below, 'Mr. le Duc d'Orleans Egalite'; both over pencil erasures.
Etched, in reverse, by S. D'Agincourt with the same inscription, but differing titles; two states in the Bibliothèque Nationale.
The Prince Regent acquired, on July 6, 1812, 'A Drawing, Portrait of Philippe Duc d'Orléans', for £4 4s., on October 12 of the same year 'A Drawing Duc d'Orléans' for 10s. 6d.; and on May 4, 1808, 'A Drawing Duke of Orleans', for 7s. 6d. (Archives Invoices 27877, 27889 and 27464) (all from Colnaghi).
Louis Philippe Joseph, Duc d'Orléans, born 1717, took the name Egalité in 1792 and was guillotined in 1793.

The following drawings were placed together unmounted and untrimmed in a recent paper folder inscribed 'Angelica Kauffman'. They were without indication of provenance.

389. DESIGN FOR A FRONTISPIECE OR MEMORIAL CARD

Pencil, pen and brown and grey washes. 9 × 6¼ in. (22.9 × 15.9 cm.)   (17989)

390. (?) HECTOR'S FAREWELL TO ANDROMACHE

Pen and grey wash heightened with white on toned paper. 10⅛ × 11⅝ in. (25.7 × 29.5 cm.)   (17984)

391. ARIADNE AND BACCHUS

Pencil and pen within border. 6½ × 7¾ in. (16.5 × 19.7 cm.)   (17993)

392. (?) THE MEETING OF DIDO AND AENEAS

Pen. 7⅝ × 9⅛ in. (19.4 × 23.2 cm.)   (17985)

393. TROILUS AND CRESSIDA

Pen, the title in pencil at foot. Watermark 1781. 7 × 8¾ in. (17.8 × 22.2 cm.)   (17991)

394. TWO WOMEN DRAPED, WITH TWO CHILDREN

Pencil and pen, the paper coloured at the back. 9¾ × 12⅛ in. (24.8 × 30.8 cm.)   (17988)

395. TWO SKETCHES OF A MOTHER AND CHILD

Pen. 9½ × 7 in. (24.1 × 17.8 cm.)   (17990)

396. A WOMAN SEATED, DRAPED

Pen. 9 × 7⅛ in. (22.9 × 18.1 cm.)   (17986)

397. MUSIC. A WOMAN PLAYING THE LYRE, A MAN HOLDING A SCROLL OF MUSIC

Pen and grey wash. Circular, diam., 7⅜ in. (18.7 cm.).   (17994)

398. A MOTHER WITH TWO CHILDREN

Black and white chalk on paper toned grey. 9⅜ × 13 in. (23.8 × 33 cm.)   (17996)

399. A SUPPLIANT

Black and white chalk on buff paper. 13 × 10 in. (33 × 25.4 cm.)   (17992)

400. MELPOMENE, SEATED, HOLDING A MASK

Black and white chalk on toned paper. 12½ × 10½ in. (31.8 × 26.7 cm.)   (17983)

401. THE DEATH OF CLEOPATRA

Black and white chalk on grey paper. 12½ × 18¼ in. (31.8 × 46.4 cm.)   (17995)

402. (?) THE GLORIFICATION OF ST. FRANCIS

Pen. 5⅝ × 4⅛ in. (14.2 × 10.4 cm.)   (17987)

403. TWO DESIGNS FOR (?) AN OVERMANTEL IN POMPEIAN STYLE with decorations and lunettes of Orpheus and other musical subjects.

Pen, grey and brown washes and gouache on a black ground. 14 × 18¾ in. (35.6 × 47.6 cm.)   (17997, 17998)

JOSHUA KIRBY, see No. 4

WILLIAM KIRBY (d. 1771)

A series of drawings, architectural in character, shewing plans, elevations and reconstructions of ancient buildings in Rome, uniformly mounted and dated 1767 and 1768, some signed W. Kirby and others Giovanni Stern, or unsigned, preserved in the Royal Library, would appear to be the 'Architectural Drawings of the Pantheon by Mr. Sterne, with others of the Sybill's Temple at Tivoli', bought for 83.27 Roman Crowns by Richard Dalton at Rome, Surveyor of the King's pictures (Archives Document 15603) before 1771. Entered in Inventory 'A', p. 162 (1816).
William Kirby, younger son of Joshua Kirby (q.v.) was sent to Italy to study architecture at the Royal expense. On his return the King appointed his wife housekeeper at Richmond Lodge and gave Kirby a house at Kew. He died suddenly from an accident in 1771. (Whitley, *Artists and their friends*, Vol. I, p. 225.)

Sir GODFREY KNELLER (1646–1723)

404. LOUIS XIV, head only, turned half right.   *Figure 30*

Black and red chalk on brown paper, damaged. 17¾ × 13 in. (44.2 × 33 cm.)   (13310)
Inscribed, top left corner in ink: 'Louis the XIIIId. Drawn (*sic*) by the Life at Versallis (*sic*) in the year 1684 by G. Kneller.' On the back an unintelligible inscription: words in Italian, as deciphered by Mr. Cecil Gould.
From Hampton Court: *cf.* Waagen II, p. 368.
Possibly the drawing for the portrait now in the possession of Col. Nigel Stopford-Sackville, Drayton House, Lowick, Northants, engraved by P. Vanderbank.

Sir GODFREY KNELLER, Attributed to

405. KING GEORGE I (?), head, full face, slightly inclined to right.

Black and coloured chalk on green-blue paper. 14½ × 9⅜ in. (36.7 × 24 cm.)   (13253)
Neither artist nor sitter, suggested anonymously on the modern mount, carries any conviction.

L. KNYFF (1650–1721), After

406. WINDSOR CASTLE AND TOWN FROM THE RIVER

Pencil and grey wash. 8⅛ × 17⅞ in. (20.7 × 40.5 cm.)
                                                                 (17395)
Unfinished copy of the Knyff-Kip print.

'LAMBERT'

407. WINDSOR CASTLE FROM THE RIVER

Pen and watercolour. 14 × 20⅞ in. (35.3 × 52.6 cm.)
                                                                 (17417)
A recent pencil note at the back, perhaps from some earlier mount, reads 'Lambert del. 1797'. While the topography betrays a pure pasticheur, both costume and style suggest a much earlier date than 1797 and might not be inconsistent with James Lambert of Chichester (1725–1788).

WILLIAM LANE (1746–1819)

408. STUDY FOR A GROUP OF MUSICAL PERFORMERS

Salomon, Pinto, Weischell, Shield, Linley, Parke and Ashe; around a bust of Apollo on a pedestal inscribed 'Handel, Haydn, Mozart'.   *Plate 67*

Black and coloured chalks on pink paper, rubbed. 17 × 22½ in. (43.4 × 56.5 cm.)   (13500)
Signed: W. Lane delt.

Lane exhibited a picture of this subject at the Royal Academy, 1810 (No. 544).
Purchased May 1, 1817, by the Prince Regent from the artist for £42 11s. (Archives Invoice 26991).

Fig. 30. Kneller: Louis XIV (Cat. No. 404)

MARCELLUS LAROON (1679–1772)

409. A FRENCHMAN AT BOW STREET *Plate* 68

Pencil. 14⅛ × 20½ in. (36.2 × 51.8 cm.) (13309)

Signed: M. Laroon F. 1740, and inscribed in the Colnaghi hand, 'A Curious and Interesting Drawing by Laroon of a French Gentn Brought at night before the Justice at Bow S[t].'

Purchased by the Prince Regent from Colnaghi on January 18, 1813, £2 2s. (Archives Invoice 27911), title as inscribed on drawing.

410. RIDERS AND BEGGARS

Pencil, pen and brown wash. 18¼ × 13 in. (47 × 33 cm.)
(13308)

Signed in border: Marcellus Laroon . . . (erasure) Fecit 1735.

411. A CONVERSATION

Pencil, pen and grey wash, with margin. 15⅜ × 11¼ in. (39 × 28.7 cm.) (13287)

Signed in the margin at foot: M. Laroon f. and inscribed in pencil below, 'Marcellus Laroon born 1678 Died 1771 aged 93' and '20'.

Sir THOMAS LAWRENCE, P.R.A. (1769–1830)

412. THE PRINCE REGENT, half length, profile to left, in armour. *Plate* 9

Black, white and red chalk on prepared canvas. 40⅞ × 33⅜ in. (104 × 85 cm.)

Lord Chamberlain's Department, No. 704.

No. 676 in the Carlton House Inventory (after 1830 and before 1837), and presumably the 'Drawing on Canvas of his Majesty in Armour' claimed by the King from Lawrence's estate and delivered in January, 1830, on payment of 100 guineas (South Kensington Ms. 86, H. 19, kindly indicated by Mr. Kenneth Garlick).

The drawing has every appearance of being a preparation for an oil painting, and the head has sufficient resemblance to the portraits in Garter robes and that in uniform at Londonderry House to suggest that it is a first, discarded study for the portrait exhibited in 1815. Moreover, it corresponds in almost every detail, notably the *pentimenti*, with the lithograph (in reverse) by R. J. Lane, which in the larger private issue of 1828 carries a facsimile inscription stating that 'for this drawing His Majesty graciously sat to me in the year 1814'. The proof on which Lawrence wrote the original inscription is in the Royal Library, accompanied by a letter from Lane, presenting it to Queen Victoria. Lane's smaller version (published, O'Donoghue, Vol. II, p. 316, No. 110) of the lithograph dated 1829 carries another facsimile inscription, also signed by Lawrence, which inserts that the drawing was designed for a medal. The chief point of difference from Lane's lithographs is in the neckwear, which is there clearly the collar of the armour worn by the Regent, but in the drawing is a closely-fitting stock. In this detail, which seems to have presented some difficulty in all the representations, the drawing comes nearer to the sketch in oil at the National Portrait Gallery (No. 123), which is said in the catalogue to have been 'made for the coinage', and is accordingly dated 1821 by Armstrong, notwithstanding that Lane's lithographs give the date 1814, and F. C. Lewis's stipple engraving of 1839 (Plate 2 of his *Twenty Imitations of Lawrence*), which comes nearest to the oil sketch, is also stated to be 'from an original

drawing'. There would appear to be no authority beyond the inscription on Lane's lithograph of 1829 for connecting the oil sketch with the coinage. Nor is there any resemblance between the head on Rundell & Bridge's Peace Medal of 1814 (followed by the Waterloo medal) and these portraits, except in the direction and perhaps in the hair. The head in the medal is older, heavier and entirely different in character and expression. Lawrence's memory may have been confused when he inscribed (if he did) the lithograph of 1829; otherwise it must be supposed that the medal referred to was never executed. Even so a life-size drawing on canvas would not seem most adapted for the purpose.

Another portrait of the King in black, white and red chalk was Lot 406 in the Lawrence Sale on June 18, 1831, among some twenty highly-praised 'Large Drawings from the Life on Canvas' (bought by Norton, 9½ gns.). Lawrence, according to Wilkie, habitually made careful drawings of the heads on paper and then transferred them to canvas.

413. CONSTANTINE HENRY PHIPPS, First Marquess of Normanby (1797–1863), bust, facing half right.

Black and red chalk, grey wash. 11⅝ × 8⅞ in. (29.6 × 22.6 cm.) (13501)

Signed: T. L. and inscribed 'Normanby'.

414. ROBERT PLUMER WARD, M.P. (1765–1846), bust, full face. *Figure* 31

Black and red chalk, grey wash. 11¾ × 8⅞ in. (29.7 × 22.5 cm.) (13502)

Exhib.: R.A. 1934, No. 733 (1189).

Fig. 31. Lawrence: Robert Plumer Ward, M.P. (Cat. No. 414)

415. LADY ELIZABETH FOSTER, DUCHESS OF DEVON-
SHIRE (1759–1824), half length, facing half left.

Pencil, charcoal and red chalk. $10\frac{1}{4} \times 8\frac{1}{4}$ in. (sight)
(26 × 21 cm.)

Engraved by F. C. Lewis (published February 1, 1828) after
Lawrence (O'Donoghue, Vol. II, p. 51, No. 1; print reproduced in *Sir Thomas Lawrence's Letterbag*, opp. p. 184). The
engraving is larger than the drawing.

The drawing, which has been laid down, is neither signed
nor dated; the date 1806 is given in the Inventory of Pictures (Lord Chamberlain's Department), where it is called
Mary, Countess Grey (No. 2354).

SIR THOMAS LAWRENCE or G. H. HARLOW

416. 'ELIZA O'NEIL', head and shoulders, almost full face.

Pencil, stump and red chalk. $7\frac{1}{2} \times 6$ in. (19.2 × 15.3 cm.)
(13612)

This and the following are traditionally described as portraits by G. H. Harlow (1787–1819) of Eliza O'Neil, actress
(1791–1872), and Anna Bishop, singer (1814–1884). The
latter identification is impossible, whether Harlow or
Lawrence is the artist; nor are the two drawings in fact
uniform in scale or manner. The present drawing is the
weaker in handling throughout, that called 'Anna Bishop'
might well be by Lawrence himself.

417. 'ANNA BISHOP', head only, full face.

Pencil, stump and red chalk. $7\frac{1}{2} \times 6$ in. (19.2 × 15.2 cm.)
(13613)

See on the preceding.

THE EARL OF LEICESTER (1753–1811), *see* Nos.
615, 616

BERNARD LENS II (1659–1725)

418. WINDSOR CASTLE FROM THE NORTH; THE WEST
END ONLY   *Plate* 74

Grey wash, some pencil. $7 \times 13\frac{3}{4}$ in. (17.8 × 34.8 cm.)
(17414)

Inscribed in ink, 'Part of Windsor castell', in an early hand,
and (?) '80' in the top right corner. In pencil on the front
'Wyke' under 'Windsor Castell', '236' centre top, and on
the back 'Bernard Lens' over an erasure and 'No. 105' in
ink.

This drawing and No. 697, though approximately of the
same size, and perhaps at some date cut to form a pair, are
on different paper, and in different styles.

Although no drawing so forceful and free in character is
known by either of the Bernard Lens (whose identity is very
difficult to distinguish), the signature at the back is too
much like that in the inscription on the drawing of Bone
Well at the British Museum (L.B.1) to be disregarded. The
drawing is however much closer to the manner of the
Blackheath by T. Wyck (1897–8–31–1) at the British
Museum, whose name may have been placed on the front,
when the inscription on the back was hidden in the book
whence it has evidently been removed.

BERNARD LENS III (1682–1740)

419. WINDSOR CASTLE FROM THE NORTH-WEST

Grey wash, within ruled border. $9\frac{3}{4} \times 14$ in. (24.8 × 35.6
cm.)
(17965)

Inscribed at the foot in brown ink, 'Windsor Castle' and '4',
and, in pencil in a dealer's hand, 'Berks'.

Very similar drawings inscribed by the same hand but with

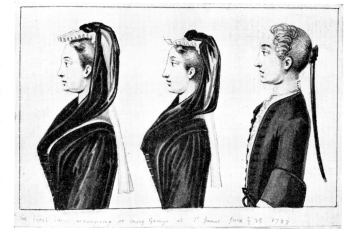

Fig. 32. Bernard Lens III: 'The first dayes' mourning June
25 1727' (Cat. No. 421)

neat pen hatching as well as wash are in the British Museum.
From the L. G. Duke Collection; acquired from the Squire
Gallery, 1948.

420. An album (adapted) containing seventeen views of
England, etc.

The sketches are not uniform, five, *c.* 7×9 in. (17.8 × 22.9
cm.), and smaller, are in grey with descriptions and artist's
name in different hands. Two are in pen and brown wash,
$4\frac{3}{4} \times 7\frac{1}{2}$ in. (12.1 × 19.1 cm.), and inscribed below in the
same hand as in No. 421, with descriptions in ink; 'B. Lens
1704' added, later, in pencil. The other English views are of
different sizes, in grey wash and with inscriptions and dates,
if any, in various hands. One only, Bridgnorth, is inscribed
in the same hand as the two in brown wash and is signed
and dated 1718. Another drawing is inscribed, 'An exact
prospect, of Gibraltar, with the Enemy's Trenches before
it', in a similar hand in ink, with the date 1704 added
recently in pencil. The last two drawings, in brown, are
Italian or imaginary views, with antiquities, and are clearly
by another later and considerably more experienced hand,
perhaps Italian.

Acquired from F. Edwards, 1911.

Similar collections of English views are in the British
Museum and private collections, and are mentioned in the
catalogue of the sale after Bernard Lens' death in 1740
(*Walpole Society*, Vol. XXII, p. 100).

421. THE EXACT HEAD DRESS OF YE BRITISH COURT
LADYES & Quality Drawn from the Life at the Court,
Opera and Theater in the Years 1725: 26: 27.

Figures 32, 33

An oblong volume in contemporary calf binding, contain-
ing, inserted, title-page and forty sheets, *c.* $4\frac{1}{8} \times 6\frac{1}{4}$ in. (10.2
× 15.7 cm.), each sheet showing from two to four busts to
the waist in pen and grey wash. The figures are almost
exclusively in profile, all are of women except pp. 36–39,
men, and p. 40, *Figure 32*, which shews two women and one
young man, and is inscribed, apparently in the artist's handwriting, 'the first dayes mourning for King George at St.
James June ye 25 1727', in pencil in the lower border of the
drawing. Some of the other figures are similarly inscribed
with numbers, which are not in serial order, and eight others
with names—Mrs. Lee (p. 14), Countess of Cardigan
(p. 16), Miss Vane (p. 19), Duchess of Richmond (p. 25),
Miss Bret (p. 28), Lady Denbigh (p. 34), Lady Mary
Wilmore and Lady Dudley (p. 35), *Figure 33*. Some of these

Fig. 33. Bernard Lens III: Headdresses of the year 1727
(Cat. No. 421)

names are repeated in pen, also in a contemporary hand, below, on the paper of the book. The names should be regarded as indicating that the headdress was worn by the lady rather than that a portrait is to be found in the features. One of the more mature ladies represented on the first page carries a folded paper inscribed 'Admetus Opera'. That opera was first performed in January, 1727.

The title, as given, and 'by Bernard Lens', are inscribed in pencil within a cartouche on the first sheet. It bears the number '116' in the lower margin, apparently uniform with the numbers under some of the figures referred to in the previous paragraph.

A manuscript memorandum dated September 30, 1850, unsigned, but in the writing of J. H. Glover, states that he had just found this volume, which had been sent on approval by a bookseller, on the table of an official (Mr. Wilbraham Taylor, Secretary to the Privy Purse) who had left the office, 'and knowing its value and the length of time it had been *kicking about*, thought it desirable to take care of it'.

There is a very similar volume in the Department of E.I.D. at the Victoria & Albert Museum (E.I.D. 1652–1926). It contains thirty pages only, including the title page, which is more elaborate and completed with an inscription in ink and specifies the years as 1725 and 1726 only. Some of the figures are identical, if differently arranged, and most shew the head and shoulders only; they are more delicately drawn.

BERNARD LENS III, Ascribed to

422. GRENADIER WITH BAYONET. Two views of the same position.

Oil on brown paper. (*a*) 9 × 4⅞ in. (22.5 × 13 cm.); (*b*) 9 × 4⅞ in. (22.7 × 12.5 cm.)   (17253, 17254)

Similar to the figures etched in outline by Bernard Lens, 1736, in 'The Grenadier's Exercise with the Grenade', and republished, with elaborations, by A. B. Lens, his son, in 1745. (A washed copy of the former and a coloured of the latter are in the Royal Library.)

PETER PAUL LENS (fl. 1729–1750),
son of Bernard Lens III

423. 'MOGGEDORIO THE GOOD CLERK'   *Figure* 34

Pencil and body colour. 9½ × 6¼ in. (24.1 × 16 cm.)
(17235)

Signed: P. Lens. Pinx. 1737, and inscribed on the back:

'Original drawing of Moggadorio, extremely curious 15/–.'
Exhib.: B.F.A.C. 1931/32, No. 64.

Acquired by the Prince of Wales on July 6, 1810, from Colnaghi, 'Moggedorio the good Clerk an original Drawing by Lens' for 15s. (Archives Invoice 27540).

ROBERT LODER

424. JOHN AUBREY, after Faithorne.
Pencil. Oval, 6⅞ × 5½ in. (17.3 × 14 cm.)   (13512)
Signed: Robt. Loder fecit.
After Faithorne's drawing in the Ashmolean Museum (Poole, *Oxford Portraits*, I, 1912, No. 450. Bell, *Walpole Society*, Vol. XIV, pl. 386).
Perhaps the 'drawing by Aubrey' bought by the Prince Regent on February 7, 1813, from Colnaghi for 1½ guineas (Archives Invoice 27977).

PHILIP DE LOUTHERBOURG, R.A.
(1740–1812)

Seven small watercolours, four being on cards, shewing details of uniforms, in Military Drawings, Vol. IV, p. 63 (Nos. 16429–16435). Inscribed on border 'De Loutherbourg del'. On three, names are pencilled—'Genl. Lake', 'Genl. Leigh', 'Col. Doyle', and on another 'Yorkshire Grey'.

Fig. 34. P. P. Lens: Moggedorio the good clerk (Cat. No. 423)

F., J., OR T. MACKENZIE (1809)

425. THE HOUSES AT THE BACK OF ST. GEORGE'S CHAPEL (Denton's Commons, removed 1859).

Pencil. $8\frac{5}{8}$ × 9 in. (21.8 × 22.8 cm.)   (17484)

Inscribed in pencil: 'T. Mackenzie 1809', and 'back of St. George's Chapel Windsor', and on the back, 'Windsor 1809', in another hand.

Reprod.: St. John Hope, *Windsor Castle*, 1913, pl. LXXXVIII, when in his collection.

Probably F. Mackenzie (1788–1854) was intended by the inscription, no J. or T. Mackenzie being recorded. A nondescript performance, it is included for its topographic interest as shewing the condition of the houses at the beginning of the 19th century (see Hope, *op. cit.*, p. 505).

THOMAS MALTON, JUNIOR (1748–1804)

426. THE SEAT OF SIR JOHN ELVILL, BART., AT ENGLEFIELD GREEN, SURREY

Pen and watercolour, soiled. $9\frac{7}{8}$ × $14\frac{5}{8}$ in. (25.2 × 37 cm.)   (14714)

With a false signature of comparatively recent and well-known type, 'P. Sandby' and 'Frogmore House' perhaps in the same hand, both in ink. In an older hand, on the back, in pencil 'Duke of Gloster's in Winsor (*sic*) Park'.

In all essentials identical with the engraving by W. Watts after T. Malton, November 1, 1784, pl. LXVI, of Watts' *Seats*, but if the original drawing, not accurately followed. Cf. *Sandby Catalogue*, p. 56.

COLONEL COOTE MANNINGHAM (1766–1809)

427. CARISBROOKE CASTLE, ISLE OF WIGHT

Watercolour. 12 × $17\frac{3}{4}$ in. (30.5 × 45 cm.)   (17063)

Inscribed on the back: 'Drawings by Col. Manningham received from His Majesty Aug. 23rd. 1798'.

This and the following drawings are included on p. 159 (after 1816) of the George III Inventory 'A', where this drawing is called 'View of an ancient Castle'. The artist had clearly received instruction or assistance from William Payne.

Coote Manningham born 1766; served as Adjutant General in the attack on San Domingo, 1795. Returned to England 1798, wounded, promoted Colonel and appointed A.D.C. to King George III. Raised the 'Rifle Corps' in 1800. Major-General 1805. Equerry to the King from 1800 till his death in 1809 from wounds received at Corunna.

428. FORT ROYAL, the lines of Port au Prince, Bizoton, L'Islet, the Bay and Leogane Point, from Port Robert.

Pencil and watercolour, within lined and washed border' backed with linen. $24\frac{1}{2}$ × 51 in. (61.3 × 130.5 cm.)   (17012)

Signed below the drawing: 'Coote Manningham Adjutant General', and inscribed with the title as given.

429. CAPE NICHOLAS MOLE FROM THE POINT OF PRESQU'ISLE ST. DOMINGO

Pencil and watercolour. $19\frac{1}{2}$ × $42\frac{3}{4}$ in. (49.5 × 109 cm.)   (17011)

Signed on the mount: 'Coote Manningham Adjt. General' with the title as given.

430. THE LOSS OF H.M.S. UNDAUNTED ON THE MORANT KEYS, AUGUST 31ST, 1796

Watercolour. $13\frac{7}{8}$ × $21\frac{1}{2}$ in. (35.2 × 54.5 cm.)
(*Souvenir Album*, VI, p. 68)

Signed: Coote Manningham Adjt. General, and inscribed with the title as given, on the washed mount.
Inventory 'A', p. 159, with title as given.
Identical with the drawing attributed to W. Anderson in Sir Bruce Ingram's collection, exhibited at Colnaghi's, March, 1936, No. 8, illustrated in the catalogue, with the title, 'Stranding of a Frigate'. In view of the similarity of No. 427 to the work of Payne and the puerility of the only other known drawing by Manningham (in Mr. Iolo Williams' collection), it is more likely that the professional, Anderson, worked up the nautical sketches of the amateur than that a drawing of Manningham's should have been wrongly attributed to Anderson.

431. THE JAMAICA, SLOOP OF WAR, GOING TO THE RELIEF OF IROIS, SEPTEMBER, 1796

Watercolour. $13\frac{1}{2}$ × $19\frac{3}{4}$ in. (34.2 × 50.50 cm.)
(*Souvenir Album*, VI, p.69)

Companion to the preceding, and similarly signed and inscribed.
Inventory 'A', p. 159, with title as given.
Three other pairs of exceedingly capable seascapes, measuring *c.* $7\frac{3}{4}$ × $11\frac{7}{8}$ in., $10\frac{1}{2}$ × 15 in., and $19\frac{1}{8}$ × $27\frac{3}{4}$ in., the last pair varnished and one of the first pair initialled 'C.M.', are on pp. 66, 67, 70 and 71 of *Souvenir Album*, VI. They are presumably the drawings described in Inventory 'A', p. 159, as two large and four small seascapes.

F. J. MANSKIRSCH (1768–1830)

Fifteen watercolours of military costumes are in Military Drawings, Vol. IV, pp. 21–24 (Nos. 16272–16286), signed 'F. J. Manskirsch'.

ALEXANDER MARSHAL (fl. 1660–1690)
Figures 35–38

432. Two volumes containing, on guards, 159 folio sheets of flower, etc., drawings, in watercolour and gouache. The sheets have been considerably cut down, carefully mended and renumbered. Additions have been made either by pasting small drawings of animals, insects, etc., upon the sheets with flowers, in which case the added fragments may have come from a similar collection, or, on the first page and at the end of the second volume, by applying larger drawings, some on vellum, on fly leaves of the book itself, i.e. not on guards as are the remainder of the sheets.

According to a note in J. H. Glover's hand on p. 142 of Inventory 'A', the volumes were presented to King George IV by John Mangles, of Hurley, Berkshire. A note at the beginning of Volume I at the head of an index, probably by John Mangles, states that 'the work was painted about the year 1680 by Marshall the most esteemed painter of natural history of that time from the celebrated gardens at Haerlem for the Prince of Orange, afterwards William the Third, by whom it was on his leaving Holland presented to a Dutch nobleman the misfortunes of whose family during the late revolutions alone would have induced them to part with it'. A further note signed by John Mangles, April 27, 1820, states that the books were purchased for him at Brussels by his friend Ross Donnelly in 1818, and continues with a fantastic affiliation, as descendant or pupil, of the painter of this work with Otho Marcellis (Marseus van Schrieck, 1619–1678).

Fig. 38. A. Marshal: Figures lifting a beam (Cat. No. 432)

Figs. 35–37. A. Marshal: Fruit (Cat. No. 432)

Each sheet contains three or more careful drawings of flowers in watercolour or gouache with, in some cases, animals, butterflies, insects, birds or reptiles. The flowers are arranged as for a herbarium, and the other objects are introduced apparently merely to fill vacant spaces. In only three cases are the flowers inscribed with their names above or below them; but as a rule, but by no means universally, the names in Latin and English are written in a 17th-century hand on the back of the sheet behind the drawings. Five of the vellum drawings inserted at the end, and a large fantastic figure drawing in blue wash at the end (*Figure* 38) bear the signature of Alexander

Marshal, the initials in monogram, or are marked with a monogram alone. The three inscriptions mentioned above as alone placed with the drawings are, however, in the same ornamental hand as these signatures, and since the natural history drawings on vellum would appear to be by the same hand as the main body of flower drawings, there is no reason to doubt that all are by Alexander Marshal, by whom there was in Tradescant's Museum 'a book of Mr. Tradescant's choicest flowers and plants, exquisitely limned in vellum' (*Musaeum Tradescantianum*, 1656, p. 51). He is otherwise chiefly known by the picture of the Siege of Magdeburg (R.A. British Art, 1934, No. 28 (122), Professor T. Bodkin) and certain careful almost miniature copies in bodycolour.

The connexion with the Prince of Orange and his garden at Haarlem may be merely an inference from a note on the back of a drawing of a bird on p. 2, 'a indian fowll which was presented the Prince of orenge'. Had the books remained in the Netherlands there seems little reason for the use of the English language. Further, a note on the back of folio 151 says 'this flower was sent me by Generall Lambert august 29 1659 from Wimbleton'. It is very noticeable that the English names are given in a very French form, colour becoming 'couleur', sensitive becoming 'sensible', pansies 'penses', while such phonetic spellings as 'yealeo', 'read', 'enemone', 'Croofoott', etc., are to be found on every page. If these English inscriptions are, as is possible, in the hand of Alexander Marshal himself, that artist becomes even more mysterious than before.

Exhib.: National Book League, *Flower Books*, 1950, No. 47.

JOHN MAURER (fl. 1713–1761)

433. ST. JAMES'S PALACE AND THE MALL, LOOKING EAST

Watercolour. 8⅞ × 16¾ in. (22.6 × 42.7 cm.)   (17273)

Exhib.: B.F.A.C., 1919, 'Old London', No. 42(*b*).

Identical, but for some small differences in the figures, with the print by Maurer of 1741 (B. M. Crowle, *Pennant*, Vol. IV, p. 157). Presumably with No. 434 the drawings bought by King George IV from Colnaghi on February 14, 1820, for £1 11s. 6d. each (Archives Invoice 28255).

434. ST. JAMES'S PARK AND BUCKINGHAM HOUSE, LOOKING WEST

Watercolour. 9¼ × 16⅞ in. (23.7 × 42.8 cm.)   (17272)

Exhib.: B.F.A.C., 1919, 'Old London', No. 42(*a*).

Identical but for some small differences in the figures with the print by Maurer of 1741, 'A perspective View of the Great Canal' (B.M. Crace Collection, Vol. XII, No. 84). A monochrome drawing of approximately the same size at the British Museum shows a view of the canal looking east (Crowle, *Pennant*, Vol. IV, p. 103).

435. ST. JAMES'S PARK, THE HORSE GUARDS

Pen and grey wash. 6 × 11 in. (15.2 × 28 cm.)   (17274)

Exhib.: B.F.A.C., 1919, No. 48(*a*).

Reprod.: *Connoisseur*, XCII, August, 1933, p. 145.
Reduced version of the drawing engraved 1740 as 'A Perspective View of the Parade in St. James Park' (B.M., Crowle, *Pennant*, Vol. IV, pp. 22 and 102), with a different procession.
The drawing shows Whitehall Gate which was demolished in 1723.

436. BUCKINGHAM HOUSE

Pen and grey wash. 6 × 11⅛ in. (15.2 × 28.2 cm.)   (17275)

Exhib.: B.F.A.C., 1919, No. 48(*b*).

Drawing for or from the print of the same size, 'A Perspective View of Buckingham House in St. James's Park', by Maurer, 1746.

BARNABY MAYOR (d. 1774)

437. Ten drawings: Border of title page, a Roman Soldier, and eight pencil figures shewing pike and musket drill.

Pencil. 11½ × 15½–18½ in. (Mil. Vol. V.)   (16666–16675)

Presumably intended for engraving.
A pencil inscription at the foot of the drawing for the title page has been erased. Several of the others are priced 7/6 (two 17/6) in the lower left corner.

LADY MORDAUNT (Mary Ann Holbech) (c. 1778–1842)

These four drawings were extracted from a volume, Lot 145, one of eight which were sold at Sotheby's on December 1, 1948, as the property of the late Mary Louisa, Lady Mordaunt, of Walton Hall, Warwickshire. The sketches were uniformly mounted and inscribed. The volumes were lettered with the word 'Sketches' only and contained no name of artist or proprietor, and no inscription beyond the names of localities and dates—from 1801 to 1819 with one exception noted below—written in the same hand on the mounts below the drawings.

Except for watercolours by the same hand in three volumes which were of various sizes, the drawings were in monochrome, mostly of the same size, and such differences in

manner as they showed were quite consistent with development over a long period. In spite therefore of one drawing of a Welsh subject, which was inscribed on the mount, 'Dynevor about 1789', the initials M.M. on three drawings of Bathford of 1813 may be taken to identify the artist as Mary Ann, the elder daughter of William Holbech of Farnborough in Warwickshire, who married in 1807 Sir Charles Mordaunt, Bt. Her date of birth is not given; she died June 10, 1842, aged 64 (*Gent. Mag.*, July, 1842, p. 110). Drawings of Farnborough and other Warwickshire localities were contained in the collection. Others were of Great Britain (six volumes), Switzerland (one), Tyrol and North Italy (one). A drawing by her is in the British Museum.

These four sketches with their well-chosen subjects, assured and easy drawing and delicate washes, are excellent examples of the amateur skill of the period, and they show the advantage of a restricted medium. The artist may well have come into touch with Lord Aylesford (see No. 32) in her earlier days, and with Lady Long at a later date, perhaps receiving, with her, instruction from David Cox.
The drawings were acquired in 1948 from F. T. Sabin.

438. WINDSOR CASTLE FROM BISHOPSGATE

Pencil and sepia wash. 12 × 19 in. (30.5 × 48 cm.)   (17621)

Inscribed: Windsor, May 1819, on the mount, and '43' on the back.

439. WINDSOR CASTLE FROM THE NORTH WEST
Plate 76

Pencil and sepia wash. 11⅜ × 18¼ in. (28.5 × 46.2 cm.)   (17622)

Uniform with the preceding and also inscribed 'Windsor May 1819'; '42' on the back.

440. WINDSOR CASTLE FROM THE NORTH, the river in the foreground.

11½ × 19⅜ in. (29.7 × 49.3 cm.)   (17623)

Uniform with the preceding and also inscribed 'Windsor May 1819'; '44' on the back.

441. WINDSOR CASTLE FROM THE NORTH, THE WEST END ONLY

12¼ × 19 in. (31 × 48.2 cm.)   (17624)

Uniform with the preceding, but slightly larger; inscribed 'Windsor, 1819'; '41' on the back.

MOORE, CHARLES, *see* No. 483 under Pugin

GEORGE MORLAND (1763–1804)

442. HIEROGLYPHIC LETTER dated December 12, 1785, from Margate.
Figure 39

Pen and watercolour. 12⅛ × 7⅞ in. (30.9 × 20 cm.)   (17571)

The letter on the reverse is signed G. Morland. Inscribed at the top, in ink, 'By George Morland, The Painter', and on the reverse, at foot, 'Curious' in the Colnaghi hand and 'Morland' in ink, erased.
Bought by the Prince Regent on January 13, 1812, from Colnaghi for £6 6s. 'A Curious Hieroglyphical Letter of George Morland Painter' (Archives Invoice 27671).
The *verso* reads: 'I thinks as how this Letter in Hieroglyphicks, or properly a Hieroglyphical Letter will serve to amuse *all an ye*. Answer it as soon as you can and let me know how many characters thou hast found out, I think

Fig. 39. Morland: A hieroglyphic Letter (Cat. No. 442)

Sophy will find more than any of ye, however I think t'will not puzzle you more than a Letter Lauzun sent to me the other day, tho not in Hieroglyphical Characters, the Spelling being so bad, made it, if possible ten times harder to explain; he had forgot Webbs name, so directed for me at Mr—a Miller &c; the Frames come down on Fryday Night last; I have wrote to Young to send me a Frame for A Portrait, now Painting, as soon as he can possibly make it, get my dadday to ask him if he has received the Letter and to hurry him as much as possible, I shall be Six Shillings out of Pocket by Sherbournes Frames, tho t'was mentioned particularly they were not to exceed 15 shillings in price. I have become a Collector of Fossils, which are very common amongst the Rocks at, and about this place. I went into a Cavern yesterday to Look for some, but the Echo occasion'd by the roaring of Neptune contending with Boreas, who was very powerful indeed, made me glad to retreat. Margate is become so very dead, that gives one an idea of A place infested by A plague, where people are affraid of stiring from thier Houses, I generally begin and finish a stain'd Drawing every evening, and I think to doo the same at home every night that's not fit to March out. Write as soon as you can, I never mind paying the Post.

Non Plus

Adieu

G. Morland.'

JOHN HAMILTON MORTIMER (1741-1779)

443. A CONCERT. Singers above musicians who have on their music books 'English, Swiss, Italian, German, Prussian'. All facing more or less left.

Pen on buff paper. 8¼ × 11⅛ in. (21.1 × 28.2 cm.)
(17660)

Inscriptions as on the print, a pencil number '86' at top. Engraved in facsimile by L. Bates, no date (B.M. Sat., V, 6356—Addenda). A date (?) 1779 on the music held by one of the orchestra is misread as 4679 in the facsimile.

FREDERICK NASH (1782-1856)

444. Five architectural subjects in watercolour on inter-leave pages from an extra-illustrated *Pennant's London*.

Size of the original page 21⅛ × 14⅝ in. (53.8 × 36 cm.)

(1) Courtyard of St. James's Palace. Signed: F. Nash.
(17125)

(2) Melbourne House (the Albany). Signed: Nash.
(17126)

(3) St. Stephen's Walbrook. Signed: Nash.   (17127)

(4) Council Chamber, Kensington Palace. Signed: Nash.
(17128)

(5) The Old Bed Chamber, Kensington Palace. Signed: Nash.   (17129)

JOHN NASH (1752-1835)

445. PROJECT FOR THE STATUE OF KING GEORGE III IN POSITION AT THE END OF THE LONG WALK

Watercolour and pencil, faded, within lined and washed border. 13⅞ × 20¾ in. (35.2 × 52.5 cm.)   (17309)

Inscribed at the back 'Statue of George 3 Windsor Park', in ink.

The statue, much as in Carlini's model, on a classical pedestal.

Presented to the Royal Library in July, 1944, by Mr. John Summerson, F.S.A., A.R.I.B.A., who acquired it in the Isle of Wight from a former domestic in the Pennethorne family. John Pennethorne, pupil of Nash, died at Yarmouth (I.o.W.) in 1888.

446. PROJECT FOR MRS. JENNING'S HOUSE IN WINDSOR PARK

Pencil, pen and grey wash, with lined border, creased. 12¼ × 21½ in. (31.3 × 54.9 cm.)   (17462)

Inscribed at the back in pencil and in ink: 'Mrs. Jenning's Windsor Park' in a similar manner to the preceding, and 'by Nash' in a later hand.

A highly ornamental villa in the Regency Chinese taste.

JOHN CLAUDE NATTES (1765-1822)

447. THE BELL TOWER IN WINDSOR CASTLE AND PART OF THAMES STREET

Pencil. 8⅞ × 12⅞ in. (23 × 32 cm.)   (17388)

Interesting as showing the houses formerly on the Castle side of Thames Street.

448. WINDSOR CASTLE AND THE GATE OF THE HUNDRED STEPS AND MR. RAMSBOTTOM'S HOUSE (now Bank House).

Pencil. 8⅞ × 12⅞ in. (22.7 × 32 cm.)   (17389)

449. IN WINDSOR CASTLE (THE NORMAN GATE FROM THE WEST)

Pencil. $9 \times 12\frac{3}{4}$ in. (23×32.4 cm.)   (17390)

450. UNDER AN ARCH OF EATON BRIDGE, LOOKING DOWN THE RIVER THAMES, 1813

Pencil. $8\frac{7}{8} \times 12\frac{7}{8}$ in. (23×32.5 cm.)   (17386)

451. THE SAME, LOOKING TOWARDS SUNNING HILL, 1813

Pencil. $8\frac{7}{8} \times 12\frac{7}{8}$ in. (23×32.5 cm.)   (17387)

Numbered '32' at foot left.

These five drawings, with titles, as given, inscribed in ink at foot, appear to have been extracted from the large collection of drawings by Nattes acquired in seven volumes from the representatives of Sir F. Gore Ouseley in 1919, and probably occasioned the acquisition of the whole.

Of these seven volumes, six consist of large drawings (up to 16×23 in.) stitched together or inserted in blue paper albums, in the latter case together with drawings of half the size. They are in pencil, pen, and wash, with a few watercolours, and a considerable proportion of offsets. No order of date or of locality has been attempted in the arrangement, offsets being frequently separated from the originals. Some drawings by pupils and other artists can be recognized among them. For example, two drawings in Vol. 6 with a watermark subsequent to the death of Nattes are probably by H. W. Burgess, who, if not a pupil, formed his drawing-master style on that of Nattes. Drawings by Coney in the Royal Library are also believed to have come from this collection.

There are 414 drawings in these six volumes. Several are signed, and some bear the name Nattes without initials, impressed with a stamp. Two have the address '23 Welbeck Street'. Of those with inscriptions one is dated 1784 and another 1801, but the large majority of dates are between 1791 and 1799. A number of the subjects are in Lincolnshire and Leicestershire, but there are also several in Kent, Surrey and Sussex, London, Bath, Durham, Warwick, Weymouth, York, and neighbourhoods, a few are Scottish, Welsh, or Irish views; there are also Italian subjects and compositions. Some are the subjects of Nattes' topographic prints.

The seventh volume is a travelling sketchbook, $11\frac{1}{4} \times 8\frac{1}{4}$ in. (28.6×21 cm.), containing a title-page and 149 sketches of Montpellier and district, mainly in pencil, but in some cases penned or washed in brown or grey. Each subject is described at foot in French and dated from November, 1821, to January, 1822. The list of Nattes' sketchbooks preserved at the Victoria and Albert Museum mentions five sketchbooks of Montpellier and district of 1822, each containing from 146 to 150 sketches, of which 'No. 18' with 149 sketches would appear to be this.

JOHN PRESTON NEALE (1771–1847)

452. THE TOWN HALL, WINDSOR

Pencil and grey wash, unfinished. $4 \times 3\frac{3}{8}$ in. (11.5×8.9 cm.)   (17456)

Inscribed in ink: Neale, Town Hall, Windsor.

The Library also contains the sixty-one drawings, elevations and views by Neale, illustrating *The History and Antiquities of the Abbey Church of St. Peter Westminster* (1818 and 1823), by E. W. Brayley and J. P. Neale, and the coat of arms by Willement heading the dedication. The drawings are of the same size as the prints and with two exceptions, which are in colour, are in pen and brown wash heightened with white. Thirteen are signed with dates from 1816 to 1821. They were acquired from Ryman Hall, Oxford, 1907.

R. NEWTON

453. 'PULL DEVIL, PULL BAKER.' The devil left, and a parson right, tugging at a tortured citizen.

Pencil. $10\frac{1}{4} \times 13\frac{7}{8}$ in. (26×35.5 cm.)   (17668)

Signed: R. Newton delin, within the drawing.

Exhib.: B.F.A.C. 1931-32, No. 158.

Carefully drawn, perhaps a copy, but there is no corresponding print at the British Museum.

WILLIAM NEWTON (1735–1790)

454. RANELAGH ROTUNDA: THE INTERIOR

Pen and grey wash. $12\frac{1}{4} \times 22\frac{1}{2}$ in. (31.8×57.1 cm.)   (17064)

Signed: Wm Newton fecit 1755. W. Jones arcitect (*sic*).

Perhaps the 'View of the Rotunda at Ranelagh, drawing' bought by the Prince Regent from Colnaghi, April 6, 1812, for £1 11s. 6d. (Archives Invoice 27857).

A cartouche below the drawing, within its border, has 'Ranelagh Rotundo Built MDCCXL Destroyd MDCCCV' (*sic*). An old inscription at the back describes Newton as Jones' pupil and the translator of Vitruvius.

Clearly connected with the print of 1761 by A. Walker after W. Newton, but with important differences which preclude it from being regarded as the drawing from which the print was made.

FRANCIS NICHOLSON (1753–1844)

455. WINDSOR CASTLE AND TOWN FROM THE RIVER, LOOKING SOUTH EAST

Pen and watercolour. $15\frac{1}{4} \times 20\frac{3}{4}$ in. (38.6×52.5 cm.)   (17370)

Acquired locally in 1938.

W. O'KEEFE (*c.* 1800)

456. A DUET. Madam Strainem, Signor Grimaci Squall.

Pencil. Watermark A. Blackwell 1799. $9\frac{1}{2} \times 13\frac{5}{8}$ in. (24×34.6 cm.)   (17669)

Signed in border below: O'Keefe invt. and inscribed with the title as given. Above the characters—

> 'How Sweet is the pleasure
> How sweet the Delight'
> 'When Soft love and Music
> Together Unite.'

Priced 3/6.

A print by O'Keefe of November 1, 1794, five years earlier (B.M. Sat. VII, 8565), has the same subject differently treated, and the names transposed.

ISAAC OLIVER (OLIVIER) (*c.* 1556–1617)

457. QUEEN ELIZABETH, full length standing, three-quarter face to left, crowned, in pearl-embroidered dress, holding the sceptre in her left hand, the orb in her right.

Figure 40

Pen and brown ink, with brush in grey, the coarser washes in the cloak and shadow probably an addition. Incised with stylus. On paper. $11\frac{3}{4} \times 8\frac{1}{8}$ in. (29.7×20.8 cm.) (17018)

Fig. 40. Isaac Oliver: Queen Elizabeth (Cat. No. 457)

Drawing for the engraving (in reverse) by Crispin de Passe (O'Donoghue, Vol. II, p. 147, No. 15) after Isaac Oliver.

Exhib.: R.A. 1934, No. 524 (1113); Victoria and Albert Museum (Hilliard), 1947, No. 199.

Lit.: O'Donoghue, *Catalogue of Portraits of Queen Elizabeth*, 1894, pp. 24 and 171.

Reprod.: *Connoisseur*, XCI, June, 1933, opp. p. 360.

Removal from the frame has disclosed a press mark and an inscription in ink, 8Nᵗ L 68, which identifies the drawing with Lot 68 on the eighth night of Dr. Richard Mead's sale, January 18, 1755, *et seq.*, among the drawings, 'One of Queen Elizabeth by Peter Oliver' (£2 12s. od.). The wrong Christian name may have been due to another portrait of the Queen by Peter in Lot 66 on the seventh night. This provenance is already suggested by the inscription on Vertue's engraving for Rapin's *History of England*, 1732. According to Colvin (*Early Engravers and Engraving in England*, 1905, note to pl. IV) from the Hardwicke collection (Sale 28 June, 1888, Lot 769, bought Colnaghi £180).

The drawing is closely followed by de Passe's engraving, an unfinished proof of which in the Royal Library has the cloak and other accessories in outline only. The sceptre in the left hand shews that the drawing was expressly made for the purpose of engraving; and confirms the suggestion of O'Donoghue that both it and the earlier engraving by William Rogers (in the same direction as the drawing, but with the sceptre in the right hand) derive from some common original which has been lost.

The richly embroidered dress, though traditionally supposed to be that worn by the Queen at the Thanksgiving Service at St. Paul's after the Spanish Armada, was her customary array at the Opening of Parliament.

458. AFTER HOLBEIN: THE DANCE OF DEATH (THE PRINCE). Copy, same size, coloured, of the woodcut by Holbein (*c.* 1524).

Watercolour with gold on paper, within narrow border in imitation of a bevelled frame. 2½ × 2⅛ in. (6.3 × 5.1 cm.). Torn and repaired. It is mounted on a small bevelled wooden panel, branded with King Charles I's cypher CR. Vanderdoort (Bathoe), 1757, p. 54, No. 75. Believed to be 'A Peece of a Duke in Limbning, a Death in it', valued at £10 and sold to Mr. Bass, October 8, 1651 (P.R.O. L.R. 2, 124, f. 132 *v*.). It is not in any of the subsequent inventories. *Reprod.*: *Connoisseur*, XCI, June, 1933, frontispiece (in colour).

459. MOSES STRIKING THE ROCK   *Plate* 73
Brown and grey wash and white. 8¼ × 13¼ in. (21 × 33.3 cm.)   (13529)
Signed on an inset: Isac: Olivier Fec.
King James II Cat. No. 636: 'A drawing in black and white of the journeying of the children of Israel by Isaac Oliver.'
Reprod.: *Connoisseur*, XCI, June, 1933, No. V.

460. NYMPHS AND SATYRS   *Plate* 75
Black and white on brown paper. 8⅛ × 13⅞ in. (20.5 × 35.7 cm.)   (13528)
Signed: Ollivier.
King James II Cat. No. 638: 'A drawing in black and white of Satyrs and women sporting. By Isaac Oliver.'
Exhib.: R.A. 1934, No. 523 (1097).
Reprod.: *Connoisseur*, XCI, June, 1933, No. VI.

PETER OLIVER (1594–1647)

461. AFTER TITIAN: THE D'AVALOS ALLEGORY. (The Marquis of Guasto and his mistress, or Duke of Alva and his family.)

Watercolour. 4⅞ × 4⅞ in. (sight) (12.3 × 12.3 cm.)

Inscribed, in gold, top left corner: Titiano, and at foot, 1629, P. Olivier F.

After the picture then in King Charles I's collection, now in the Louvre.

Vanderdoort (Bathoe, 1757), p. 34, No. 4 gives the date as 1629, but no measurements. Ashmole MS. 1514, f. 116, gives 5¼ × 5⅛ in.

Sir Richard Holmes (*Burlington Magazine*, Vol. IX, May, 1906, p. 110, with reproduction) says that of the nine limnings by Peter Oliver from pictures in Charles I's collection which were enumerated by Vanderdoort, this alone has remained in the Royal collection since it was painted. According, however, to P.R.O. L.R. 2, 124, fol. 161 *verso*, it was sold in the Commonwealth sale for £51 to Colonel Hutchinson on May 24, 1650, and must have been returned at the Restoration if it is to be identified with the limning (5 × 5 in.) mentioned in the Charles II MS. Inventory, *c.* 1665, as in the King's Closet at Whitehall, with a black and white version, also by Peter Oliver. They are both included as at Kensington in a 'List of the Pictures belonging to the Crown taken by Mr. Walton' between 1704 and 1710, p. 48, and in Vertue's list of 1743 (Bathoe, 1758), Nos. 590 and 668.

Reprod.: *Connoisseur*, XCI, June, 1933, No. IX.

462. AFTER CORREGGIO: VENUS, MERCURY AND CUPID

Watercolour and body colour. $7\frac{5}{8} \times 5\frac{7}{8}$ in. (19.3 × 12.4 cm.).

In Charles I frame, with small label, numbered '8'.
Inscribed top right in gold, Anton: Coregium Invent: Imitatus Est. Petrus Olivarus 1634.
Vanderdoort (Bathoe, 1757), p. 35, No. 8, the date being given as 1636, and the size 8 × $5\frac{1}{4}$ in. Sold in the Commonwealth sale for £50 to Embree, May 21, 1650. Bohn Sale, March 26, 1885, Lot 1177, bought Holmes, £21.
The original picture, which belonged to Charles I, is now in the National Gallery.
Reprod.: *Connoisseur*, XCI, June, 1933, No. VII.

463. AFTER CORREGGIO: JUPITER AND ANTIOPE

Watercolour and body-colour. $8\frac{1}{4} \times 5\frac{3}{8}$ in. (21.2 × 14.4 cm.).

Charles I frame, with two labels, the smaller numbered '6'.
Signed in gold at top right corner: 'An°. Do. 1633, Anton: Coregium. Imitatus est. Petr. Olivarius.
Vanderdoort (Bathoe, 1757), p. 35, No. 7, with date 1633 and measurements 9 × 6 in. Perhaps sold for £80 to Mr. Bagglay on October 23, 1651. Purchased with the preceding at the Bohn Sale in 1885, Lot 1176, £265.
After the painting by Correggio, which was in Charles I's collection, and is now in the Louvre.
Reprod.: *Connoisseur*, XCI, June, 1933, No. VIII.

464. AFTER RAPHAEL: ST. GEORGE AND THE DRAGON

Gouache, $8\frac{5}{8} \times 6\frac{1}{4}$ in. (21.7 × 16.1 cm.).

Reprod.: *Connoisseur*, XCI, June, 1933, No. X. See also Williamson, *Portrait Miniatures*, 1897, p. 31.

Acquired at the Hamilton Palace Sale, July 15, 1882, Lot 1667, without name of artist, by Sir Richard Holmes, who in the *Burlington Magazine*, Vol. IX, 1906, p. 110, describes it as much injured by exposure. The purchase is referred to by Queen Victoria in a letter to the Empress Frederick of July 31, 1882, as having the mark of Charles I upon it. This mark is no longer visible, nor is the date 1628, which is recorded by Vanderdoort (Bathoe, 1757), p. 33, No. 2, on Peter Oliver's limning after Raphael's *St. George* with dimensions $9\frac{1}{2} \times 7$ in. Presumably, too, the limning was signed as were Nos. 461–463. Perhaps, therefore, if this is the same limning, these indications have disappeared under restoration.

465. AFTER TITIAN OR PARIS BORDONE: THE LOVERS

Watercolour. $4\frac{13}{16} \times 3\frac{15}{16}$ in. (12.1 × 9.9 cm.).

Signed top left corner, in gold: P. Olivier Fe. 1637.

After a picture which was in Charles I's collection and is now in store at Hampton Court (reprod. *Burlington Mag.*, Vol. V, 1906, frontispiece, and Cust, *Royal Pictures*, Vol. I). Not mentioned by Vanderdoort.
Holmes (*loc. cit.*) mentions that the colours of the draperies differ from those in the original picture.

466. AFTER TITIAN: MADONNA AND CHILD, WITH ST. JOHN AND ST. CATHERINE

Watercolour, faded. 5 × $6\frac{1}{4}$ in. (sight) (12.7 × 15.8 cm.).

Signed in top left corner: Pe: Olivier Fe 1639.

Bought for £60 at the Pierpont Morgan Sale, Christie's, June 24, 1935, Lot 186 (reproduced).
The original picture, not in Charles I's collection, is *Klassiker der Kunst*, p. 215.

467. AFTER TITIAN: ST. LUKE PREFERRING A GENOA GENTLEMAN TO CHRIST

Grey wash with touches of red and white. $5\frac{5}{8} \times 6\frac{5}{8}$ in. (16.9 × 21.9 cm.)   (13526)

Inscribed: Tissano invt. at top left, 1639 P. Olivier fe; at foot.
Reprod.: *Burlington Magazine*, IX (1906), pl. II, No. 7.
From the picture at the time in Charles I's collection (Vanderdoort (Bathoe, 1757), p. 105), now at Hampton Court (Collins-Baker, 1929, p. 147). Among Queen Caroline's pictures at Kensington, No. 38 (Bathoe, 1758, p. 5). $6\frac{1}{2} \times 8\frac{1}{2}$ in.

468. THE VIRGIN, CHRIST AND ST. JOHN; ST. JOSEPH IN THE DISTANCE

Brown and grey wash, with touches of red and white, in black border. $9\frac{1}{2} \times 6\frac{7}{8}$ in. (24.3 × 17.4 cm.)   (13527)

Signed: P. Olivier Fe: 1640.

After a picture ascribed to Raphael (Passavant, No. 272).

469. AFTER VAN DYCK: KING CHARLES I, HEAD AND SHOULDERS, FACING HALF RIGHT

Plumbago. Slightly abraded in places. Oval, $3\frac{1}{4} \times 2\frac{5}{8}$ in. (8.3 × 6.5 cm.)   (17628)

Signed: P.O 163– (cut).

From the double portrait by Van Dyck at Euston, or rather from one of the other versions of that picture in which the King wears a round ruff.
The Snelling plumbago (No. 98 in the Seal sale, Christie's, February 16, 1949), which is dated 1647, is nearer the prints after Van Dyck's picture at Euston than is this.
Given to H.M. King George V by H.M. Queen Mary, 1920.

PETER OLIVER, Ascribed to

470. THE MADONNA AND CHILD, SEATED ON CLOUDS

Watercolour. $10\frac{1}{2} \times 8$ in. (26.7 × 20.2 cm.)
Presumably George III Inventory 'A', p. 151 (1816), 'a miniature of a Madonna and Child by Peter Oliver'.

471. TWO PUTTI, HEADS AND SHOULDERS

Black and red chalk. $3\frac{1}{2} \times 5\frac{1}{2}$ in. (8.8 × 13.8 cm.)   (13525)

Purchased on a 'Hogarth' washed mount, where it bore the number '1589. E. e. 22' and '4n/L9', and was accompanied by an oval drawing (No. 13525A, 7.5 × 5.9 cm.) of *St. George and the Dragon*, in pencil and grey wash, apparently of the XVIII century and perhaps English, numbered '547 (? 1547) E. e. 46 . . . In L 46 (1st night, Lot 46)'.

JOHN OPIE, R.A. (1761–1807), After

472. LOUISA, MARCHIONESS OF SLIGO (1767–1817)

Black and red chalk; squared with the stylus, and rubbed. $9\frac{7}{8} \times 8\frac{1}{4}$ in. (25.3 × 21.1 cm.)   (14035)

Perhaps by S. W. Reynolds for his mezzotint in the same direction (O'Donoghue, Vol. IV, p. 117, No. 1).

WILLIAM PARRY (1742–1791)

473. PAUL SANDBY SKETCHING, SEATED, A BOY HOLDING AN UMBRELLA OVER HIM

Black chalk. $11\frac{1}{2} \times 9\frac{1}{2}$ in. (29.1 × 24 cm.)   (13550)

Inscribed in ink in an old hand, 'Paul Sandby by Parry'. For the inscription see the *Sandby Catalogue*, No. 253, where this drawing is reproduced (at the end of the volume). There is no indication of the provenance of this drawing, which does not appear to have been known to William Sandby. Parry, always spoken of as 'pupil of Sir Joshua Reynolds', was the son of the famous Welsh harper. He was helped by Sir Watkin Williams Wynn, who was also a patron of Paul Sandby.

E. PEARSALL (1821)

474. NAPOLEON I AT ST. HELENA, full length, profile to left.

Watercolour. 7½ × 5½ in. (19.2 × 13.8 cm.)　　(17013)
Signed: E. Pearsall.

A document preserved with the drawing states that it was made just before Napoleon's death, sent to Lord Londonderry, Foreign Minister, given by him to his secretary, R. Wood, Esq., and by him to his nephew General Sir David Wood, who presented it to Queen Victoria. (Framed with two watercolour views of Longwood House (Nos. 17014, 17015) and other Napoleonic relics.)

HENRY PICKERING (fl. 1767–1790), After

475. MARGARET WOFFINGTON, head, full face.

Plumbago. 3¾ × 3 in. (9.6 × 7.7 cm.)　　(17026)
Reproduced Williamson, *Portrait Miniatures*, 1897, facing p. 148, as 'attributed to Zoffany', but clearly a weak copy of the mezzotint portrait of Margaret Woffington by J. Faber, Junr., after Henry Pickering. (O'Donoghue, Vol. IV, p. 524, No. 8.) The attribution to Zoffany was not made in the Royal Library.
Margaret Woffington, actress (1714(?)–1760).

FRANCIS PLACE (1647–1728)

476. A BRIDGE, PERHAPS OF ROMAN CONSTRUCTION
Pen and grey wash, one figure in brown. 2½ × 13¾ in. (6.5 × 35 cm.)　　(14300)
An undecipherable note in ink on one of the piers of the bridge.
Acquired from Squire's Gallery, October, 1932.

NICHOLAS POCOCK (1741–1821)

477. H.M.S. VICTORY
Watercolour. 7¼ × 9 in. (18.5 × 23 cm.)
　　(*Souvenir Album*, VI, p. 2)
Inscribed at the back 'His My Ship Victory 100 Guns, Admiral Lord Nelson's Ship at the Battle of Trafalgar', with details of tonnage, draft, etc., and 'The Design by Mr. Pocock No. 12 great George Street Westminster 20th Novr. 1806.'

478. H.M.S. ORION
Watercolour. 7¼ × 8¾ in. (18.5 × 22 cm.)
　　(*Souvenir Album* VI, p. 2)
Similarly inscribed to the preceding, but with 'Captain Codrington's Ship at the Battle of Trafalgar', and without details of tonnage, etc.

ALEXANDER POPE (1763–1835), Ascribed to

479. 'MR. KEMBLE', half length, seated, facing to right, holding a volume lettered 'Hamlet'.
Pastel. 10⅜ × 8½ in. (27.3 × 21.5 cm.)　　(17034)
The name and date 1783 on a label at the back of the modern frame.

480. 'MRS. SIDDONS', half length, facing half right.
Pastel. 10¾ × 8½ in. (27.4 × 21.8 cm.)　　(17035)
The name, etc., as on the preceding. The portrait is unrecognizable as Mrs. Siddons.

AUGUSTUS CHARLES PUGIN (1762–1832)

481. CARLTON HOUSE: THE ARMOURY
Watercolour. 9½ × 12⅜ in. (23.2 × 31.2 cm.)　　(17092)
Modern inscription on the mount: 'A. Pugin Delt. 1814'. Acquired by the Prince Regent from Colnaghi on August 1, 1814, for £10 10s. (Archives Invoice 28017), with the artist's name and the title as given.
Congreve's Rocket (so inscribed) is on the floor in the foreground.

482. LOWER REGENT STREET: THE IMPROVEMENTS OPPOSITE CARLTON HOUSE　　*Plate* 91
Watercolour. 11¼ × 22⅞ in. (28.5 × 58 cm.)　　(17093)
Signed: A. Pugin delt. 181 . . . (the figure cut off).
Engraved and published by Colnaghi, 1817, 'this plate representing the improvements opposite Carlton House is, with permission, dedicated to H.R.H. the Prince Regent'. The print omits the Achilles statue and the figures differ. Probably the anonymous 'Drawing, view of Waterloo Place with the New Improvt', bought by the Prince Regent from Colnaghi on May 13, 1817, for £15 (Archives Invoice 28149).

483. THE BODY OF KING GEORGE IV LYING IN STATE
Watercolour. 6 × 8 in. (15.3 × 20.5 cm.)　　(13537)
The hall, entirely draped and carpeted in black, is illuminated only by candles in a candelabra and sconces.

Three drawings by Pugin, one by Charles Moore (1800–1833) and a frontispiece by E. Harding (q.v.) have been inserted as additional illustrations in the Royal Library copy of Nash and Brayley's *Illustrations to Her Majesty's Palace at Brighton*, 1838.

ALLAN RAMSAY (1713–1784), Attributed to

484. A ROYAL PRINCE (?) wearing star and ribbon of the Garter and holding a cutlass.
Black and white chalk on blue paper, the features not indicated. 7¼ × 5⅛ in. (18.3 × 13 cm.)　　(13930)

485. A BOY HOLDING A STICK　　*Figure* 41
Black and white chalk on blue paper. 7¼ × 5⅛ in. (18.2 × 13.1 cm.)　　(13931)
Uniform with the preceding but the ribbon of the Garter not indicated under the coat as there. The attribution, made anonymously on the recent mount, is conjectural.

Fig. 41. A Boy holding a stick (Cat. No. 485)

Fig. 42. Biagio Rebecca: The Opera House, the Auditorium
(Cat. No. 486)

BIAGIO REBECCA (*c.* 1735–1808)

486. THE OPERA HOUSE: THE AUDITORIUM
                                                    Figure 42

Pen and watercolour. 26⅛ × 21¼ in. (66.5 × 54 cm.)
                                                    (17079)

This and the following are probably the 'Drawing, the
Inside of the Opera House', and 'Ditto, the Inside of the
Concert Rooms at the Opera House', bought by the Prince
of Wales from Colnaghi on July 9, 1804, for £7 7s. and
£8 8s. respectively. The figures in the latter would account
for the difference in price (Archives Invoice 27269).
The auditorium does not correspond with the plate of the
theatre (1816) in Wilkinson's *Londina Illustrata*, and no illustration of the Concert Room is available. Perhaps these are
projects, not carried out, for the building to be erected after
the fire in 1787. The attribution now made of the drawings
to Rebecca is based on the allegorical figure subjects
carefully executed on the ceiling.
Rebecca made many decorative paintings at Windsor
Castle. The reference to him by Angelo (*Reminiscences*, 1828,
I, p. 194, etc.), among the instructors of the Royal Princesses
appears to be due to a mis-reading of Pyne (*Frogmore*, p. 13).

487. THE CONCERT ROOM AT THE OPERA HOUSE
                                                    Figure 43

Pen and watercolour in washed border. 23½ × 31¼ in.
(59.9 × 79.5 cm.)   (17080)
See No. 486.

HUMPHRY REPTON (1752–1818)

488. VIEW FROM THE PRINCIPAL FLOOR OF CARLTON
HOUSE, 1808, AS EXISTING AND WITH PROPOSED
IMPROVEMENTS

Watercolour with coloured mount. 14½ × 19½ in. (27 × 41
cm.)   (17091)

Signed; H. Repton 1808, and described on labels beneath
the drawing and the overset design.

489. THE CONSERVATORY, CARLTON HOUSE

Pencil, pen and watercolour, the ruler and compasses
freely used. Cut to shape. 10½ × 22 in. (26.6 × 55.5 cm.)
                                                    (17090)

More highly finished than Repton's watercolour projects
for the Brighton Pavilion, etc., but sufficiently akin in
general idea to justify inclusion in his circle.

The original manuscript, with watercolours, of the *Designs
for the Pavilion at Brighton* by H. Repton, 1808, is in the
Royal Library with a letter from the artist, of December 13,
1815, from Harestreet near Romford, apologizing for its
long absence, with the engraver, from the Prince's Library.
The manuscript is closely followed in the publication save
that on p. 31 the series of columns is not shewn; in the
next plate the elevation of the West Front is only shewn
in part (with a pencil addition) but is accompanied by a
plan; and a paragraph on windows is omitted from the
book.

Fig. 43. Biagio Rebecca: The Concert Room at the Opera House (Cat. No. 487)

S. W. REYNOLDS (1773–1835), After

490. KING GEORGE IV

Pencil and brown wash. 6¾ × 5⅜ in. (17.3 × 13.8 cm.)
(13938)

A careful copy, in the manner of the Hardings, from the mezzotint portrait by S. W. Reynolds 'after a picture by Sir T. Lawrence in his late Majesty's collection', published 'July 15, 1830, by Giraldon-Bovinet & Co.' (B.M., Whitman 105A).

The portrait copied is neither the picture in the Waterloo Chamber (Collins-Baker, p. 208) nor the version in St. James's Palace, in which the sitter is shown wearing a ruff.

See also No. 472.

JOHN INIGO RICHARDS, R.A. (1771–1809)

491. ST. JAMES'S PARK FROM ROSAMOND'S POND, 1771

Pen and watercolour on joined pieces of paper. 16¾ × 21⅞ in. (42.5 × 55.5 cm.)   (17067)

Signed: J. Richards, R.A., at foot right, and inscribed in ink on the old mount with the title and date as given.

Acquired by the Prince Regent from Colnaghi on March 18, 1811, for £2 2s. (Archives Invoice 27615), artist named and title as given.

492. A GOTHIC HALL, 1794   Plate 92

Pen and watercolour. 16⅝ × 21 in. (42.4 × 53.4 cm.)
(17123)

Signed: J.R. R.A. 1794 (repeated on back of mount).

Perhaps the 'Drawing Interior of a Castle with Armoury' bought by the Prince Regent from Colnaghi on April 8, 1816, for £2 2s. (Archives Invoice 28092).

JONATHAN RICHARDSON (1665–1745)

493. ALEXANDER POPE, profile to right, in wig.

Plumbago on vellum. 2½ × 3 in. (8.1 × 7.6 cm.)   (13538)

Inscribed 'Pope's' on an overset label.

494. THE SAME, profile to left, his own hair, with wreath.

Plumbago on vellum. 3⅜ × 2⅝ in. (8.6 × 6.6. cm.) (13539)

Similarly inscribed on overset and, on the back, under the mount, . . . 1737.

495. THE SAME, nearly full face, in wig.

Plumbago on vellum. 4 × 3 in. (10.1 × 7.6 cm.)   (13540)

Inscribed on the back, under the mount, '15 Feb. 1736' (or '1738').

496. JOHN MILTON, nearly full face, his own hair, and wreath.

Plumbago on vellum. 3½ × 2⅞ in. (9.1 × 7.2 cm.)   (13541)

'Milton' on overset label.

No. 494 has the mark of the Richardson Collection (Lugt 2184). An inscription transferred from an old frame to the back of the present mount reads: 'H. Walpole's Sale/Purchased by me at Strawberry Hill/sketches from life by/Richardson/of Alexander Pope.' These appear to be the four drawings, from Strawberry Hill, in the catalogue of the Bale Sale, May 24, 1881, Lots 1430 and 1431 (bought Holmes £7 7s. each), where the word 'Milton' was said to be in Horace Walpole's handwriting. This is doubtful, nor can the drawings be identified with anything in either of the Walpole sales. No. 67 of Lot 1266 on p. 120 in the sale of June, 1842, a portrait of Pope, is B.M. 1902-2-8-17. Another portrait of Pope by Richardson in Lot 72, p. 224, of the April sale, was accompanied by family portraits and one of Bolingbroke, all four bequeathed by Pope to Richardson. The drawings are so small, however, that they might have been included in some lot without special mention.

The head, No. 494, is similar to the larger portrait of Pope by Richardson from Strawberry Hill quoted above, etched by him (O'Donoghue, Vol. III, p. 490, No. 39), and may be connected with the portrait by Richardson in the National Portrait Gallery (No. 1179). No. 495 is similar to the etching by Richardson (O'D., No. 33). The head of Milton, No. 496, is perhaps a copy from the engraving by J. Simon after Faithorne or R. White (O'D., Vol. III, p. 243, No. 28), and differs from Richardson's own etchings of the subject (O'D., No. 24, and O'D., No. 29), though they may be also after Faithorne. The drawings of Milton by Richardson at the British Museum (L.B. 28 and 29), from a painting and a bust, differ considerably from the present drawing.

RIGAUD, see Rocque, No. 506

STEPHEN RIOU, see Zuccarelli, No. 705

RIVERS (worked 1800–1812)

497. ELIZABETH FARREN, COUNTESS OF DERBY (1763–1829), half length, facing half right, in turban and slashed sleeves.

Brush, grey and blue background. Oval, 3 × 2½ in. (7.7 × 6.3 cm.)   (17027)

'A drawing of Miss Farren' was acquired by the Prince of Wales from Colnaghi on December 1, 1808, for 7s. 6d. (Archives Invoice 27766).

Engraved, or copied from an engraving, in stipple of the same size and in the same direction, by Ridley after Rivers, published by Vernon and Hood, June 1, 1800 (example in the Royal Collection).

JAMES ROBERTS (fl. 1766–1809)

498. PRINCESS AMELIA AS A CHILD, half length, facing quarter right.

Pencil and watercolour. Oval, 5¼ × 4¼ in. (13.1 × 10.7 cm.)
(13921)

Signed in pencil: J. Roberts delt. 1793.

Presented by the Hon. Hew Dalrymple, 1923, to H.M. Queen Mary, and by her to the Library.

499. GARRICK, IN THE CHARACTER OF ABEL DRUGGER profile to left.

Pencil. 5 × 4 in. (12.9 × 10.1 cm.)   (13608)

Perhaps the study for the head in the drawing by Roberts at the B.M. (L.B. 65) from which a small print was engraved by Thornthwaite (O'Donoghue, Vol. II, p. 282, No. 116) as a plate to Bell's *British Theatre*, 1777.

JAMES ROBERTS, Ascribed to

500. 'MRS. SIDDONS', half length seated, facing half right.

Watercolour. Oval, 5⅜ × 4¼ in. (13.5 × 10.7 cm.) (13545)

Much refreshed in colour, if not altogether spurious.
On November 29, 1819, the Prince Regent acquired from Colnaghi 'Mrs. Siddons as Belvidere a Drawing' for £1 11s. 6d. (Archives Invoice 28308).

GEORGE ROBERTSON (1742–1788)

501. NORTH WEST VIEW OF WINDSOR CASTLE

Pen and black and white chalk, much rubbed. Oval, 17⅜ × 22⅞ in. (44 × 47 cm.)   (17367)

Engraved by James Fittler and published September 2, 1782, by John Boydell.

502. WINDSOR CASTLE: THE QUEEN'S HOUSE

Pencil, pen, black and white chalk, torn and very much rubbed. 16⅞ × 22¾ in. (43 × 57.5 cm.) (17368)

Companion to the preceding.

WILLIAM ROBINS (fl. 1715–1740)

503. COLLEY CIBBER (1671–1757), half length standing, nearly full face.

Plumbago. Oval, 4¼ × 3⅛ in. (10.7 × 8.2 cm.)   (17024)

Signed: W. Robins Delin 1715, with a number '40' (or '48').

Reproduced, according to Long (*Dictionary of Miniature Painters*, p. 370), in Lord Ronald Gower, *Great Historical Galleries*, Vol. III, pl. 33.
'A drawing by Robins, Colley Cibber, his son and daughter' was acquired by the Prince Regent from Colnaghi on September 27, 1813, for £2 5s. (Archives Invoice 27940).

504. THEOPHILUS CIBBER (1703–1758), half length standing, nearly full face.

Plumbago. Oval, 4⅜ × 3⅜ in. (11 × 8.5 cm.)   (17023)

The signature with Nos. 503 and 505, but the number is '45'.

505. 'COLLEY CIBBER'S DAUGHTER', half length, standing to left, nearly full face.

Plumbago. Oval, 4⅜ × 3⅜ in. (11 × 8.7 cm.)   (17025)

The signature and date as in Nos. 503 and 504, the number '46'.

The numbering of these three miniatures shews that they are connected together as is implied by the invoice. Colley Cibber is said to have had several children, some of whom survived infancy. This may be a representation of one of them who is unknown to fame; it cannot, as claimed on the modern frame, be a portrait of his youngest daughter, later well known as an actress under the name of Charlotte Charke, since she was married 'when very young' in 1729,

while the girl in this portrait can scarcely have been born later than 1700. On the other hand, the identification of the personages may be merely a guess of the vendor.

JOHN ROCQUE (d. 1764) or J. RIGAUD
(c. 1681–c. 1754)

506. CLAREMONT, WITH PORTRAIT OF THOMAS HOLLES PELHAM, DUKE OF NEWCASTLE   *Plate* 95

Pen and grey wash. 11⅜ × 19⅛ in. (29 × 49 cm.) (17463)

Inscribed in pencil in a modern hand with the title as given and 'by J. Rogers engraved'.

This fine drawing shows the house precisely as in the engraving by J. Bonneau after J. Rocque, published by the latter in 1750, allowance being made for the smaller scale and inferior workmanship of the engraving. The forecourt, entrances and drives have, however, been entirely remodelled, and these improvements, if not merely a project which was not carried out, indicate a later date for the drawing. The foreground and figures are also entirely different, those in the drawing being considerably more important.

The accomplished drawing of figures, the buildings and trees would seem to indicate a more practised draughtsman than Rocque—so far indeed as he can be judged from his engravings. Certain features, e.g., the mannered feathery foliage of the trees on the left and the noticeably high lights on those to the right and the ease and general disposition of the figures suggest that the drawing is the work of Jacques Rigaud, who was working in England from about 1720 to 1753. Certain of the figures in the drawing are repetitions of, or very similar to, those in the series of prints of Stowe, engraved by Baron after him in 1739. The kicking horse and man behind it occur, precisely, in the sixth plate of Stowe, and the horse with a foal in the foreground of the drawing is shewn exactly but with another companion in the same plate. While only one figure in the central group—the younger man on the left—is identical or almost so with figures in the Stowe series (Nos. 4 and 7), the whole group, with the children, is more than recalled in those prints. So closely indeed do the figures resemble in their general character those in Rigaud's prints, and so different are they from the figures in the contemporary topographic prints of the same kind, that the divergences in the individual similar figures is a stronger indication of common origin than complete identity would be. The artist himself would be more inclined to vary his figures slightly than would a copyist. Until more is known regarding Rocque as a draughtsman it is impossible to speak with certainty, but if this drawing is not by him but by Rigaud, it would seem that he must have used Rigaud's drawings for the two engraved views of Claremont 1750 and 1754, and Rigaud must also be the author of a further view of the Bowling Green at Claremont in the same series which is at the Victoria and Albert Museum (D. 259/90). It was stated by the dealer who sold it to Dr. Percy to have been engraved, a copy having been seen by him at the British Museum. This is probably an error, through confusion with the two known prints; no engraving of the 'Bowling Green' is at the British Museum or is otherwise recorded.

Rocque describes himself on his prints of 1754 as Chorographer to H.R.H. the Prince of Wales—and in 1764 as Topographer to His Majesty. His many maps are well known. His engravings of views after drawings by himself were characterized by Strutt, who quotes only those of Wanstead House, as 'in every respect very indifferently executed'; as a rule they are confined to rather bald insets or surrounds to his plans.

MICHAEL ANGELO ROOKER (1743–1801)

507. AFTER SANDBY: NEW LODGE (THE BELVEDERE), built by the late Duke of Cumberland on Shrub Hill in Windsor Forest.

Pen and watercolour. Faded. $5\frac{1}{4} \times 7\frac{3}{8}$ in. (13.3×18.7 cm.) (17445)

Signed: MARooker 1776.

Identical with the engraving by M. A. Rooker after Paul Sandby, title as given, for the *Copper-Plate Magazine*, June, I, 1777.

See *Sandby Catalogue*, No. 116.

508. THE SAME, THE BUILDING TO THE LEFT
Pen and watercolour. $5 \times 7\frac{1}{4}$ in. (13×18.5 cm.) (17446)

Uniform with the preceding. Probably also after Sandby.

509. AFTER SANDBY: WINDSOR CASTLE: THE NORTH TERRACE, LOOKING EAST

Pen and watercolour. $4\frac{3}{4} \times 6\frac{7}{8}$ in. (12.1×17.5 cm.)
(17444)

See *Sandby Catalogue*, No. 8.
Uniform with the preceding.

THOMAS ROWLANDSON (1756–1827)

BIBLIOGRAPHY:

J. Grego: *Rowlandson the Caricaturist*, 1880.
A. P. Oppé: *Thomas Rowlandson, his Drawings and Water-colours*, 1923.
B. Falk: *T. Rowlandson, his Life and Art* [1949].

510. THE SCHOOL OF ELOQUENCE (THE GRAND DE-BATING SOCIETY) *Plate* 79

Pen with brown ink, traces of pencil. $11\frac{5}{8} \times 19\frac{1}{2}$ in. (29.5×49.6 cm.) (13719)

Bills on the wall are inscribed 'Orator's Hall, Grand Debating Society, Political Moral &c. . . . School of Eloquence' and 'State of the Nation,'; a flagon on the floor right, 'Robin Hood'.

Lit.: Oppé, pl. 1 and pp. 8 and 9.
Exhib.: B.F.A.C. 1931/32, No. 95.
Engraved with the title 'School of Eloquence', Grego, I, p. 98, 'published by Archibald Robertson, July 18, 1780'. An undated and coarse reprint in the Royal Library has 'A. Robertson fecit', and is without either Rowlandson's name or the publisher's.
Bought by the Prince Regent from Colnaghi, March 23, 1812 (with No. 511), for 15s., 'A Drawing of the Grand Debating Society' (without name of artist) (Archives Invoice 27835).
In technique and even in some of the countenances closely connected with the drawing, the *Life School at the R.A.* of 1776 (*Studio*, November, 1942, p. 147). These are among the earliest known drawings by Rowlandson and are reminiscent of Mortimer.
The caricature is supposed to be connected with a debating society which was established in Carlisle House, Soho Square, after the failure of the notorious Madame Corneille, and was presided over by the unsuccessful Irish portrait painter, W. (Blarney) Thomson (Edwards, *Anecdotes*, 1808, p. 69; W. H. Pyne, *Wine and Walnuts*, 1824, Vol. II, p. 56).

511. A MIDNIGHT CONVERSATION

Pen with black ink and watercolour over pencil. $11\frac{3}{4} \times 17\frac{1}{2}$ in. (29.6×44.3 cm.) (13713)

A signboard in a picture on the wall is marked 'Lock Hospital, Supported b . . . lick'. The date 1780, written on the back of the present mount, may be either copied from the back of the drawing or an inference from No. 510.
Companion to the preceding, with which it was acquired for £1 1s., the name of the artist being stated in this case with the title, as given above.

512. A CARICATURE

Pen and watercolour over pencil. $11\frac{1}{4} \times 7\frac{5}{8}$ in. (28.8×19.2 cm.) (13699)

Inscribed Rowlandson in pen on the old wash mount.
Exhib.: B.F.A.C. 1931/32, No. 86.
The colours have a political connotation. Probably represents Major John Cartwright, a radical politician. See *The Drum Major of Sedition* (B.M. Sat., VI, 6476, also by Rowlandson), dated March 29, 1784.

513. BOOKSELLER AND AUTHOR *Plate* 80
Pen and watercolour. $9\frac{1}{8} \times 11\frac{1}{8}$ in. (23.1×30.8 cm.)
(13704)

A pencil note at the back of the modern mount, 'Author and Bookseller—Rowlandson—£2.12.6', may have been transferred from the back of the old mount.
Reprod.: Oppé, pl. 8.
Engraved, September 25, 1784 (B.M. Sat., VI, 6722, Grego, I, pp. 148, 149), with some differences in detail and general effect.
The print of 1784 entitled *Poet and Bookseller*, and a companion *Manager and Author*, bear the name of H. Wigstead, who had exhibited drawings with these titles at the R.A. of that year. In the following year he exhibited further drawings (subsequently similarly engraved), of which the *St. James's Chronicle* wrote emphatically that they were clearly by Rowlandson, and ridiculed both Wigstead for claiming them as his own and the R.A. for admitting them under his name (Whitley, *Art and Artists in England*, Vol. II, p. 396). The practice was no new one with Rowlandson. According to the *Morning Chronicle* of June 1, 1784, he had exhibited at the R.A. 1783 in the name of W. Mason (Whitley's notes at the British Museum). Mason's only exhibit in that year was a *Scene in a Country Town at the time of a race* (No. 392). This was also engraved (by V. Green after W. Mason, Esq., on July 26, 1783, B.M. Sat. VI, No. 8243) and that print has long been suspected to be the work of Rowlandson at any rate in part.

514. TWO MEN ASLEEP ON A SOFA *Plate* 86
Pen and grey wash over preliminary pencil work. $6\frac{3}{4} \times 11\frac{1}{8}$ in. (17.3×28.3 cm.) (13695)

A pencil inscription in the top left corner: 'For (?) a bottle that Mistress Pr . . .' (?).
Exhib.: R.A. 1934, No. 697 (1212).
The right hand figure recurs, in reverse, in the print *Nap in Town* of 1785 (Grego I, 176), where the second figure is replaced by a woman.

515. GROG ON BOARD

Pen and watercolour over pencil, damaged, discoloured and creased. $11\frac{1}{4} \times 16\frac{1}{4}$ in. (29.3×41.4 cm.) (13712)

Inscribed below in pencil in the Colnaghi hand, 'Original Drawing'.

A variant of the subject engraved with this title in 1785 and 1789 (Grego, I, 168 and 253). A coarse example perhaps not, as it stands, entirely from Rowlandson's hand.

516. OVERSET (The Cockermouth Post Coach)
Plate 82

Pen and watercolour over pencil. $9\frac{1}{4} \times 13\frac{1}{2}$ in. (23.5 × 34.3 cm.)   (13707)

Inscribed 'Cockermouth Post Coach' on the panel of the coach door.

Lit.: Oppé, p. 12.

According to a note taken in 1922 the drawing bore an inscription 'Original Drawing. C. H. gave Rolandson (*sic*) 3 guineas for it'. The drawing has now been laid down and the inscription has not been transferred to the modern mount. At the same time, or previously, the drawing would appear to have been considerably trimmed.

A variation of the engraved subject *By Authority Persons and Property Protected*, 1785 (Grego, I, 168).

517. THE ENGLISH REVIEW
Plate 77

Pencil, pen and watercolour; bleached in cleaning. $19\frac{3}{4} \times 35$ in. (50.6 × 89 cm.)   (13720)

Exhib.: R.A. 1786, No. 575; International Exhibition, 1862, No. 822; Edinburgh (King's Pictures), 1948, No. 121.

Lit. and reprod.: Grego, I, pp. 10, 11; Oppé, pl. 19 and pp. 10, 11; Falk, *Thomas Rowlandson*, p. 40 (both in colour).

There is no trace of this drawing and its companion in the Lord Chamberlain's Inventory nor in that of Carlton House. An unnamed writer, quoted by Desmond Coke (*Confessions of an Incurable Collector*, 1928, p. 106) as a contemporary, speaks of the two drawings as already, when exhibited at the R.A., 'Carefully framed for the Royal collection'.

518. THE FRENCH REVIEW
Plate 78

Pencil, pen and watercolour, bleached and discoloured. $19\frac{3}{4} \times 35\frac{1}{4}$ in. (50.4 × 89.5 cm.)   (13721)

Exhib.: R.A. 1786, No. 583; International Exhibition 1862, No. 821; R.A. 1934, No. 691 (800); Paris 1938, No. 144; Edinburgh (King's Pictures) 1947, No. 119; Paris (English Life) 1948, No. 569.

Lit. and reprod.: Grego, I, pp. 10, 11; II, p. 413; Oppé, pl. 17, 18, and pp. 10, 11; Falk, p. 24 (both in colour).

Less highly wrought than its companion, it has lost even more colour through exposure and drastic cleaning. Both remain, however, outstanding examples of Rowlandson's early and most distinguished manner.

In the general disposition of these drawings and in some of the incidents Rowlandson seems to be inspired by Moreau's *La Revue à la Plaine des Sablons*, which, though not engraved until 1789, was exhibited at the Salon of 1781. The influence may have been indirect; if not, this exhibition would provide a date for one at any rate of Rowlandson's visits to Paris.

519. MRS. ROBINSON SITTING FOR HER PICTURE
Figure 44

Pen and grey wash, on buff or soiled paper. $4\frac{3}{4} \times 6\frac{3}{4}$ in. (12.2 × 17.2 cm.)   (13696)

Inscribed above, in brown ink: 'Mrs. R . . . sitting for her picture', and signed at foot right, 'T. Rowlandson'. A letter in ink, perhaps 'y' in lower left corner.

Reprod.: Falk, facing p. 45, who seems to read 'Mrs. Rowlandson'.

Fig. 44. Rowlandson: 'Mrs. R. sitting for her picture' (Cat. No. 519)

520. THE STOLEN KISS (a death-bed incident)

Pen and grey wash over rough pencil. 5×8 in. (12.6 × 20.2 cm.)   (13697)

The elongation of the girl's arm and the figure of her lover kissing it behind the sick man's shoulder are clearly a characteristic afterthought.

521. 'HIGH SPIRITS'
Plate 83

Pen with brown ink, and watercolour, loose washes, mainly grey, on washed mount. $8\frac{5}{8} \times 7\frac{1}{8}$ in. (22 × 13 cm.)   (13709)

An excellent example of Rowlandson's free descriptive penwork, probably about 1790.

522. ANY THING WILL DO FOR AN OFFICER

Pen and watercolour. $7\frac{7}{8} \times 6\frac{3}{8}$ in. (19.9 × 16 cm.) (13711)

Inscribed in pencil in the Colnaghi hand on the washed mount, 'original drawing'.

Engraved and published by Fores, 1796, with the title as given. The example in the Royal Library, Grego, II, p. 62, without date, and not by Rowlandson, contains above the title (which is not on the drawing) the following explanatory legend: 'Some schoolboys who were Playing at Soldiers found one of their number so ill made and so much under size that he would have disfigured the whole body if put into the ranks—what shall we do with him asked one—do with him says another why make an Officer of him'. The figure would seem however to have been intended as a caricature of a French General.

523. TRAVELLERS AT THE DOOR OF A MANSION

Pen and watercolour. $10\frac{5}{8} \times 12\frac{1}{4}$ in. (27 × 31.1 cm.)   (13694)

Reprod: Oppé, pl. 42; *Connoisseur*, XCII, August, 1933, pp. 9, 10; Falk, p. 48 (in colour).

An elaborate watercolour, but while there is extreme carefulness in parts, others are quite careless. About 1795.

524. 'SUNDAY MORNING'
Plate 81

Pen and grey wash, the flesh pink. $3\frac{3}{4} \times 5\frac{3}{8}$ in. (9.6 × 13.5 cm.)   (13703)

Signed and dated, at foot right: Rowlandson 1798.

Reprod.: Oppé, pl. 49.

Fig. 45. Rowlandson: Buck's Beauty (Cat. No. 526)

525. HAYMAKERS AT REST, OR, EASE AND ELEGANCE *Plate* 84

Pen with coloured inks and watercolour, over pencil, on washed mount. $4\frac{1}{2} \times 7\frac{1}{4}$ in. (11.3 × 18.4 cm.) (13708)

Signed and dated at foot right: Rowlandson 1798.

526. BUCK'S BEAUTY AND ROWLANDSON'S CONNOISSEUR *Figure* 45

Pen and watercolour. $7\frac{1}{4} \times 10\frac{7}{8}$ in. (27.8 × 18.5 cm.) (13698)

A Colnaghi inscription 'The Original Drawing' at the top has been erased since 1923.
Engraved in stipple by P. Roberts, 1800. Grego, II, p. 407.
Reprod.: Oppé, pl. 56.
A drawing of unusually good quality and no doubt the original from which the print was made, the many 'pentimenti' being carefully reproduced.

527. KING GEORGE III RETURNING FROM HUNTING THROUGH ETON

Pen and watercolour. $14\frac{7}{8} \times 20\frac{7}{8}$ in. (37.8 × 53 cm.) (13717)

Signed or inscribed at foot right, almost cut off.

Exhib.: R.A. 1934, No, 692 (794), pl. CLXII; Australia and New Zealand 1948–49 (Empire Art Loans Exhibition Society), No. 35.
Reprod.: Oppé, pl. 71.
A replica in the Fitzwilliam Museum, Cambridge, is signed and dated 1800, and inscribed in Rowlandson's writing, 'Windsor Castle from Eton Town'.
Engraved as 'Return from the Chase: Scene at Eton'.
Acquired 1909 from Messrs. Sabin.
As usual with Rowlandson, the topography and portraiture have been much generalized.

528. RAG FAIR *Plate* 87

Pen and watercolour. $7\frac{1}{4} \times 10\frac{5}{8}$ in. (18.3 × 27 cm.). The drawing appears to have been soaked. (13692)

The three shops on the left to centre have boards, lettered: 'MOSES MONCECO Old Clothes Hats Wigs Sold or Exchanged—WIDOW LEVY deler in Old Breeches Bad Silver bought and Exchanged Moses Fartado'—and on the corner shop, on the right 'RAG FAIR', and the shopkeeper's name 'PETER SMOUGH'.
A print of *Rag Fair* was published by Ackermann in 1801. Grego, Vol. II, p. 33.
Lit.: *Connoisseur* XCII, August, 1933, p. 9 (reproduced); Falk, p. 60.

529. THE POST-HOUSE

Pen and watercolour, on washed mount. $14\frac{3}{8} \times 21\frac{1}{8}$ in. (32 × 48.5 cm.) (13718)

The inn sign inscribed 'Post House'.
Many replicas of the whole or parts.
Reprod.: Macaulay, *Life among the English* (1942), p. 24; Falk, p. 32 (both in colour).

530. THE UNWELCOME VISITOR

Pen with inks of various colours, and watercolour. $10\frac{1}{4} \times 7\frac{3}{4}$ in. (26 × 19.9 cm.) (13701)

Acquired with artist's name and title as given above by King George IV from Colnaghi on March 31, 1828, for 15s. (Archives Invoice 28370).

531. FERRY BRIDGE, YORKSHIRE, partly under construction or repair.

Pencil, pen and watercolour, partly extending to the washed mount at top and left. $6\frac{1}{2} \times 13\frac{7}{8}$ in. (16.7 × 35.4 cm.) (13686)

The title presumably copied from the back of the old mount now covered.

532. TARR POINT (Torpoint, Plymouth). *Plate* 88

Pen with coloured inks and watercolour. $7\frac{1}{4} \times 10\frac{7}{8}$ in. (18.5 × 27.6 cm.) (13688)

Inscribed by Rowlandson in capital letters in ink, at foot left, TARR POINT, a pencil inscription erased.
Lit.: *Connoisseur*, XCII, July, 1933, pp. 9 and 50; reprod. (in colour), p. 11.

533. WELL AT HARROWGATE, YORKSHIRE

Pen with coloured inks and watercolour. $6\frac{1}{4} \times 9\frac{3}{8}$ in. (16 × 23.8 cm.) (13687)

The title, as given, in pencil on the washed mount.

534. FISH-MARKET AT BRIGHTHELMSTONE

Pen (mainly black) and watercolour. Traces of pencil, not followed. $7\frac{5}{8} \times 11\frac{7}{8}$ in. (19.4 × 30.1 cm.) (13689)

Inscribed by Rowlandson in ink with the title, as given, at foot, left; the same words in pencil, above, erased.
Exhib.: R.A. 1934, No. 695 (805).

Lit. and reprod.: *Connoisseur* XCII, p. 9; and reprod., p. 8;
    R.A. *Souvenir*, p. 80; Falk, p. 173.
Replica, in reverse, at the Victoria and Albert Museum
(catalogued as Margate, P. 115–1931), with slight differences
and over pencil indications and perhaps offset).

535. A RUINED CASTLE

Pen with coloured inks and watercolour; nearly mono-
chrome. $5\frac{3}{4} \times 9\frac{3}{8}$ in. (14.5 × 23.8 cm.)   (13685)
Colchester Castle has been suggested.

536. HAMPTON COURT FROM THE SOUTH BANK OF THE RIVER; the Castle Inn in the right foreground.   *Plate* 90

Pen and watercolour; unfinished and faded. $11\frac{1}{4} \times 17$ in.
(28.3 × 43.2 cm.)   (13691)
'The Castle Inn by Davis' inscribed on a board above the
door.
Reprod.: *Connoisseur*, XCII, July, 1933, p. 8.
This drawing and No. 537 are companions and had
evidently suffered before cleaning and mounting.

537. HAMPTON COURT: THE WEST FRONT, FROM THE TOW PATH   *Plate* 89

Pen with inks of various colours, and watercolour (much
faded). $11\frac{1}{4} \times 17$ in. (28.3 × 43.3 cm.)   (13690)
Reprod.: Falk, p. 173.

538. OLD KEW PALACE

Pen and watercolour over pencil. Washed and faded.
$10\frac{5}{8} \times 16\frac{1}{4}$ in. (27 × 41 cm.)   (14313)
Acquired in 1941 from Frank Davis.
Kew Palace, begun in the Gothic style by James Wyatt in
1803 for King George III, was never finished and was
pulled down in 1829.
Replica at the Victoria & Albert Museum, D.797.

539. STAG HUNTING SCENE IN A PARK

Pen with coloured inks and watercolour. $9\frac{3}{8} \times 13\frac{1}{4}$ in.
(23.8 × 33.6 cm.)   (13693)
A pencil inscription on the back of the modern mount,
'Lanhydrock, Bodmin, Cornwall', is perhaps copied from
the back of the drawing.

540. AN INDIGNANT HUSBAND

Pen and coloured inks and watercolour; much soiled and
torn. $9 \times 13\frac{1}{4}$ in. (23.2 × 33.8 cm.)   (13705)
Inscribed in the lower centre in pencil, 'An Original
Drawing', in a Colnaghi hand. 'Rowlandson' in pencil, cut
away, in the left bottom corner may have been in the same
hand.
A free late drawing with marked disproportions.

541. THE CHAMBER OF GENIUS   *Plate* 85

Pen with brown ink and watercolour over pencil. $8\frac{5}{8} \times 13$
in. (22.1 × 28.1 cm.)   (13706)
Engraved 1812. Grego, Vol. II, p. 227.
Reprod.: Oppé, pl. 85; Falk, opp. p. 45.
Presumably 'A Drawing of an Artist in his Study by
Rowlandson', bought by the Prince Regent from Colnaghi
on February 6, 1811, for £1 11s. 6d. (Archives Invoice
27673).

542. THE SHRIMP GIRL

A loose adaptation from Hogarth's picture. The print by
Bartolozzi is in reverse.

Pen with brown ink and watercolour; rubbed. $9\frac{1}{2} \times 7$ in.
(24.3 × 17.8 cm.)   (13702)
Reprod.: Falk, p. 56 (in colour).

543. 'PEG WOFFINGTON', half length seated, seen from behind, her face magnified in a mirror.

Pen ink and watercolour; soiled. $10\frac{5}{8} \times 8\frac{5}{8}$ in. (27.3 ×
22 cm.)   (13605)
Inscribed by the artist in ink at foot: 'Portrait of Peg
Woffington the celebrated Actress.'
Reprod.: Falk, p. 16 (in colour).
The portrait is based on the mezzotint by J. Faber, junr.,
after Eccardt (O'Donoghue, IV, p. 524, No. 1).

544. DR. MONSEY

Pen with brown ink and watercolour, over slight pencil and
(?) red chalk. Oval, $4\frac{1}{8} \times 3$ in. (10.4 × 7.1 cm.)   (13714)
This drawing is a copy of a portrait engraved by Bromley
'from a sketch by Mr. Forster' published in March, 1789
(O'Donoghue, Vol. III, p. 256). The head and hat are in
reverse, but the coat and buttons retain the direction of the
print. The right shoulder also seems to follow the print,
while the left is altered to fit the oval shape which cuts off
the arms and hands, while the chair has been eliminated.
Such copies and pastiches were frequently made by Rowlandson in his later days, probably with the intention of
passing them off as original studies from the life.
Messenger Monsey, M.D., F.R.S. (1693–1788), physician
to the Chelsea Hospital.

545. A CONTRE-TEMPS

Pen and watercolour over pencil. $7\frac{5}{8} \times 9\frac{7}{8}$ in. (19.5 × 25
cm.)   (13715)
A copy or, conceivably, worked over by another hand.

ROWLANDSON, After

546. A BRACE OF BLACKGUARDS

Pen and watercolour. $10\frac{1}{4} \times 8\frac{5}{8}$ in. (26.1 × 22 cm.)
                                                          (13710)
Close to the aquatint of 1789, etc., for which and the
supposed identification of the sitters with George Morland
and Rowlandson, see Grego, Vol. II, pp. 229–30 and 392.
This is a coarse repetition of a type which cannot be attributed to Rowlandson's own hand.

547. THE CONSULTATION

Pen and watercolour. $9 \times 7\frac{1}{2}$ in. (22.8 × 13 cm.)   (13700)
A forgery or copy.

548. SADLER'S FLYING ARTILLERY

Pen and watercolour in ruled margin. $10\frac{3}{4} \times 16\frac{3}{4}$ in.
(41.5 × 27.3 cm.)   (17692)
Signed in lower margin: W.B. del, and inscribed with the
title as given and 'To protect Cavalry either in advancing
or retreating'.
Identical with the print sometimes included with Rowlandson's *Loyal Volunteers* 1798/9, in the same direction and
in spite of the initials no doubt a copy.

ROWLANDSON, Ascribed to, after Buck

549. 'TAMBORINA'

Pen and watercolour within a washed border. $8\frac{5}{8} \times 12\frac{1}{4}$ in.
(21 × 31.8 cm.)   (13716)
Inscribed in pencil on the border, 'Original Drawing by
Rowlandson', in the Colnaghi hand.

Nothing in the drawing, with its weak and thin line and rather clumsy washes, explains its ascription to Rowlandson. It is a close copy of the well-known print by A. Buck.

WILLIAM WYNNE RYLAND (1738-1783), After

550. AFTER RAMSAY: KING GEORGE III IN CORONATION ROBES, standing full face.

Pencil, torn and rubbed. $19\frac{5}{8} \times 13\frac{3}{8}$ in. (50 × 33.7 cm.)
                                                        (13928)

Presented by H.M. Queen Mary in 1919.
A careful copy of the engraving from Lord Bute's picture of 1761 (O'Donoghue, Vol. II, p. 305, No. 95) shortened at the foot.

PAUL AND THOMAS SANDBY

For drawings by the Sandby Brothers acquired before 1947, see *Catalogue of Sandby Drawings at Windsor Castle* by A. P. Oppé, 1947. For drawings acquired since 1947 see the Supplement in the present volume, p. 113-117, Nos. S.419-S.435.

J. SAUNDERS, *see* No. 93

JAMES SAYER (1748-1823)

551. NEW SOUTH SEA FISHERY, OR A CHEAP WAY TO CATCH WHALES (*c.* 1790)

Pen and brown wash. (In a volume of caricature prints by Sayers.) $14\frac{1}{4} \times 21\frac{1}{2}$ in. (36 × 55 cm.)
The Spanish Convention of 1790. Pitt and Dundas are represented in a rowing boat fishing with bags of millions for whales off the Pacific Coast of North America from Norton Sound to Guatemala. Buoys labelled '10 Leagues' are placed off the coast. A ship inscribed 'Convention' lies in the offing. Pitt is saying, 'I fear Harry this fishery will never answer'; Dundas replies, 'Never mind that Billy the gudgeons we have caught in England will pay for All.' There are verses in the lower margin, and the title as given is inscribed at the top.
In pencil the vendor has written 'Original Drawing by Sayre' (gone over).

JOHN CHRISTIAN SCHETKY (1778-1874)

552. THE ROYAL GEORGE YACHT LEAVING PORTSMOUTH HARBOUR, 13 AUGUST, 1819

Watercolour, with border below. $8\frac{3}{4} \times 11\frac{7}{8}$ in. (22 × 30 cm.)   (*Souvenir Album*, VI, p. 2)
Signed: J. C. Schetky, and inscribed with title as given, in border.

553. THE ROYAL GEORGE YACHT AT ANCHOR, COWES ROADS

Watercolour. $8\frac{5}{8} \times 12$ in. (21.8 × 30.5 cm.)
                                    (*Souvenir Album*, VI, p. 2)
Signed and inscribed as the preceding.

554. EMBARKATION ON BOARD THE ROYAL YACHT 'VICTORIA AND ALBERT', PORTSMOUTH HARBOUR, OCTOBER 14, 1844

Watercolour. $11\frac{7}{8} \times 18\frac{1}{4}$ in. (28.5 × 46.4 cm.)
                                    (*Souvenir Album*, IV, p. 23)

Queen Victoria describes the embarkation at night, in her *Journal*, October 14, 1844: 'It was quite dark and we were lighted by lanterns to our barge. When we reached the

Yacht, we found her entirely lit up with blue lights, which had a lovely effect on the water.'

555. VISIT TO THE FRENCH FLEET OFF SPITHEAD, OCTOBER 15, 1844

Watercolour. $11\frac{7}{8} \times 17\frac{1}{2}$ in. (30 × 44.5 cm.)
                                    (*Souvenir Album*, IV, p. 23)

556. THE NAVAL REVIEW AT SPITHEAD, 21ST JUNE, 1845. Four drawings.

Watercolour, *c.* $9\frac{1}{2} \times 13\frac{1}{2}$ in. (24.1 × 34.3 cm.)
                                    (*Souvenir Album*, VI, pp. 9, 10)

557. H.M.S. 'SUPERB', OFF THE NAB LIGHT, 23RD JUNE, 1845

Watercolour. 8×14 in. (20.5 × 35.5 cm.)
                                    (*Souvenir Album*, VI, p. 10)

558. ST. MARY'S, SCILLY ISLES

Watercolour. $10\frac{7}{8} \times 19\frac{1}{4}$ in. (27.5 × 48.9 cm.)
                                    (*Souvenir Album*, V, p. 31)

Queen Victoria visited St. Mary's on August 13, 1847.

559. DOUGLAS BAY, ISLE OF MAN

Watercolour. $9\frac{3}{4} \times 13\frac{1}{2}$ in. (25 × 34.5 cm.)
                                    (*Souvenir Album*, V, p. 33)

560. THE NAVAL REVIEW AT SPITHEAD, 11 AUGUST, 1853

Watercolour, within border, inscribed with the names of the ships. $10\frac{3}{4} \times 15$ in. (27.3 × 38 cm.)
                                    (*Souvenir Album*, VI, p. 13)
Signed: J. C. Schetky.

561. PLYMOUTH: THE DEPARTURE OF THE PRINCE OF WALES FOR CANADA, JULY 11, 1860

Watercolour. $8\frac{5}{8} \times 13\frac{1}{2}$ in. (21.6 × 34.5 cm.)
                                    (*Souvenir Album*, VI, p. 16)

562. THE NAVAL ACTION OFF HELIGOLAND, MAY 9, 1864

Monochrome. $13\frac{1}{2} \times 21\frac{1}{8}$ in. (35.5 × 54.1 cm.)
                                    (*Souvenir Album*, VI, p. 22)
Signed and dated: John Christian Schetky Marine Painter in Ordinary to Her Majesty Queen Victoria, April 1866.

563. BELVOIR CASTLE FROM DEVON HILL

Pencil, pen and grey wash, touched with Chinese white. $14\frac{1}{2} \times 21\frac{3}{8}$ in. (36.5 × 54 cm.)   (17068)
Signed in pen: John Christian Schetky—Marine painter in ordinary to Her Majesty, April 1866—and the title, as given, in pencil on the mount.
A monument of his 89th year.

JACOB C. SCHNEBBELIE (1760-1792)

564. ST. GEORGE'S CHAPEL: THE WEST END, from the Horseshoe cloisters, 1786.

Pen and watercolour, creased and faded. $10\frac{3}{4} \times 15\frac{1}{2}$ in. (27.5 × 39.5 cm.)   (17375)
Signed: Schnebbelie delt 1786.
Reprod.: St. John Hope, *Windsor Castle*, 1913, pl. XCII.
Apparently based on the print by W. Watts after Paul Sandby, published December 1, 1777, by Kearsly.

565. WINDSOR CASTLE: THE QUEEN'S LODGE AND SOUTH EAST TOWER, 1787

Pen and watercolour. $8\frac{1}{4} \times 11\frac{7}{8}$ in. (21 × 30 cm.) (17374)

Inscribed on the back of the washed mount: 'The Queen's Lodge and South East Tower of Windsor Castle and part of the East Terrace—Drawn by J. Schnebbelie. Draw'g Masr. (March 3d 1787)—No. 25 Park Street. Gros'r Sqr.–'

ROBERT BLEMELL SCHNEBBELIE (d. 1849)

566. INTERIOR OF THE LATE THEATRE ROYAL, DRURY LANE . . . destroyed by Fire 24th Feb. 1809. From a sketch by John Winston.

Watercolour. $8\frac{5}{8} \times 10\frac{7}{8}$ in. (21.9 × 27.5 cm.) on a sheet 12 × $14\frac{3}{4}$ in. (30.5 × 37.5 cm.) (17132)

Engraved 1820, Wilkinson, *Londina Illustrata*, Vol. II, No. 180, by Dale 'from an original drawing by, and in the possession of, John Winston Esqr.'; the title as given above. Though identical with the engraving and inscribed 'Original' in pencil in the same (?) Librarian's hand as is the word 'copy' on the mount of No. 567, this careful drawing is on the same paper as is that copy and bears every sign of being by the same hand. The 'Original sketch' referred to in the inscription on No. 567 was no doubt that by John Winston, Esq., referred to on the engraving.

567. INTERIOR OF DRURY LANE THEATRE. From a sketch by John Winston.

Watercolour on Whatman paper. $12\frac{1}{8} \times 9\frac{5}{8}$ in. (24.4 × 30.9 cm.) (17133)

Inscribed in Schnebbelie's hand: 'Drawn (after an Original Sketch) by Robert Blemell Schnebbelie 18th Novr. 1817 26 (?) H.' The mount is inscribed in pencil 'Copy' and '15/–'. Almost identical with the preceding but unfinished, without figures in the centre and with empty chairs in the boxes. The number in Schnebbelie's inscription may denote that it is the twenty-sixth repetition, for the purpose of extra-illustration.

568. INTERIOR OF THE THEATRE ROYAL COVENT GARDEN AS ALTERED PREVIOUS TO THE OPENING ON 15TH SEPT. 1794, destroyed by Fire Sept. 20, 1808. From a sketch by John Winston.

Watercolour. $7\frac{3}{8} \times 9\frac{1}{2}$ in. (18.9 × 24 cm.) (17131)

Inscribed on the mount in pencil 'Covent Garden' and '15/–'.

Engraved 1819, Wilkinson, *Londina Illustrata*, Vol. II, No. 183, by Springsguth, 'from an original drawing by and in the possession of John Winston Esqr.' Uniform with No. 567, which is signed by Schnebbelie (after an original sketch) and clearly by the same hand, and made for the same purpose, on the same Whatman paper.

569. INTERIOR OF THE REGENCY THEATRE with spectators, Othello played on the stage.

Watercolour, on the same paper as the preceding. $6\frac{5}{8} \times 8\frac{3}{4}$ in. (16.8 × 22.4 cm.) (17069)

Signed and inscribed: 'Regency Theatre sketched 25th April 1816 by Robert Blemmell Schnebbelie.'

Engraved 1817 by Cook for Wilkinson's *Londina Illustrata*, Vol. II, No. 199.

570. THE KING'S THEATRE, HAYMARKET (the Opera House): View of the Eastern Exterior as altered by Nash in 1819.

Pencil, pen and watercolour. $7\frac{5}{8} \times 10\frac{1}{2}$ in. (19.5 × 26.7 cm.) (17071)

Signed and dated: 'Robert Blemmell Schnebbelie 1819.'

Inscribed at the back in pencil: 'King's Theatre.' '15/–.'

Engraved 1820 by Howlett for Wilkinson's *Londina Illustrata*, Vol. II, No. 189.

Exhib.: B.F.A.C. 1919, 'Old London', No. 24.

571. SPECIMENS OF ARCHITECTURE IN CROSBY HALL

Pen and watercolour on Whatman paper. 17 × $11\frac{3}{4}$ in. (43 × 29.9 cm.) (17070)

Signed: 'Sketched on the 3rd November 1817 by Robert Blemell Schnebbelie.'

Engraved 1819 by Cook, for Wilkinson's *Londina Illustrata*, Vol. I, No. 81.

The central 'specimen of architecture', a window boarded up with advertisements of Kemble, Kean, etc., performing in 1817, was no doubt the reason for the acquisition of this drawing as a theatrical subject.

HEINRICH WILHELM SCHWEICKHARDT (1746–1797)

572. A FARM HORSE

Black and coloured chalk on blue paper. $6\frac{3}{8} \times 8\frac{1}{2}$ in. (16.3 × 21.5 cm.) (13288)

Signed: H. W. Schweickhardt.

Acquired by the Prince of Wales from Colnaghi, January 12, 1803, for 15s.: 'A Drawing of a Horse by Schweichardt' (Archives Invoice 27213).

JAMES SEYMOUR (1702–1752)

573. A HOUND

Pencil on brown paper. $7\frac{1}{4} \times 11\frac{7}{8}$ in. (18.6 × 30.2 cm.) (13556)

Inscribed in the Colnaghi hand, in pencil on the drawing itself, 'Original by Seymour'.

Four drawings of horses and one of a dog by Seymour were acquired by the Prince of Wales from Colnaghi on September 9, 1803, at prices ranging from half a guinea to three guineas (Archives Invoice 27242).

574. GROOM HOLDING HORSE

Pencil, on washed mount, folded and torn. $10\frac{3}{4} \times 7\frac{5}{8}$ in. (27.5 × 19.5 cm.) (13559)

Inscribed on the drawing as the preceding.

575. HORSE AND GROOM, GALLOPING TO RIGHT

Pen over pencil with washed mount. $6\frac{5}{8} \times 10\frac{5}{8}$ in. (16.8 × 27.3 cm.) (13560)

Inscribed on the drawing as the preceding.

576. GROOM LEADING SADDLED RACE HORSE TO LEFT

Pencil and white chalk. 10 × $13\frac{1}{8}$ in. (25.7 × 33.3 cm.) (13554)

Signed: J. S. 1747, and inscribed on the drawing as No. 573. Highly finished and possibly prepared for gouache colouring.

577. HORSE WITH HUNTSMAN RIDING TO LEFT AT FOOT PACE

Pencil, old wash mount with remains of original washed border at foot. $7\frac{5}{8} \times 10$ in. (19.5 × 25.5 cm.) (13558)

Inscribed on the drawing, 'Original Drawing by Seymour', in the same hand as No. 573.

580. FOUR SEPARATE STUDIES OF BIRDS: duck swimming, cock crowing, pheasant feeding and two cocks fighting.

Black and red chalk. $9\frac{1}{4} \times 13\frac{7}{8}$ in. (23.5 × 35.4 cm.)
(13555)

Probably not English. The mount is either that of the 17th century Italian drawings in the Royal Collection, or a recent imitation.

SAMUEL SHELLEY (1750–1808)

581. HEAD OF A LADY   *Figure* 47

Black and red chalk. $8\frac{3}{8} \times 5\frac{7}{8}$ in. (21.3 × 15 cm.) (14735)

Inscribed in pencil at foot: Portrait sketch by Samuel Shelley for a miniature.

GEORGE SHEPHERD (exhib. 1800–1830)

582. THE NURSERY, GOLDEN LANE; (wrongly called 'The Fortune Play House'); exterior view.

Watercolour, ruled off and extended on each side in pencil. $8\frac{1}{8} \times 8\frac{5}{8}$ in. (20.8 × 22 cm.) (17073)

Signed: G. Shepherd 1811.

Engraved by Wise after Shepherd 1811, including the pencilled extensions, in Wilkinson's *Londina Illustrata*, Vol. II, No. 173, as the Fortune Play House. See *Catalogue* B.F.A.C., 1919, *Old London*, No. 28.

Fig. 46. Seymour: A hunt Servant (Cat. No. 578)

578. A HUNT SERVANT WITH DEAD HARE
Figure 46

Pen over slight pencil; old washed mount. $9\frac{1}{8} \times 6\frac{5}{8}$ in. (23.1 × 15.9 cm.) (13553)

Exhib.: Country Life 1937, No. 478 (reprod. *Souvenir*).

Though not inscribed as are the preceding, the drawing is on a similar washed mount and may be identified with 'A Drawing by Seymour' acquired by the Prince of Wales from Colnaghi on October 25, 1803, for 7s. 6d. (Archives Invoice 27717).

Similar rough pen drawings by Seymour are in the British Museum.

JAMES SEYMOUR, Ascribed to

579. HEAD OF A CHARGER   *Figure* 48

Black and white chalk on brown paper, a pencilled rectangle cuts through the forehead of the horse. $16 \times 10\frac{1}{4}$ in. (45.6 × 26.2 cm.) (13557)

Probably a study for a large equestrian portrait without connection with Seymour. Large heads of horses, in pen, by him are at the British Museum, but they are drawn with less sensitiveness and painter-like mastery. The drawing may well be Flemish of the late 17th or early 18th century. A likeness to the head of Charles II's charger in the statue in the Quadrangle of Windsor Castle, extending even to the metal work of the bit which differs only in one ornament, may be merely accidental. That statue was cast in 1679 by one John Ibach, perhaps of Bremen (St. John Hope, *Windsor Castle*, 1913, Vol. II, p. 555, note 4).

Fig. 47. Shelley: Portrait of a Lady (Cat. No. 581)

Fig. 48. Head of a Charger (Cat. No. 579)

583. WINDSOR CASTLE: EDWARD III GATEHOUSE WITH PART OF THE UPPER WARD, the Round Tower in the background.

Pencil, within a ruled margin on three sides, which divides off part of the buildings on the left. 8½ × 13⅛ in. (21.3 × 33 cm.)   (17448)

Inscribed in the margin at the foot 'Windsor Castle G. Shepherd', and again, '7 G. Shepherd'. Remains of pencilled words on the drawing.

Compared with No. 617 (ascribed to Turner), which is taken from almost the same viewpoint, this sketch shows a further stage in the Gothic embellishment of the State Entrance, which was later swept away for Wyatville's porch. The statue of Charles II had not yet been removed from the centre of the quadrangle to its present position.

G. SHEPHERD, Ascribed to

584. THE OLD PLAY HOUSE, PORTUGAL STREET, Lincoln's Inn Fields, exterior view.

Watercolour within washed border, the whole inset in another sheet. 8 × 9½ in. (20.4 × 24.4 cm.)   (17072)

Inscribed below border with the title as given.

Exhib.: B.F.A.C. 1919, 'Old London', No. 26.

A view of the building with an adjoining chapel was engraved 1811 after Shepherd for Wilkinson's *Londina Illustrata*, Vol. II, No. 175. This puerile representation may shew still further degradation of the building.

585. GROCERS' HALL, EXTERIOR

Watercolour. 8⅜ × 11⅛ in. (21.3 × 28.3 cm.) on a large sheet (35.6 × 62.3 cm.) for extra-illustration.

Inscribed in pencil 'by Shepherd', '365'.

SHEPHERD, Manner of

586. THE BEAR GARDEN (at Bankside, Southwark)

Watercolour. 5¼ × 7½ in. (13.4 × 19 cm.)   (17141)

Conceivably the 'enlarged Drawing of a very scarce View of London, called "the Antwerp View" ', engraved October 1810 for Wilkinson's *Londina Illustrata* (Vol. II, No. 166), without name of artist or engraver, but more probably a copy of the engraving itself.

587. 'ELEANOR GWYNN'S HOUSE', PALL MALL

Pencil and watercolour, within washed border. 10 × 8¼ in. (25.5 × 21 cm.)   (17139)

An anonymous drawing made and inlaid for extra-illustration, perhaps in the Shepherd workshop.

JOHN KEYSE SHERWIN

(*c.* 1751–1790), Ascribed to

588. FRANCESCO BARTOLOZZI, R.A., bust, profile to left

Pencil and red chalk. 8¾ × 7⅛ in. (22 × 13.2 cm.) (13304)

If this is the 'Portrait of Bartolozzi, a drawing', bought for the Prince Regent from Colnaghi on March 24, 1817, for one guinea (Archives Invoice 28143), the attribution to Sherwin is more recent. Since, moreover, the sitter can scarcely have been more than 35 years of age, either he is not Bartolozzi or the artist is not Sherwin, who was at least 23 years the younger man.

JOSIAH SLATER (exhib. 1806–1833)

589. PRINCESS AMELIA (1783–1810), half length, facing half left.

Pencil and wash. 8¾ × 7¼ in. (22.5 × 13.4 cm.)   (14737)

Inscribed in pencil, at foot, 'J. Slater 17 Newman St.'

Very closely connected with the memorial portrait of the Princess engraved by J. S. Agar after Anne Mee, published 1811 (O'Donoghue, Vol. I, p. 43, No. 5).

590. PRINCE EDWARD OF SAXE-WEIMAR (1823–1902), half length, facing half left.

Pencil and slight wash. 9½ × 6⅝ in. (24.1 × 16.9 cm.)   (14738)

Signed at foot right: Jos^h Slater 1832.

JOHN SMART (1741–1811)

591. MRS. GRUEBER, bust, turned half left.

Pencil and watercolour, on card. 2½ × 2½ in. (6.2 × 6.2 cm.)   (17595)

Inscribed: Mrs. Grueb . . . faintly in pencil on the back with the remains of an erased inscription and various other, modern, markings.

Presented by H.M. Queen Mary, February, 1948.

Presumably from the sale at Christie's, December 17, 1936, when Smart's store of his preparations for miniatures on ivory was sold by his descendants.

FRANCIS SMITH (exhib. 1770–1773)

592. THE AUDIENCE OF THE GRAND SIGNIOR: the introduction. The ambassador and his suite wearing Turkish robes. *Plate 70*

Watercolour, within ruled border. 17¾ × 27¾ in. (44 × 70.5 cm.) (17143)

Engraved by R. Pranker 1769, and loosely followed in the engraving by J. Fougeron, without artist's name, in Lord Baltimore's *Tour to the East in the Years 1763 and 1764*, published 1767.

F. Smith exhibited 'A View of Constantinople, representing the Grand Signior's Seraglio, with a great part of the city . . . taken on the spot in 1764', at the Royal Academy in 1770 (No. 175).

These undoubtedly authentic drawings, though clumsy and stiff, are impressive in a somewhat Oriental manner, but they do not exhibit any of the characteristics of the artist described by Colonel Grant in *English Landscape Painters*, n.d., Vol. I, p. 70.

593. THE AUDIENCE OF THE GRAND VIZIER *Plate 72*

Watercolour, within ruled border. 17½ × 66⅛ in. (44.5 × 66.5 cm.)

Engraved, etc., as on the preceding.

CAPTAIN SMITH, 1802

A large drawing, in pencil, pen and brown wash, unfinished, 'Death of Major General Mansel in the plain Cateau (Beaumont) April 25th 1794', is in Military Drawings, Vol. IV, p. 86 (No. 16494). The artist's name, date and title are written on the back in different hands, also '1794–7'.

THE LADY CAROLINE SPENCER

594. GROUP OF THREE WOMEN, HALF LENGTH; AFTER GUERCINO

Pen, with brown ink and brown wash, some red, in ruled border. 8¼ × 8⅞ in. (21 × 22.5 cm.) (13565)

Signed on border: Caroline Spencer 1782.

A pencil addition to a list of the contents of a portfolio in the Library which has been inserted as p. 168 in Inventory 'A' mentions this and the following seven drawings as having belonged to Queen Charlotte. Both the list and the pencil addition are in the hand of J. H. Glover, who was Royal Librarian from 1836 to 1860.

595. A WOMAN SEATED, READING; AFTER GUERCINO

Pen with brown ink and brown wash, some red, within ruled border. 11½ × 8¾ in. (29.2 × 21.4 cm.) (13566)

Signed in border: Guercino inv. Caroline Spencer 1782.

Presumably Lady Caroline Spencer, eldest daughter of the 4th Duke of Marlborough (1763–1813), married 2nd Viscount Clifden, March 19, 1792.

THE LADY ELIZABETH SPENCER

596. A SEATED WOMAN; AFTER GUERCINO

Pen with brown ink and brown wash, also some red, in ruled border. 12 × 9 in. (30.4 × 22.7 cm.).

Signed, within border: Elizabeth Spencer 1782.

597. A WOMAN HOLDING A BOWL OVER A TABLE ON WHICH IS A CORONET; AFTER GUERCINO

Pen, with brown ink and brown wash, some red, in ruled border. 10⅜ × 9⅜ in. (26.5 × 23.8 cm.) (13564)

Signed, within border: Eliza Spencer 1782.

Presumably Lady Elizabeth Spencer, second daughter of the 4th Duke of Marlborough (1764–1812), married John Spencer, 1790.

THE LADY GEORGIANA CHARLOTTE SPENCER

598. Four pencil drawings, three 3⅛ × 4¾ in. (8 × 12 cm.) ruins; and one, a goldfinch 3⅛ × 2¾ in. (8 × 7.1 cm.), all presumably copies, on one mount. (13568–13571)

A label preserved with the drawings is inscribed in ink, 'Georgiana Charlotte Spencer fecit 1781'.

Presumably Lady Charlotte Spencer, third daughter of the 4th Duke of Marlborough (1769–1802), married Rev. Edward Nares, April 16, 1797.

THOMAS STOTHARD, R.A. (1755–1834)

599. DESIGN FOR A FRIEZE AT BUCKINGHAM PALACE: 'SUMMER'. Apollo in his chariot, centre, pastoral scenes on left and right.

Pen and brown wash over pencil. 2¼ × 19¾ in. (5.7 × 50.1 cm.) (13573)

Another version of this subject is in the British Museum (L.B. 106 (*b*)) among thirteen designs, the last important work of the artist, for the decoration in sculpture of the Great Staircase, the Drawing-room and the Throne room of the palace. This design, and three other friezes above the Great Staircase, were carried out in low relief by A. J. Stothard, the son of the painter. (H. Clifford Smith, *Buckingham Palace*, n.d., p. 132.)

600. DESIGN FOR A LUNETTE AT BUCKINGHAM PALACE: A NEST OF CUPIDS

Reproduced on p. 16.

Pen and brown wash over pencil. 5½ × 7⅞ in. (14 × 20 cm.) (17322)

Identified by Mr. H. Clifford Smith as a design for one of the four lunettes executed in high relief by Bernasconi above the cornice of the Grand Staircase at Buckingham Palace. Acquired from Messrs. Spink, May, 1945.

Fig. 49. Stothard: A lunette at Buckingham Palace (Cat. No. 601)

The subject of this frieze occasioned a remark by King George IV that Stothard's sprightliness had not diminished in his old age (Mrs. Bray, *Life of Stothard*, p. 181; H. Clifford Smith, *op. cit.*, p. 132; and *Country Life*, September 7, 1945, with a reproduction of this drawing).

601. A SIMILAR DESIGN: CUPIDS, FLOWERS AND BUTTERFLIES *Figure* 49

Pen and brown wash over pencil. $5\frac{1}{2} \times 7\frac{5}{8}$ in. (14×19.5 cm.) (17353)

Uniform with the preceding, and no doubt also a design for the same purpose.
Acquired from Messrs. Spink, June, 1946.

602. A DESIGN FOR A TYMPANUM AT BUCKINGHAM PALACE: CUPIDS AND FLOWERS, WITH ARCHITECTURAL SETTING

Pen and brown wash over pencil. $6\frac{5}{8} \times 16$ in. (16.8×40 cm.) (17327)

Signed at foot: Thos. Stothard.

Acquired from Messrs. Spink, February, 1946. (Previously at Squire's Gallery.)
Reprod.: *Country Life*, July 4, 1947 (H. Clifford Smith).
The shape of this tympanum corresponds with those in the Blue Drawing Room at Buckingham Palace.
This drawing, together with a similar design in the British Museum (L.B. 110), may be two of the 'three designs of

Boys and Foliage' mentioned in an account of 1830 (Mrs. Bray, *op. cit.*, p. 183) for work in the South Drawing-room which was not carried out. See also H. Clifford Smith, *op. cit.*, Pl. 175).

603. DESIGN FOR (?) A DIPLOMA: The Royal Arms surmounting a plinth and soffit, on which are seated female supporters holding a hammer and (?) folded compasses.

Pen and brown wash. $6\frac{3}{4} \times 10\frac{3}{4}$ in. (17.5×27.4 cm.) (17564)

Acquired Sotheby's, March 19, 1947 (Mrs. Thorn Drury), Lot 1.

604. DESIGN FOR A TICKET: Mediæval knights swearing fealty to a royal crown, surrounded by emblems in the border.

Pencil, pen and brown wash. $2\frac{3}{4} \times 4\frac{5}{8}$ in. (9.4×12.8 cm.) (17336)

It has been suggested that this is a preliminary design for the admission ticket to Westminster Abbey for the Coronation of King George IV, which shows, in its central medallion, the king enthroned with, on each side, allegorical female figures, while a winged figure descends from above and places a crown on his head. The suggestion is an old one, but neither the incident depicted nor the emblems in the margin (which are military on the left with a caduceus, and naval on the right with the Libra) seem sufficiently

Fig. 50. Architectural Design (Cat. No. 609)

connected with the occasion to justify the drawing being considered as a preliminary and entirely discarded sketch. The arms at the foot are too slightly drawn to allow any identification. The ticket, if such it be, would seem rather to be connected with some celebration of an Order of Knighthood. Pencil inscriptions on scrolls connecting the emblems in the margin are almost illegible, but appear to be Latin tags: 'Hostes ad faedera co . . .', 'sub justo temper . . .', '. . . fert omnia'.
Presented to the Royal Library in May, 1946, by Mr. I. A. Williams.

605. THE ROYAL FAMILY, 1787

Pencil, pen and watercolour. 15 × 21 in. (38 × 53.2 cm.)
(17606)

Sketch for the mezzotint—T. Stothard pinxt. 1787, J. Murphy sculpt 1794, published by John Jeffryes, June 4, 1794 (O'Donoghue, Vol. V, p. 36).
The disposition of the group is much as in the print, but, except for the three princes on the left and the Princess Royal on the right, the personages are all altered in position or attitude. The picture, if it ever existed, has left no other record and, despite this print and another portrait of the King, engraved by Testolini after Stothard, Mrs. Bray, in her life of the artist, p. 23, speaks as though he had received no commissions from King George III.
From the collection of L. G. Duke, who is understood to have purchased it at Exeter. Acquired from Squire's Gallery, July, 1948.

606. KING GEORGE III ENTHRONED AND SURROUNDED BY THE CARDINAL VIRTUES. Design for Messrs. Rundell and Bridge's Transparency, 1810. *Plate 93*

Watercolour, slight pen. 7¼ × 13¼ in. (18.6 × 33.6 cm.)
(17636)

Purchased at Sotheby's, July 13, 1949, Lot 17. Previously Christie's, October 1, 1948, Lot 50.
Mrs. Bray (*op. cit.*, p. 50) describes the large transparency displayed by Messrs. Rundell & Bridge, the Royal silversmiths, in front of their house at Ludgate Hill in honour of the King's jubilee in 1810. In it 'King George appeared, seated on a throne, surrounded by the Cardinal Virtues. To the right and left of the sovereign were seen spiral columns, to one of which History was engaged in attaching the names of the Naval and Military Victories of his reign; Mars and Neptune were reclining at his feet'. Except for the absence of the two last-mentioned deities the present sketch corresponds exactly with this description. A preliminary sketch of the Virtues in the collection of the present writer shows the figure of Neptune also, and has a slight indication of the whole composition separately at the top.

GEORGE STUBBS (1724–1806), Ascribed to

607. COW IN SHED

Pencil on buff paper, 5⅜ × 6¾ in. (14.2 × 17 cm.).
(13574)

608. LION

Pencil on buff paper, 6⅛ × 8⅞ (15.5 × 22.4 cm.) (13575)

WILLIAM TALMAN (d. 1719–20), Attributed to

609. ARCHITECTURAL DESIGN. On the front, a monumental gateway, inscribed with the name and titles of Queen Anne, repetition and details. On the reverse, an ornamented fountain with plan and sketches of buildings. *Figure 50*

Pen. 6¾ × 9¾ in. (17.2 × 24.5 cm.) (17590)
The architraves inscribed ANNA D : G : MAG : BR:FRA . . . (*cancelled*) HIB : REGINA, and the same with initials only; and over the central windows DIEU ET MON DROIT twice.
The drawing was acquired in November, 1947, from Messrs. Spink as anonymous. It cannot be related to any known building, nor has the artist been identified with certainty, but, as has been pointed out by Mr. Summerson, it has affinity with a group of drawings at the R.I.B.A. once considered to be by Thomas Archer (*d.* 1743), but now attributed to William Talman.
The use of the motto DIEU ET MON DROIT for a building connected with Queen Anne is unusual, since that monarch preferred SEMPER EADEM.

SIR JAMES THORNHILL (1676–1734)

610. DESIGN FOR A CEILING: 'AUTUMN' *Plate 99*

Pen and brown wash with white on green-grey paper. A slight sketch of the same, in pen on the reverse. 7⅝ × 15⅝ in. (19.5 × 37.2 cm.) (14749)
Signed on the drawing: Jno Thorn^ll Fct.

611. HERCULES. Design for an overmantel at (?) St. James's Palace *Figure 51*

Pen and brown wash. 9½ × 7¾ in. (24 × 19.8 cm.) (17634)
Inscribed in Thornhill's handwriting at the top: 'Next ye Guard room at St. James's over ye Chimney.' At foot a scale of feet and inches.
Acquired from Messrs. Colnaghi, April, 1949.
The design shows a bust of Hercules, with the skin of the

Fig. 51. Thornhill: An Overmantel (Hercules) (Cat. No. 611)

Nemean Lion over his shoulder, in high relief on a medallion surrounded by a garland of fruit and flowers and surmounted by a lion's mask and ribbons, the whole over a plinth and within a rectangular panel. On the reverse is a pencil sketch of approximately the same design over a fireplace and within Corinthian columns supporting an architrave. In the view of the King's Presence Chamber opposite p. 10 of Vol. III of Pyne's *Royal Residences*, a sculptured head in high relief within a similar garland and panels stands over the fireplace, but there is no plinth nor Corinthian columns. The ornament has disappeared from the room. Thornhill is not known to have done any work for St. James's Palace, nor is the King's Presence Chamber (now known as the Tapestry Room) next to the Guard Room; it would therefore be possible to read the abbreviation as 'Sir' not 'St.', were it not unlikely that the house of a mere 'Sir James' would possess a Guard room.

PIETER TILLEMANS (1684–1734)

612. LANDSCAPE, TREES AND ROCKS

Black chalk, grey and brown washes. $11\frac{1}{4} \times 14$ in. (28.5 × 35.4 cm.)   (6643)

Signed in pencil at foot left: . . . ter Tillemans.

From the volume of Miscellaneous Italian and Flemish landscapes in King George III's Collection, which also contained the drawing by Chatelain, No. 119, and that by Crone, No. 161.

The artist was much employed in England, but this drawing is entirely Italo-Flemish in character and has no English bearing.

CHARLES TOMKINS (1757–after 1804)

613. THE HORSE ARMOURY AT THE TOWER OF LONDON

Watercolour. $11\frac{1}{2} \times 19\frac{5}{8}$ in. (29 × 50 cm.)   (17155)

Signed: C. Tomkins 1804.

Acquired by the Prince Regent from Colnaghi as 'Drawing of the Horse Armoury in the Tower by C. Tomkins' on April 12, 1813, for £4 4s. (Archives Invoice 27840).

Other drawings by Tomkins of rooms in the Tower of London are in the British Museum, illustrations to Crowle's *Pennant*.

LORD GEORGE TOWNSHEND (1723–1807), Fourth Viscount and (1787) First Marquess Townshend.

GEORGE TOWNSHEND (1753–1811); Lord Ferrers (1774), Earl of Leicester (1784), 2nd Marquess Townshend (1807).

LORD JOHN TOWNSHEND (1757–1833).

A collection of caricatures, formed about 1794, and containing caricatures by the First Marquess Townshend, his two sons and possibly others, remains in the possession of the Marquess of Townshend at Raynham. By his kind permission its contents have been studied and the following anonymous drawings have been identified.

614. ROBERT NUGENT CRAGGS, EARL NUGENT, BORING HIS AUDITORS   *Figure* 52

Pen, folded before mounting. $6 \times 5\frac{1}{8}$ in. (15.2 × 13 cm.)   (17716)

The title inscribed on the back of the mount.

Fig. 52. George, Marquess Townshend: Robert Nugent Craggs (Cat. No. 614)

A duplicate, no doubt by the caricaturist himself, of two drawings at Raynham inscribed 'Lord Clare by Mr. John Townshend' (p. 164) and 'Lord Nugent' (p. 41). Robert Nugent, born *c.* 1702, assumed the name of Craggs on marriage, 1736; created Baron Nugent of Carlanstown 1767, Earl Nugent and Viscount Clare in 1776. He died in 1788. He affected to be a poet (*Complete Peerage*, Vol. XI).

615. Three pen and ink drawings, single figures of men (two over soft pencil), all on paper several times folded; two are priced on the back 1s. and 1s. 6d. One is a later version of a subject shown in two drawings apparently by Lord George Townshend in the Raynham album; the other two drawings, less caricatured in the faces, are more closely related to the drawings there ascribed to his eldest son George (Lord Leicester) and John. The soft underlying pencil work of one of them suggests a relation to the drawings described below.   (17717–17719)

616. A series of three pen drawings (without pencil indications) and twelve pencil drawings have been preserved with an original wrapper inscribed in ink, 'Skitches / by Earl of Leacester Brighton 1807 & 8' (the 'a' of 'Leacester' apparently inserted—there is no 'i'); and on the other side, in pencil, 'Caricature Drawings (Portraits) by the E of Leicester 1807 & 08.' in a different, later hand. It cannot be said with certainty that the parcel has remained undisturbed, but the bulk of the drawings were within the wrapping when it was opened in 1941 and it clearly fits them. If the oblique stroke after 'Skitches' in the puzzling inscription be taken for the numeral '1' the single drawing

by the Earl of Leicester indicated by it may have been removed from the parcel and been merged among the anonymous caricatures. The stroke is more probably a meaningless effort by the illiterate writer, rightly omitted from the pencil inscription.   (17720)

The drawings, measuring approximately 12½ × 8 in. (32 × 20 cm.), are all single portraits, with the exception of a couple dancing and a card-party of four. The latter is on paper watermarked 1801, and most of the drawings show costume of that late period. On the other hand, two pencil drawings of fat figures wearing the ribbon of the Garter are also dated 1801 by the watermark, though they show Georgian costume. One of them, though perhaps of Lord North, recalls figures supposed to be William, Duke of Cumberland, among the drawings at Raynham. Two of the ink drawings, although less caricatured, also resemble drawings in the Raynham album, as does a pencil portrait inscribed 'Lord Thurlow', of whom there are several drawings in that book. One of the pen drawings with a legend showing that it represents a master scolding his servant is also, though more careful, in the manner of Lord George Townshend. Of the remaining drawings one may represent Lord Derby, another (in ink) is inscribed (apparently in error) 'Louis 18?'; a free pen drawing of an Englishman in Oriental costume and posture smoking a hookah is inscribed by the artist 'Ali Day Behauder', and another, in pencil and also scarcely caricatured, has the legend 'Fifty to ten and I say done first' in pencil. One drawing, without inscription, but watermarked 1802, is a studied portrait without trace of caricature.

While the album at Raynham contains nothing of the same nature, there are sufficient points of resemblance in individual drawings to justify a tentative suggestion that either the First Marquess, noted as a savage caricaturist in his early days, retained his power but softened his manner in old age, or, more probably, that his eldest son, who appears in the Raynham album as a more gentle and timid draughtsman than his father, developed his artistic talents and exercised them perhaps for the amusement of the Prince of Wales at Brighton during the years mentioned in the inscription on the wrapper.

JOSEPH MALLORD WILLIAM TURNER, R.A. (1775–1851), Ascribed to

617. WINDSOR CASTLE: EDWARD III GATEHOUSE WITH PART OF THE UPPER WARD, THE ROUND TOWER IN THE BACKGROUND

Pencil and grey wash, on vellum paper. 8 × 10¾ in. (20.5 × 27.3 cm.)   (17447)

Inscribed at foot: 'J. M. W. Turner' (not a signature) and at the back 'Windsor Castle Berks' and 'Dr. M' '(? Dr. Monro)'.

Reprod.: St. John Hope, *Windsor Castle*, 1913, Vol. I, pl. XIV.

There are drawings by Turner of Windsor and neighbourhood dating from 1791 and 1792 at the British Museum of approximately the same size (Finberg I, p. 13).

The drawing shews the beginnings of the replacement of Hugh May's Restoration window by Wyatt for King George III.

COLONEL TURNER

Four watercolours of uniforms, signed Turner or Col. Turner, and dated 1799–1803, are in Military Drawings, Vol. IV, p. 62, *et seq.* (Nos. 16425–16428).

JOHN VANDERBANK (1694–1739)

618. BRITANNIA OFFERING THE CROWN TO (?) KING GEORGE I; A FIGURE OF JUSTICE WITH SCALES IN THE BACKGROUND

Pen over rough pencil, rubbed in places. 11½ × 7⅛ in. (29.3 × 18.3 cm.)   (17999)

Inscribed 'Vanderbank' at foot left.
Acquired Sotheby's, March 27, 1946, Lot 71.
Presumably a design for a decoration or a title-page. The features of the monarch are unidentifiable.

See L. van Puyvelde, *Dutch Drawings* No. 66, for a drawing in black chalk dated January 5, 1759, of Sir Richard Blackmore after the engraved portrait by Vanderbank.

JOHN VARDY (1700–1765)

619. INTENDED BOAT HOUSE AT THE WEST END OF THE GREAT PIECE OF WATER IN WINDSOR GREAT PARK, 1754

Pen and watercolour. 12¾ × 14¼ in. (32.5 × 35.7 cm.)   (17461)

Signed: John Vardy invt 1754; the title as given above.
Elevation with scale.
John Vardy was employed as Clerk of the Works at Kensington Palace, Hampton Court, St. James's and Whitehall.

CORNELIUS VARLEY (1781–1873), Manner of

620. ST. ALBANS CATHEDRAL: the South Transept and Presbytery from the South-East.

Pencil and watercolour, unfinished. 10¼ × 15¼ in. (26 × 38.7 cm.)   (13760)

JOHN VARLEY (1778–1842)

621. NORTH-WEST ASPECT OF WINDSOR CASTLE FROM THE BROCAS CLUMP

Watercolour on Whatman paper dated 181– much faded. 13¼ × 20⅞ in. (sight) (33.5 × 53 cm.)   (14751)

Presented in 1941, through the National Art Collections Fund, by Miss E. M. Spiller, whose grandfather was a cousin of the artist (N.A.C.F. Report, 1942, No. 1250).
The remains of a fine early drawing.

622. LANDSCAPE COMPOSITION: EVENING

Watercolour (heavily gummed), on rough paper. 11⅝ × 35¾ in. (30 × 90 cm.)   (14752)

Inscribed by the artist on a label pasted on the back of the frame: 'No. 2 Composition Evening J. Varley.'
About 1825.

WILLIAM FLEETWOOD VARLEY (? 1777–1858)

623. AN OLD HOUSE NEAR WINDSOR

Pencil. The lower corners cut off. 6⅝ × 9¼ in. (16.5 × 23.3 cm.)   (17486)

Inscribed: Near 'Windsor Berks', and 'Wm. Varley 1805', on the drawing at foot, and on the back.

GEORGE VERTUE (1684–1756)

624. WILLIAM PINKETHMAN AS DON LEWIS IN 'LOVE MAKES A MAN' BY COLLEY CIBBER; three-quarter length standing, right hand on stick.   *Plate 97*

Pen and grey wash with some watercolour. $11\frac{7}{8} \times 8\frac{5}{8}$ in. (30.3 × 22 cm.) (13579)

Unknown collector's mark, (?) Lugt 2920.

Inscribed: 'William Penkethman, Comedian, ob. 1725; drawn from the life at Lord Oxford's' below the drawing and signed 'G. Vertue . . .' partly erased. 'Love Makes a Man' on label above.

Engraved by E. Harding in stipple, 1794, as frontispiece to F. G. Waldron, *Shakespearean Miscellany*, 1802 (O'Donoghue, III, 471, No. 2).

Acquired by King George IV from Colnaghi 'drawing by Vertue of Wm. Pinkethman' on May 16, 1821, for £14 14s. (Archives Invoice 28323).

Fig. 53. Vertue: William Pinkethman. British Museum (*Cf.* on Cat. No. 624)

The British Museum have a version in red chalk and pen, the face entirely different, another inscription (illegible) above, but otherwise identical, *Figure* 53. It is closely incised with the stylus, and perhaps is a preliminary sketch from which the outline of the present drawing was traced.

625. AFTER HOLBEIN AND VAN LEEMPUT: THE WHITE-HALL FRESCO of Henry VII and Henry VIII and their wives Elizabeth of York and Jane Seymour.

Pen and watercolour, with gouache. $18 \times 21\frac{3}{4}$ in. (45.7 × 57.3 cm.) (13581)

Signed: A°. D^{ni}. 1737 f. G. Vertue Lond^{ni}.

Engraved by Vertue (O'Donoghue, Vol. V (1922), p. 31). Perhaps the 'Drawing of Henry by Vertue' purchased from Colnaghi for £15 15s. on February 24, 1802, for the Prince of Wales and framed in gilt for £2 2s. (Archives Invoice 27184).

626. AFTER VAN DYCK: CHARLES I AND HENRIETTA MARIA

Red chalk, a perpendicular fold in the centre. $15\frac{1}{2} \times 22$ in. (39.5 × 56 cm.) (13580)

Inscribed in border: G. Vertue.

Probably the drawing for the engraving by Vertue of 1742 which O'Donoghue (Vol. I, p. 394) describes as a reworking of R. Van Voerst's plate (of 1634).

627. AFTER HOLBEIN: KING EDWARD VI

Watercolour. $17 \times 10\frac{1}{4}$ in. (43 × 25.6 cm.) (sight) (17094)

Signed: GV. f. 1745 in gold.

Carlton House Inventory, 1819, No. 293.

A copy of the Windsor picture (Collins-Baker, p. 162), fairly accurate but showing considerably more at the top and, at the bottom, the legs down to the feet and the border of the carpet extending over the whole foreground. Inscriptions: EDWARDUS VI REX ANGLIAE and H.H. 1545 on the furniture, and MARCUS AURELIUS ROMAE around the relief are not now visible on the picture.

628. PRINCE HENRY, DUKE OF GLOUCESTER

Brush and grey wash. Oval, $5\frac{1}{2} \times 3\frac{7}{8}$ in. (sight) (14.2 × 10 cm.) (17095)

Identical with the print by Vertue (O'Donoghue, Vol. II, p. 509, No. 4), and in the same direction.

Henry, Duke of Gloucester, 1639–1660, son of King Charles I.

629. KING CHARLES II

Brush and grey wash. Oval, $5\frac{5}{8} \times 3\frac{7}{8}$ in. (sight) (14.2 × 10 cm.) (17096)

Identical with the print by Vertue after Lely (O'Donoghue, Vol. I, p. 398, No. 61), and in the same direction.

GEORGE VERTUE, After

630. KING'S GATE, WESTMINSTER, DEMOLISHED 1723

Pencil, pen and watercolour. $13\frac{1}{8} \times 9\frac{7}{8}$ in. (33.3 × 25.2 cm.)

The title, as given, inscribed in pencil at the top.

Exhib.: B.F.A.C. 1919, (Old London), No. 25.

Copy of Vertue's engraving, for the Society of Antiquaries, 1725, no doubt made for the purpose of extra-illustration about 1810.

G. VERTUE, Ascribed to

631. THE KING'S HOUSE AT GREENWICH

Pen and grey wash. $12\frac{1}{2} \times 20\frac{5}{8}$ in. (32 × 52.4 cm.) (17161)

Presumably, with the following, the 'Drawing a view of the King's House at Greenwich by Vertue' and 'Drawing, Richmond House by Vertue', bought by the Prince Regent from Colnaghi on May 22, 1815, for 3 guineas each (Archives Invoice 28057), but clearly copies, with descriptive cartouches added, from the prints of the subjects engraved by J. Basire for the Society of Antiquaries, 1765 and 1767.

632. RICHMOND PALACE

Pen and grey wash. $12\frac{1}{2} \times 20$ in. (32 × 50.8 cm.) (17160)

See on the preceding.

THOMAS VIVARES (1735–? 1788)

633. A COUNTRY HOUSE

Pen and watercolour. Oval within rectangular frame, 6¾ × 9 in. (17.2 × 22.9 cm.) (17557)

Signed: T. Vivares, on the back.

Acquired with the following and three drawings by Paul Sandby (Supplement, S.419, 420 and 421) from the Randall Davies Collection, Sotheby's, February 12, 1947, Lot 366.

634. WOODLAND SCENE

Pen and watercolour in lined border. 10 × 12½ in. (25.5 × 31.7 cm.) (17558)

Inscribed at the back in pen by the artist, 'An Original Design by Thos. Vivares. St. George's row Oxford Turnpike'.

Acquired with the preceding.

635. AN IDEAL CASTLE

Pen and watercolour within washed border. 10⅝ × 13 in. (27.1 × 33 cm.) (17559)

Acquired with the preceding.

SAMUEL WALE (? 1720–1786), After

636. WINDSOR CASTLE FROM THE RIVER, DRAWN IN REVERSE; a cricket match in the foreground.

Etched, in reverse, by B. Green.

Pen, grey wash, incised with the stylus, the paper retaining tallow on the reverse side from the plate, and creased, at top and bottom, where folded around the plate. 4 × 6 in. (10 × 15.2 cm.) (17385)

Bought from Suckling in 1939.

A drawing or tracing made by, or for, the engraver in reverse for transference to his plate. Other known drawings for the same series are in the natural direction, and markedly superior in handling.

E. WELLS

637. THE NORMAN GATE, WINDSOR CASTLE, FROM THE UPPER WARD

Watercolour. 10¾ × 9 in. (27.2 × 22.7 cm.) (17408)

False signature 'Buckler' at foot; on the back, in ink, 'Entrance to the Upper Court, Windsor Castle, Entrance to the Tower on right hand. E. Wells'; also, in pencil, 'J. M. W. Turner'.

Perhaps a copy, certainly by an inexpert hand.

LIEUT. GEORGE WELSH, R.N. (1821)

638. NAPOLEON ON HIS DEATHBED

Pencil, highly finished, and mounted on a washed card. 4½ × 6⅛ in. (11.3 × 15.6 cm.) (17017)

Purchased at Sotheby's, June 18, 1934, Lot 266, the property of G. S. C. Weigall, a step-descendant of the artist, with a letter of June 18, 1821, from the artist to his mother saying that he drew it at St. Helena on the day after Napoleon's death, and that it was universally acclaimed as superior to all others of the same subject.

The drawing was engraved in 1822 and republished in the *Graphic*, September 9, 1911.

A similar drawing, attributed to J. Ward, Esq., 4th Regiment of Foot, was reproduced in a woodcut in the *Illustrated London News*, January 25, 1873. Another, less like, was in the possession of Dr. G. C. Williamson (*cf.* his *Memoirs in Miniature*, pp. 113 and 114). In sending to the Royal Family on August 2, 1934, a photograph of his drawing, which he stated to be signed by T. G. Finch, Dr. Williamson mentioned an engraving by H. Meyer from yet another and slightly different drawing, by J. W. Rubidge, which was purchased by Lieut. G. Horsley Wood, and presented by him to Napoleon III. Another portrait, by Capt. Frederick Marryat, R.N. (9½ × 11¾ in.), was in the collection of A. G. D. Fuller, Esq. (Sale, Sotheby's, December 19, 1945), of which many versions are said to exist.

BENJAMIN WEST, P.R.A. (1738–1820)

639. KING GEORGE III, profile head and shoulders, to right. *Plate 2*

Black and white chalk on blue paper. Oval, 7⅞ × 6¾ in. (sight) (20 × 17 cm.) (17591)

Signed: B. W.

This and the following drawing appear from the Inventory of Pictures at Windsor Castle, 1907 (Nos. 2461 and 2462), to have come to Windsor between 1900 and 1904. The frames have pasted at the back the bookplate or label of Francis Draper, 67, Park Street, Grosvenor Square.

640. QUEEN CHARLOTTE, half length seated at a table, facing half right. *Plate 3*

Black and white chalk on blue paper. 10⅞ × 8¼ in. (sight) (28 × 25 cm.) (17592)

Study for the portrait of the Queen with the Princess Royal exhibited at the R.A. 1777 and engraved by Valentine Green, 1778 (O'Donoghue, Vol. I, p. 411, No. 53).

641. ALLEGORICAL DESIGN ON THE REGENCY BILL OF 1788 *Figure 54*

Pen and brown wash. 13⅛ × 18 in. (33.4 × 45.7 cm.) (17721)

The shields hanging on the pillars are inscribed 'The Majority of LXXV in Parlimt 1788' and 'The Majority of XXXIII in the Lords 1788'. The reference is to the voting (75 should be 73) on December 22 and 23, 1788, upon the Resolutions which were devised to secure to the Queen a much larger share in the Regency than would have been allowed to her by the Prince of Wales and his party. This feature of the design was actually employed. Lady Duncannon wrote in her Diary on April 5, 1789 (after the King's recovery): 'At the concert at Windsor, the *desert pieces* were surmounted with Pitt's and the Chancellour's arms, and medallions with the number of their majority' (Earl of Bessborough, *Lady Bessborough and her Family Circle*, 1940, p. 50). The Chancellor (Thurlow) may be identifiable in West's drawing which may have been intended for a transparency.

B. WEST, Ascribed to

642. 'THE APOTHEOSIS OF PRINCESS CHARLOTTE: DESIGN FOR WINDOW IN ST. GEORGE'S CHAPEL.' *Plate 94*

Oil and sepia on brown paper. 8¾ × 14⅞ in. (21.2 × 37.6 cm.) (13586)

Princess Charlotte of Wales died in November 1817. If the title given on the modern mount to this drawing is correct, West must have volunteered a design to the Queen or the Regent six years after his pension had been discontinued and after the death of his wife, which marked the beginning of his own end.

Fig. 54. West: Allegorical Design on the Regency Bill, 1788 (Cat. No. 641)

RICHARD WESTALL, R.A. (1765–1836)

643. PRINCESS VICTORIA, FULL LENGTH, SKETCHING, WITH HER DOG FANNY

Coloured chalks. 20½ × 15½ in. (52 × 35.4 cm.)

Dated 1829.

Sketch for the picture dated 1830 in the Royal Collection (Collins-Baker, p. 309).

Inventory of Pictures, Lord Chamberlain's Department, No. 702.

644. THE SAME

Pencil and watercolour. 6 × 5 in. (15.2 × 12.5 cm.)

(13991)

Signed: R. W.

Small sketch for (or from) the portrait of 1830.

Purchased by H.M. Queen Mary from Squire in 1931, and presented by her to the Royal Library.

645. THE SAME (head only)

Chalks. Severely damaged by damp. 13 × 9½ in. (33 × 24.1 cm.).

Dated '1829' at foot.

Inventory of Pictures, Lord Chamberlain's Department, No. 1838.

The Library also contains two albums of drawings by Westall, who was the Princess Victoria's first Drawing-master from 1827, and, as is shewn by her diary, attended regularly about twice a week, until his death in 1836. The first album is inscribed, in the handwriting of J. H. Glover, Royal Librarian, 'Forty-three pencil drawings by Richard Westall, R.A. Drawing Master to H. M. Queen Victoria and intended as Studies for the instruction of Her Majesty by whom they have all been copied'. About half the drawings are on cards, and are of heads, hands, etc., others are on scraps of paper, three are mounted and are apparently illustrations.

The second album with an identical inscription by Glover except that it reads 'Twenty-Four coloured drawings', now contains twenty-five mounted watercolours, one of which is unnumbered, of various sizes, all but one on cards.

WESTALL, R., Attributed to

646. THE MARRIAGE OF PRINCESS CHARLOTTE OF WALES AND PRINCE LEOPOLD OF SAXE-COBURG at Carlton House, May 2, 1816. The bride to the left.

Pen with oil and watercolour on paper. 9¼ × 11⅜ in. (24 × 29 cm.)

(17619)

Presented to H.M. King George V by Princess Louise, Duchess of Argyll, 1935, and by him to the Royal Library.

The ceremony is represented, as described by Mrs. Herbert Jones, *Princess Charlotte of Wales*, 1885, p. 125, as taking place at a red-covered altar with 6-foot candlesticks in the Crimson Saloon of Carlton House. Queen Charlotte is seated to the right of the altar, the Prince Regent behind the Princess on the left. Of the other personages present, the Duke of Kent and the Lord Chancellor are recognizable. The bridegroom is in uniform and wears the ribbon of an order over his right shoulder.

647. THE SAME (partly reversed, the bride to the right).

Plate 100

Pen and watercolour; varnished. 6⅜ × 8⅛ in. (16.3 × 20.7 cm.)

(17629)

Clearly by the same hand as the preceding but shewing more figures and with the bride now on the right at the altar, and therefore nearer to the Queen and separated from the Regent. This rearrangement may have been for reversal in engraving; also, the ribbon of the Garter is worn by the Regent on his right shoulder and the Prince's sword is on his right side.

Purchased from Messrs. Colnaghi, March, 1949.

SIR RICHARD WESTMACOTT, R.A. (1775–1856)

648. KING GEORGE III EQUESTRIAN STATUE IN WINDSOR PARK, SEEN FROM BELOW

Pencil and watercolour. 7⅝ × 9¾ in. (19.3 × 24.7 cm.)

(17489)

Inscribed in pencil at foot right: 'P's thought for pedestal of Windsor statue.'

Presented to the Royal Library by Mr Iolo A. Williams in 1943 as possibly a free sketch by the sculptor of his intended design, with an inscription by one of his children.

Two drawings by R. Westmacott, junr., are in Sir William Drummond's manuscript translation of Horace. See on p. 52 (Sir William Gell).

C. JOHN M. WHICHELO (d. 1865)

649. 'ENTRANCE TO THE LIBRARY FROM THE CLOISTERS, WESTMINSTER'

Pen and grey wash. $11\frac{7}{8} \times 10\frac{1}{8}$ in. (30.2 × 25.8 cm.)
(17134)

Engraved by J. Storer without date or inscription.
Signed: J. Whichelo 1805, and inscribed with the title as given, in pencil, on the back, and, also in pencil in a later hand, 'Entrance to the Chapter House'. The building called the Chapter House formerly housed the Records, and is entered from the East Cloister.

650. NEW THEATRE, COVENT GARDEN: EXTERIOR FROM BOW STREET

Watercolour. $5\frac{5}{8} \times 8\frac{3}{4}$ in. (14.8 × 22.2 cm.) (17136)
Engraved by Wise 1813 after Whichelo for Wilkinson's *Londina Illustrata*, Vol. II, No. 184.
The New Theatre was erected in 1809.

651. NORTH-WEST VIEW OF THE THEATRE ROYAL, DRURY LANE, FROM GREAT RUSSELL STREET

Pencil and watercolour. $5\frac{3}{4} \times 9$ in. (14.8 × 23 cm.)
(17135)

Exhib.: B.F.A.C. 1919, (Old London), No. 54.
Engraved by Howlett after Whichelo, 1814, for Wilkinson's *Londina Illustrata*, Vol. II, No. 178.
The new Theatre Royal was erected in 1814.

CHARLES WILD (1781–1831)

652. ST. GEORGE'S CHAPEL, WINDSOR: THE CHOIR

Watercolour, some gouache, somewhat faded and slightly torn. The lines of the steps and some of the stalls heavily incised with stylus and ruler. $19\frac{3}{4} \times 16\frac{3}{4}$ in. (50.2 × 42.3 cm.) (17601)
Engraved 1818 by T. Sutherland, Pyne's *Royal Residences*, Vol. I, p. 182, much reduced.
Acquired with the following four drawings from Walker's Gallery, July, 1948.

653. ST. GEORGE'S CHAPEL FROM THE ALTAR

Watercolour, touches of gouache, faded and torn. Perspective lines in the stalls of the choir incised with stylus and ruler. $19\frac{3}{4} \times 16\frac{1}{2}$ in. (50.3 × 41.8 cm.) (17602)
Engraved 1819 by T. Sutherland for Pyne's *Royal Residences*, Vol. I, p. 183, much reduced.

654. CARLTON HOUSE: THE CRIMSON DRAWING-ROOM

Watercolour, some gouache, faded. Perspective lines in the fireplace incised with stylus and ruler. 16 × 20 in. (40.7 × 51 cm.) (17603)
Engraved 1816 by T. Sutherland, Pyne's *Royal Residences*, Vol. III, ii, p. 20, much reduced.

655. CARLTON HOUSE; THE CIRCULAR ROOM

Watercolour, with some gouache; somewhat faded. Incised lines as in the preceding. $15\frac{7}{8} \times 20$ in. (40 × 50.7 cm.)
(17604)

Engraved 1817 by T. Sutherland, Pyne's *Royal Residences*, Vol. III, ii, p. 24, much reduced.

656. CARLTON HOUSE: THE ROSE SATIN DRAWING-ROOM

Watercolour, faded. $16\frac{1}{8} \times 21\frac{1}{4}$ in. (41 × 53.7 cm.)
(17605)

Engraved 1817 by D. Havell, Pyne's *Royal Residences*, Vol. III, ii, p. 31, much reduced.

657. CARLTON HOUSE: THE ALCOVE IN THE GOLDEN DRAWING-ROOM

Watercolour, within narrow border. $18\frac{1}{4} \times 15\frac{1}{4}$ in. (46.5 × 38.8 cm.) (17631)
Engraved 1817 by W. J. Bennet, Pyne's *Royal Residences*, Vol. III, ii, p. 60, much reduced.
Acquired, with a collection of architectural and other drawings relating to Carlton House, Frogmore, etc., Sotheby's, April 8, 1949, Lot 10. Apparently from the collection of J. B. Nichols.

The Royal Library also possesses a volume containing a hundred watercolours which form the complete series engraved in aquatint by various artists for Pyne's *Royal Residences* published by Ackermann in 1817–1819. Fifty-nine of these are by C. Wild, twenty-five by the Stephanoffs, nine by R. Cattermole, six by W. Westall, A.R.A., and one by G. Samuel. They are of precisely the same size as the prints and may be presumed to be the models for them, whether by the artists themselves or by the engravers, but since the Library also contains elaborate pencil drawings of six of these plates after Wild, also of the same size as the engravings, it would appear that several stages were involved in the production of these plates or the repetition of the watercolours.

CHARLES WILD, Ascribed to

658. CORONATION OF KING GEORGE IV: the scene in the Abbey.

Pencil, pen and brown wash. $8 \times \frac{3}{4}$ in. (20.2 × 14.8 cm.)
(13589)

The highly stippled work in the figures, etc., is unfamiliar in Wild's drawings. The subject was treated, among others, by J. Stephanoff (engraved F. C. Lewis).
Presented to H.M. Queen Mary by Mr. C. P. Johnson in 1922, and by her to the Library.

SAMUEL DE WILDE (c. 1748–1832)

659. SARAH HARLOWE AS BEATRICE IN THE 'ANATOMIST' *Plate* 98

Pencil and watercolour. $14\frac{1}{4} \times 8\frac{7}{8}$ in. (36.2 × 22.5 cm.)
(13415)

Signed: S. de Wilde f. Sept. 1805.

Engraved in stipple by R. Cooper for Cawthorn's *Minor British Theatre*, 1807.
Bought by King George IV from Colnaghi on October 13, 1820, for £2 2s. (Archives Invoice 28291).

660. SAMUEL SIMMONS AS SIMKIN IN DIBDIN'S 'DESERTER'

Pencil and watercolour. $14\frac{1}{4} \times 9$ in. (36.4 × 22.7 cm.)
(13414)

Signed: Wilde delin Aug. 1805.

Engraved in stipple by Maddocks for Cawthorn's *Minor British Theatre*, 1806.
Bought with the preceding, at the same price.

SIR DAVID WILKIE, R.A. (1785–1841)

661. A COTTAGE GIRL SEATED   *Plate* 101

Black and red chalk on brown paper, a large portion on the right cut out and made up. $7\frac{3}{8} \times 4\frac{1}{8}$ in. (18.8 × 10.6 cm.)
(17563)

From the Julian Lousada collection (Christie's, March 7, 1947, Lot 56), probably previously in the Sir T. Baring and Lord Northbrook collections.

Reprod.: Lord R. Sutherland Gower, *Sir David Wilkie*, 1902, p. 50.

The study was perhaps made for the girl on the extreme left of the *Penny Wedding*.

662. THE ENTRANCE TO HOLYROOD PALACE, 1822

Pencil, heightened with white on grey paper. $14\frac{1}{2} \times 21\frac{1}{4}$ in. (37 × 54.1 cm.)   (17626)

Followed almost exactly in the picture of King George IV entering Holyrood, in the Royal Collection exhibited 1830. See Cunningham, *Life of Wilkie*, 1843, Vol. II, p. 89. Bought from Messrs. Colnaghi, January, 1949.

663. ARRIVAL OF KING GEORGE IV AT HOLYROOD PALACE, 1822   *Plate* 102

Pen with brown ink over pencil. $12\frac{1}{4} \times 20\frac{1}{8}$ in. (31.1 × 51.1 cm.)   (13593)

Exhib.: Edinburgh 1947 (King's Pictures), No. 120.

A sketch for the same picture.

664. KING GEORGE IV HOLDING A DRAWING-ROOM, FROM MEMORY, 1822   *Plate* 103

Pen with brown ink, and pencil, on buff paper. $16\frac{1}{4} \times 21\frac{1}{2}$ in. (36.6 × 51.5 cm.)   (14768)

Signed and inscribed in ink at foot: 'Isle of Wight—Octbr 10th 1822 D.W.'

From the collection of George Manners, Sotheby's, May 25, 1894, Lot 84. Acquired from Messrs. Dunthorne, February 22, 1939, with Nos. 665 and 671.

Wilkie describes in a letter to his sister dated August 23, 1822, the drawing-room at Holyrood House which he attended (Cunningham, *op. cit.*, Vol. II, p. 85). Another sketch from memory done on October 14, 1822, in the Isle of Wight is known to Dr. Malcolm Stearns, who has kindly communicated many of the details regarding these drawings.

665. KING GEORGE IV IN HIGHLAND COSTUME, full length, facing half right, holding sceptre, 1830.

Black chalk on buff paper. $22\frac{5}{8} \times 17$ in. (52.5 × 33 cm.)   (14769)

Inscribed (very indistinctly) 'David Wilkie' in pencil. In ink on the old mount: 'George ye 4th in his Highland Costume by David Wilkie' and 'Bought at Tippins' £3.12.6.'; and at the back, in pencil, 'The Painting I believe is at Apsley House'.

Cf. Cunningham, *op. cit.*, Vol. III, p. 38. On February 11, 1830, Wilkie informed Sir William Knighton that he had a fine-looking Highlander as a model for the whole-length portrait of the King.

Acquired with Nos. 664 and 671.

666. KING WILLIAM IV, FULL LENGTH STANDING, FULL FACE

Black chalk and watercolour, foxed. $10\frac{1}{4} \times 7\frac{1}{8}$ in. (25.8 × 18 cm.)   (13898)

Presumed first sketch for the picture in the Waterloo Chamber dated 1832 (Collins-Baker, p. 312).

667. QUEEN VICTORIA'S FIRST COUNCIL: THE WHOLE SUBJECT

Pencil, pen and sepia with touches of red chalk and white. $10\frac{1}{2} \times 16\frac{1}{2}$ in. (27.1 × 41.4 cm.)   (13591)

Probably drawn in October, 1837, at Brighton (Cunningham, *op. cit.*, Vol. III, pp. 226–229).

668. QUEEN VICTORIA'S FIRST COUNCIL: THE QUEEN SEATED, NEARLY FULL FACE, with the ribbon of the Garter.

Pencil and watercolour. $7 \times 4\frac{1}{8}$ in. (17.6 × 10.4 cm.)   (13592)

669. QUEEN VICTORIA'S FIRST COUNCIL: THE QUEEN SEATED TO RIGHT holding a paper, without the ribbon of the Garter. A dog at her feet.   *Figure* 55

Pencil, red chalk and water- and body-colour. $11\frac{3}{4} \times 7\frac{5}{8}$ in. (30.4 × 19.4 cm.)   (13590)

The Queen is represented as in the sketch of the whole subject (No. 667) and in the completed picture at Windsor (Collins-Baker, p. 311), where the dog is replaced by a footstool.

Fig. 55. Wilkie: Queen Victoria (Cat. No. 669)

WILKIE, Ascribed to

670. 'STUDY FOR THE HAND OF QUEEN VICTORIA' WITH SERPENT BRACELET

Pencil, red chalk and watercolour on brown paper. $10\frac{1}{8}$ × $4\frac{5}{8}$ in. (25.8 × 10.6 cm.)　　(13990)

Formerly No. 711 in the Lord Chamberlain's Inventory of Pictures, where it is stated to have been bought at Wilkie's Sale by Mr. William Russell, nephew of the 5th Duke of Bedford, who presented it to the Prince Consort. Transferred to the Royal Library, June, 1931.
Reprod.: Vulliamy, *English Letter Writers*, 1945, plate 8 (colour).

671. WINDSOR CASTLE, INTERIOR, THE GARTER THRONE ROOM

Gouache on buff paper, cut irregularly. $15\frac{1}{4}$ × $15\frac{7}{8}$ in. (34 × 35.5 cm.)　　(14767)

Inscribed (not by Wilkie) in pencil: 'Windsor Castle 1837'. Acquired with Nos. 664 and 665.

THOMAS WILLEMENT, *see under* Neale (No. 452)

Several illuminations are invoiced by this artist to the Prince Regent in 1816–1818.

Lt. W. WILLERMIN, Royal Staff Corps

A large drawing in pen and brown wash, of the Death of Sir Ralph Abercromby, is in Military Drawings, Vol. IV, p. 85 (No. 16495). The name has now all but disappeared from the edge of the drawing; it is given as Lieut. Villeman in the invoice of this drawing from Colnaghi for £15 15s. on July 14, 1806 (Archives Invoice 27345).

PETER DE WINT (1784–1849), Ascribed to

672. WINDSOR CASTLE FROM THE RIVER, LOOKING EAST

Sepia. 4 × $9\frac{1}{8}$ in. (11.5 × 23 cm.)　　(17418)
Purchased 1909.

The architecture is somewhat fantastic; if the attribution is correct, a popular engraving was no doubt intended.

GEORGE M. WOODWARD (d. 1809)

673. MORSELS OF MELODY. Seven subjects in two rows.

Watercolour in ruled border. $13\frac{3}{8}$ × $18\frac{1}{2}$ in. (34.4 × 47.1 cm.)　　(17677)

Signed: Woodward Delin, and inscribed by him with the title as given, in the border below. Quotations from songs above each subject in his hand; the last two perhaps completed by another. '7s.' on back.

674. A SMART

Pen and watercolour within ruled margin. $14\frac{1}{4}$ × $9\frac{1}{4}$ in. (36.5 × 23.5 cm.)　　(17690)

Signed in ink 'G. Woodward Delin' and inscribed in pen as in the print (B.M. Sat. 7784), the date of publication added in pencil. On the reverse a long description in the artist's hand of 'An Honest Fellow', relating to another print in the same series of six, published December 1, 1790 (B.M. Sat., VI, 7782–7785).

675. GENTLEMEN IN THE WHIG INTEREST. Westminster Election, 1784: Fox with four ruffians, one carrying a sack inscribed 'Old Wigs'. St. Paul's, Covent Garden, in distance. All wear blue and yellow.

Watercolour in ruled border. $10\frac{7}{8}$ × $16\frac{1}{8}$ in. (27.4 × 41 cm.)　　(17678)

Inscribed with the title as given, above, and below, 'We've these and many Gemmen more—all ready at a Spirt/With coat and waistcoat Blue & Buff—we never mind the Shirt/And a Begging we will go'. Both inscriptions apparently in Woodward's hand. At foot in ink over pencil, 'Original drawing never published'.

676. ENGLISH APATHY! Two figures; a man and woman.

Pencil within ruled borders. $10\frac{7}{8}$ × $8\frac{3}{4}$ in. (27.6 × 22.4 cm.)　　(17679)

Signature and title below; legend: 'So Miss—you are sulky and wont have me, etc.', above in pen. Uniform with Nos. 677–680, priced '3/6'.

677. IRISH PERSEVERANCE! Two figures; marriage offer to an old woman.

Pencil, a little pen. Signature and title below; legends (above) in pen. $11\frac{3}{8}$ × $9\frac{1}{4}$ in. (28.8 × 23.4 cm.)　(17680)

Uniform with 676 and 678–680, priced '3'.

678. METHOD! Two figures; master seated, and servant.

Pencil in ruled border. $12\frac{5}{8}$ × $9\frac{5}{8}$ in. (32.1 × 24.5 cm.)　　(17681)

Signature: Woodward Deln, title and legend below in pen. 'Nathan—hear what I say unto thee—Yea.—Have you prepared my Brandy and Rum?—Yea.—Does the Water boil?—Yea.—Is the Sugar sifted?—Yea.—the Lemons placed upon the table?—Yea.—the pipes and tobacco ready—Yea. And the pipe lights?—Yea.—Why then you may go to Prayers!!!'
Uniform with the preceding, priced '3/–'.

679. SAGACITY!! Two Figures; fool and friend—'Boy or Girl'?

Pencil, some pen strokes. $11\frac{3}{8}$ × $9\frac{1}{4}$ in. (29.1 × 23.2 cm.)　　(17682)

Legends (above), title and signature in pen below; a pencilled signature outside the border erased. Uniform with the preceding. Priced '4' on back.

680. POVERTY STRUCK PRIDE! Four figures, father, wife, daughter and servant.

Pencil within ruled border. 11 × $8\frac{5}{8}$ in. (27.9 × 21.8 cm.)　　(17683)

Signed in pen: Woodward Delin, below the border, with the title as given. The legends in pen above the characters. Uniform with the preceding, priced '4' on back.

681. A MORNING REHEARSAL PREVIOUS TO THE PRESENTATION. (Miss Farren and Lord Derby.)

Pencil, pen and watercolour. (Size of paper) $13\frac{5}{8}$ × 10 in. (34.3 × 25.2 cm.)　　(17684)

Inscribed with title, as given, in ink below. The paper, red border and legends above the characters are similar to those of No. 682.
Exhib.: B.F.A.C. 1931/32, No. 173.
Lord Derby married Miss Farren in 1797.

682. 'A FRIENDLY DISCUSSION OF POLITICS OR MIRACLES OF HUMAN WISDOM AND UNDERSTANDING.' 1795. A Bishop (of Rochester) and another (? the King) at a table with port and the Heads of a Bill.

Pen and watercolour over pencil. $10\frac{3}{4} \times 14$ in. (27.2 × 35.2 cm.)   (17685)
The title, as given, in pen below. 'Heads of a Bill' in pencil and pen; in red ruled border.
Bishop (of Rochester) says: 'For my part I cant see what the people have to do with the Laws but to obey them.' The other: 'You are perfectly right—for which reason I am determined to give my assent to the Bill, though I don't know a syllable it contains.' The inscriptions over the figures are in Woodward's manner and apparently in his handwriting.
For the Bishop of Rochester's Speech on Lord Grenville's Treason Bill, November, 1795, *cf.* Stanhope, *Pitt*, Vol. II, p. 363 (B.M. Sat., Vol. VIII, 8703, 9046).

683. THE DUEL. A ferocious red-coated officer, his belt teeming with pistols, apparently points out to a sexton with spade and a sack inscribed 'Razor Blades & Bullets', a doctor and a parson, the place for the grave of his antagonist, who stands R. shaking with terror while his second on his knees implores the protection of heaven.
Pen and watercolour in ruled border. $6\frac{3}{8} \times 9\frac{7}{8}$ in. (16 × 25 cm.)   (17686)
Inscribed above in pencil 'Original Drawing'. A rough pencil sketch on the reverse.

684. RIDERS ON BOLTING HORSES
Two elderly citizens seated perilously, one on the tail, and the other on the neck, of horses galloping towards a fingerpost pointing R. 'To Hornsey'.
Pen and black-brown wash in ruled border. $4\frac{7}{8} \times 9\frac{1}{4}$ in. (12.3 × 23.7 cm.)   (17687)
Inscribed 'Original Drawing' in pencil at top.
Uniform with No. 683 but rather less characteristic of Woodward's manner.

WOODWARD, Manner of
685. FALSTAFF'S ARREST (King Henry IV, Pt. 2, Act II, sc. 4).
Pencil and grey wash, many alterations. $7 \times 9\frac{1}{2}$ in. (18 × 24 cm.) on paper $8\frac{5}{8} \times 11\frac{5}{8}$ in. (21.9 × 29.5 cm.)   (17688)
Quotation in border above, reference at side (in ink).

686. FALSTAFF'S RECRUITS (King Henry IV, Pt. 2, Act 3, Sc. 2).
Pencil and brown wash. $8\frac{3}{8} \times 11\frac{7}{8}$ in. (21 × 29 cm.) on paper $9\frac{1}{4} \times 11\frac{7}{8}$ in. (23.5 × 30.2 cm.)   (17689)
Quotation in border below, title and reference above (in ink).
Not uniform with the preceding, but by the same hand, which might be Woodward's in a restrained mood. See also No. 105 (Bunbury).

687. A series (probably incomplete) consisting of seven watercolours (measuring $5\frac{3}{4} \times 6\frac{1}{4}$ in. without their borders), and showing with considerable humour the adventures of a country boy from his recitation of Romeo for a dinner in the Squire's kitchen and rehearsal before a manager (*Figure* 56) on the recommendation of the Squire, to his eventual return to the country after his failure in Hamlet and Othello.   (17691)
The inscriptions below the drawings are not all in the same handwriting, but in some cases the writing comes very near to Woodward's and the drawing, if not the careful colouring, is consistent with his authorship in a more restrained mood. There is nothing to indicate the provenance of the drawings, which have no traditional attribution.

Fig. 56. Rehearsal before a Manager (Cat. No. 687)

WILLIAM WOOLLETT (1735–1785)
688. TWO FARMHOUSES WITH CATTLE AND SHEEP
Plate 96
Pencil, pen, grey wash and watercolour. Unfinished. $7 \times 10\frac{1}{2}$ in. (17.9 × 26.6 cm.)   (13594)
'A landscape by Woolet' is entered in Inventory 'A', p. 148 (1816), and in p. 168 (1840).

689. A MOATED MANOR-HOUSE
Pencil; a perpendicular fold in the centre. $9\frac{7}{8} \times 14$ in. (25 × 35.3 cm.)   (13595)

W. WOOLLETT, Ascribed to
690. RICHMOND PARK AND PETERSHAM
Pen and black wash. $13\frac{3}{4} \times 21\frac{1}{4}$ in. (35 × 54 cm.) (17159)
Inscribed in pencil on a dealer's mount with the title as given above, and "Woollett fecit'; possibly a copy from a print by him. The locality may be intended for the Thames from the South Bank looking towards the foot of Richmond Hill and Park.

JOHN WOOTTON (1686–1765)
691. HUNTING SCENE WITH FREDERICK PRINCE OF WALES, CAPTAIN BLOODWORTH, MASTER OF THE HORSE, AND MR. CORNWALLIS, M.P., EQUERRY
Plate 104
Pencil, pen and grey wash, some white. $11\frac{1}{2} \times 19\frac{3}{4}$ in. (29.3 × 50 cm.)   (13596)

Colls.: Hone (Lugt 2793); Charles Rogers (Lugt 624)—Sale, April 15, 1799, perhaps in Lot 712.
Sketch for the picture by Wootton (Collins-Baker, p. 321) of 1734 in the Corridor at Windsor. The three names are inscribed above the figures in pencil and there are crosses, also in pencil, below the principal personages or horses. The painting departs in detail from the drawing which is of considerable importance.
Probably the 'Drawing by Wootton' acquired by the Prince of Wales from Colnaghi on January 15, 1801, for £2 12s. 6d. (Archives Invoice 27155).
Capt. Thomas Bloodworth was Groom of the Bedchamber to Frederick, Prince of Wales, from 1731–1735.
'Mr. Cornwallis M.P.' was equerry to the Prince of Wales, but left his service for that of the King in 1727, according to Hervey's *Memoirs.*

THOMAS WORLIDGE (1700–1766)

692. MR. THEOPHILUS CIBBER, THE COMEDIAN, 1735, whole length, to left, nearly full face, standing on a terrace.
Pencil on vellum. $12\frac{1}{4} \times 8\frac{1}{2}$ in. (31 × 21.6 cm.) (17029)
Signed: Thos: Worlidge Fecit 1735, and inscribed with the title as given.
The figure only engraved by R. Clamp, 1794, as 'Theophilus Cibber Comedian in the Character of a Fine Gentlemen from an Original Drawing by Worlidge in the Collection of Sir William Musgrave Bart.' (O'Donoghue, Vol. I, p. 433). This was presumably the drawing forming Lot 65 on the 23rd day of the Musgrave sale, February-March, 1800, bought Thompson £2 2s.
Acquired by the Prince of Wales from Colnaghi for £2 2s. on June 21, 1812 (Archives Invoice 27534).
Theophilus Cibber, actor, 1703–1758. See No. 504.

693. 'BEAU NASH', whole length to left, nearly full face, standing in a garden.
Pencil on vellum. The title on the modern frame only. $11\frac{1}{4} \times 8$ in. (28.5 × 20.5 cm.) (17030)
Signed: Thos. Worlidge Fecit 1736.
Uniform with the preceding but presumably the drawing 'Beau Nash of Bath by Worlidge' acquired by King George IV from Colnaghi for £1 1s. on February 14, 1822 (Archives Invoice 28343).
Richard Nash, 1674–1762, Master of the Ceremonies at Bath.

694. AFTER MERCIER: FREDERICK LEWIS, PRINCE OF WALES (1707–1751), playing the violincello.
Red and black chalk, mostly red, but the first outline apparently in black, largely erased, retouches in black. $8\frac{3}{8} \times 7\frac{1}{8}$ in. (21.4 × 18 cm.) (13874)
TW in monogram in pencil in top right corner.
This and the following drawing have long been recognized as copies, with adaptations, from the principal figures in either the picture by Nollekens at Windsor Castle (Collins-Baker, p. 236) or the version signed by Mercier in the National Portrait Gallery. The angle of the princess's right arm is gentler than in either of the pictures, but its position and still more that of the faintly-drawn left arm are ill adapted for the occupation of sketching; apart from the added hand, they would be suitable for playing a key instrument. This is the most significant difference between the drawing and the pictures. Minor points are that the inclination of both heads is slightly different, the Prince of Wales' sleeve is unfinished in the drawing and his 'cello is without tuning keys. The drawing is on a slightly larger scale than the Windsor picture.
The handling is in strong contrast to the tight miniature manner of the preceding drawings, and is more characteristic of Worlidge, to whom the initials if genuine point as the copyist.
Reproduced in the *Burlington Magazine*, November, 1948, by Mr. Ralph Edwards, who discusses fully the problems concerning the pictures.

695. AFTER MERCIER: ANNE, PRINCESS ROYAL (1709–1759) sketching at a table.
Black chalk with red for flesh, ribbons and sketch ($8\frac{7}{8} \times 7\frac{1}{4}$ in. (22.7 × 18.4 cm.) (13875)
Signed with the initials TW, the letters joined but complete.
See the preceding.

T. WORLIDGE, Ascribed to

696. A TEA PARTY IN A PERGOLA, two men and a woman seated, a boy bringing a kettle.
Pencil on vellum. $9\frac{5}{8} \times 13$ in. (24.6 × 33 cm.) (13876)
Inscribed in minute characters at foot: Thomas Worlidge fecit 1736.

THOMAS WRIGHT

A design for a palace in the Palladian style, together with alternative plans for siting it in St. James's Park, are in the collection of Architectural drawings.

JOHN WYCK (1640–1702), Attributed to

697. WINDSOR CASTLE FROM THE SOUTH-WEST, THE WEST END ONLY *Plate* 106
Pencil, pen and grey wash. $6\frac{7}{8} \times 13\frac{1}{4}$ in. (17.6 × 34.2 cm.) (17415)
A small letter 'b' twice on the roofs of a house.
Closely connected with a group of paintings of which two are represented in the Royal Library by photographs, and a third (? one of the same) is in the Fairhaven Collection (Catalogue No. 82, plate 13), and there attributed to J. Wyck. The drawing shows the left half of the scene only, more distance to the left and none of the immediate foreground. If the point of view were recognizable it might be possible to regard it as an original sketch on which the oil paintings were based. Its attribution to J. Wyck must stand or fall with that of the picture in the Fairhaven Collection. It has hitherto been regarded as anonymous, and might equally well be attributed to Leonard Knyff on the strength of its similarity to the drawing of Berkeley Castle at the British Museum (1948–11–26–10).

JOHANN ZOFFANY (1733–1810)

698. AZOFF-UD-DOWLAH, NABOB OF OUDH *Figure* 57
Black, white and red chalk on brown paper. $8\frac{1}{4} \times 6\frac{1}{8}$ in. (21.7 × 15.2 cm.) (13286)
Inscribed: Nabob of Oude.
Bought by the Prince Regent from Colnaghi on June 5, 1811, 'A drawing by Zoffany—the Nabob of Oude, 10/6' (Archives Invoice 27637).
The Nabob of Oudh was painted several times by Zoffany.

699. APOLLO DRAWING THE CHARIOT OF THE SUN. Design for a ceiling.
Pencil or black chalk and white on brown-grey, slightly greenish (as No. 701) paper, the design continued in white. $10\frac{1}{4} \times 16\frac{3}{4}$ in. (26 × 42.5 cm.) (13284)

Fig. 57. Zoffany; The Nabob of Oudh (Cat. No. 698)

Bought with the following three drawings (and Nos. 447–451, etc., Nattes, *q.v.*) from Sir Frederick Gore Ouseley's collection, Tenbury, 1919.

Two further designs with the same subject and acquired from the same source by the British Museum (1920–12–14–11/12) are inscribed in an old hand on the guard with the name of Zoffany. He is said to have painted a chapel at Coblentz on his return from Italy in 1779; these are, however, clearly secular designs.

700. VENUS, CUPIDS AND SATYRS   *Plate* 108

Black chalk and white on brown-grey paper; irregular. *c.* $13\frac{3}{4} \times 12\frac{3}{8}$ in. (34.9 × 29 cm.)   (13285)

701. TRITON AND NEREID. A design for an architectural decoration, a coved frieze.   *Plate* 109

Black chalk and white on brown slightly greenish paper. $8\frac{3}{4} \times 13\frac{7}{8}$ in. (22 × 35 cm.)   (13282)

702. CUPID AND PSYCHE; WITH VENUS AND CUPID IN A CHARIOT ABOVE

Dry brush and brown oil pigment? over black chalk. $7\frac{7}{8} \times 5\frac{1}{8}$ in. (20 × 13 cm.)   (13283)

JOHANN ZOFFANY, After

703. A GROUP OF ROYAL ACADEMICIANS   *Figure* 58

Pencil, reinforced with black chalk and pen. $8\frac{1}{4} \times 12\frac{5}{8}$ in. (20.5 × 32 cm.)   (13281)

The name Huddesford in pen at foot towards the centre.
Exhib.: R.A. (British Art), 1934, No. 620 (1288).

Perhaps the 'drawing of Royal Academicians, Sir Joshua Reynolds, etc.', acquired by the Prince Regent from Colnaghi on May 24, 1813, for 7s. 6d. (Archives Invoice 27847).

Hitherto regarded as Zoffany's sketch for the picture of the Royal Academicians in the Life School, 1772, in the Royal Collection (*Figure* 59).

Apart from Horace Walpole's statement (Whitley, *Artists and their Friends in England 1700–1799*, Vol. I, p. 271) that this picture was painted without any preliminary sketch, it it not possible to accept this supposition. The heads of the seven academicians around Sir Joshua Reynolds, namely, Hayman, Yeo, Newton, Dr. Hunter, Wilson, Zuccarelli and Moser, are clearly the same as those in the picture, and their attitudes so far as shewn are similar. But the figures are brought together from different parts of the picture, and attitudes which have meaning in the picture are meaningless in the drawing. It is inconceivable that the artist, having put together these heads and shoulders in a close group, should have separated the figures widely, completed their attitudes and found appropriate positions for them in the picture. The omission of Sir William Chambers from between the President and Francis Newton, the Secretary, has brought Newton's hand upon the end of Sir Joshua's ear-trumpet instead of on Sir William's arm, while behind him, to the left, Yeo's cane stands unsupported through the total

Fig. 58. Zoffany, after: A group of Royal Academicians (Cat. No. 703)

Fig. 59. Zoffany: The Life School of the Royal Academy (*Cf.* on Cat. No. 703)

omission of his hand against his breast as it is in the picture, where he faces the model on the other side of Sir Joshua. On the extreme right of the drawing a roll of paper is awkwardly attached to Moser's left hand, which, in the picture, is very intelligently employed in the adjustment of the model's support. The name Huddesford, written in ink at the foot of the drawing, is that of a jocular journalist who had been trained as an artist and may quite well have been the author of this pastiche. His portrait by Reynolds is N.G. 754.

The drawing inscribed 'Zoffany' at the Royal Academy, showing some of the figures as in the picture is, *pace* Horace Walpole, more plausible.

704. GARRICK AS JAFFIER IN 'VENICE PRESERVED'

Pencil. $5\frac{1}{8} \times 3\frac{7}{8}$ in. (13.1 × 9.8 cm.) (13607)

Presumably a copy of the head in the print by McArdell after Zoffany (O'Donoghue, Vol. II, p. 284, No. 144).

See also under Pickering, No. 475.

FRANCESCO ZUCCARELLI (1702–1788)

705. THE NAVAL POWER AND COMMERCE OF ENGLAND. Design for a pediment.

Pen, brown and blue washes, within ruled border. $13\frac{7}{8} \times 29\frac{1}{4}$ in. (36.2 × 74.5 cm.)

Inscribed above: 'Allegorical subject for the Basso rilievo of the pediment. Design XX.'; and below, 'Stephanus Riou invenit', left, and 'Amicitiae Causa F. Zuccarelli Delint. 1755' right; and 'This design represents the naval power and commerce of England, etc.' The former is represented by Neptune, the latter by Mercury.

Included as the last design in a manuscript volume containing twenty plans and elevations for a royal palace by Stephen Riou (d. 1780). A title-page states that the designs were invented and begun at Rome in 1751, 1752, and 1753, and finished at London in 1754. The dedication page is blank. The introduction sets out the advantages of placing a royal palace with large piazza in front, on the site of Buckingham House, with communication to St. James's and Westminster.

DRAWINGS SIGNED WITH INITIALS ONLY

W. B., *see under* Rowlandson, No. 548.

G. M. OR G. M. L.

706. 'THE RIVAL CANDIDATES AND THEIR OLD SUPPORTERS.' The Westminster Election 1784: Charles Fox and Lord Hood, accompanied by groups of sailors, sweeps and ruffians. St. Paul's, Covent Garden, and a fight in the background.

Pen and watercolour. $7\frac{5}{8} \times 10\frac{7}{8}$ in. (19.3 × 27.7 cm.) (17693)

'G.M.' or 'G.M.L.' in monogram at foot right. Title in border with 'Original Drawing never published' in ink. There was a Lord George Murray, *cf.* B.M. Sat., VII, 8284, a print after him by Rowlandson.

J. M., 1785

707. A LONG-WAYS DANCE *Plate* 105

Pen and watercolour in washed border. $12\frac{3}{4} \times 18\frac{7}{8}$ in. (32.5 × 47.5 cm.) (13763)

Signed in border: J. M. 1785.

Exhib.: Spring Gardens (Humour Exhibition), 1925, No. 7.

S. M., 1773

708. LORD SWELL'S ADVICE TO THE EARL OF BEEF CHIN SLIM . . . (illegible).

Pen. $6\frac{7}{8} \times 7\frac{3}{4}$ in. (17.5 × 19.6 cm.) (17694)

Title in border. '2/–' on back.

Signed: S. M. Delint. 1773.

Exhib.: B.F.A.C. 1931/32, No. 179.

C. L. S.

709. DANCING MASTER AND PUPIL

Pen over slight pencil. $10\frac{3}{8} \times 7\frac{3}{8}$ in. (26.2 × 19.5 cm.) (17695)

Initials (?) C.L.S. at foot left. '1/6' at back in pencil.

Somewhat in the manner of the Brethertons' etchings after Bunbury.

G. L. S. (*c.* 1772)

710. THE LAST ANNUITY PAID—OR A SALUTARY TRIP TO THE SOUTH OF FRANCE

Pen. $10\frac{3}{8} \times 16\frac{1}{8}$ in. (26.5 × 42.5 cm.) (17696)

Signed: G.L.S. — — and inscribed with the title, as given, below.

Amateur; a print signed G.L.S. in ornamented monogram, published by J. Seago, 1777, B.M. Sat., 5428, the *Poacher*, may be by the same hand; another, the engraving by Rowlandson, B.M. Sat., VI, 8150, 'Philosophy Run Mad', *c.* 1792.

711. RETURN FROM THE GRAND TOUR

Pen, uniform with the preceding. $10\frac{3}{8} \times 16\frac{7}{8}$ in. (26.5 × 43 cm.) (17697)

Inscribed 'G.L.S.' below the title, as given; 'A Tour to foreign' cancelled. The inn-sign inscribed 'Bullock'.

ANONYMOUS DRAWINGS

I. PORTRAITS AND FIGURE STUDIES

712. KING GEORGE I, whole length standing, nearly full face, scarlet surcoat, white coat embroidered with chinoiserie, left hand pointing upward. The Royal Arms on curtain right.

Watercolour. $12\frac{1}{2} \times 8\frac{3}{8}$ in. (32 × 24 cm.) (17258)

713. 'PRINCE GEORGE OF WALES PLAYING AT SOLDIERS' *Figure* 60

Pen with black and brown inks and grey wash, the left hand lower corner made up. $6\frac{1}{2} \times 9$ in. (16.4 × 22.8 cm.) (13932)

Inscribed at foot in ink: 'taken by ye life July mon ye 6'. A boy, aged about six, is seated, reading a book, between four chairs, over which are two poles and a curtain forming a rough tent with a bell hanging from it. A sword, gun and bayonet are on the carpet in the foreground, and a flag initialled G.R. on the extreme left. A ribbon around his neck may have been wrongly intended for that of the Garter, and there may be a suggestion of a Star. The date in the inscription agrees with 1744. As this drawing is traditionally held to be a portrait of George III in the Nursery, it may perhaps be the drawing 'George III when Young' bought by the Prince Regent from Colnaghi on January 13, 1820, for 15/– (Archives Invoice 28252).

Fig. 60. 'Prince George of Wales playing at Soldiers'
(Cat. No. 713)

714. PRINCE CHARLES EDWARD, IN OLD AGE, head and shoulders, profile to left, in armour with the Ribbon of the Garter and the Badge of the Thistle; in circular frame on pedestal with inscription.

Black chalk heightened with white on grey paper. $10\frac{1}{4} \times 8\frac{1}{8}$ in. (26 × 20.6 cm.) (17196)

The inscription on the pedestal reads: CAROLUS III D.G. MAG. BRIT. FRANC. ET HIBERN. REX FIDEI DEFENSOR &&& NATUS PRIDIE KAL. IAN. AN. MDCCXXI QUI POST OBITUM JACOBI III AVITIS REGNIS SUCCESSIT KAL. IAN. AN. MDCCLXVI. Exhibited by Sir Archibald Hamilton Dunbar, Bt., at the Stuart Exhibition, 1889, and the Glasgow International Exhibition, 1901, and given by him to H.M. Queen Mary, who presented it to the Stuart Collection, Windsor Castle, June, 1932.

Reproduced in Miss Henrietta Tayler's *Bonnie Prince Charlie.*

715. WILLIAM, LORD AMHERST (1773–1857), full length, standing to right in uniform holding sword; buildings (? Horse Guards) indicated in the background.

Pencil and watercolour (a miniature, unfinished); colours and material 'gravel', 'slate' indicated in pencil in the sketched background. $8\frac{1}{4} \times 7\frac{3}{8}$ in. (21 × 18.8 cm.) (13610)

The traditional identification as William Lord Amherst is not supported by the mezzotint portrait, Dunkerton after Devis (O'Donoghue, Vol. I, p. 44, No. 1), except perhaps in some details of the uniform, which may be that of the St. James's Volunteers. Lord Amherst was the popular Commandant (*cf.* Farington's *Diary*, October 15, 1803) of that Corps, and a miniature of him in that capacity by J. T. Barber was exhibited at the Royal Academy in 1800. For a note on Barber (Beaumont) see *Gent. Mag.*, 1841, Vol. 2, p. 96.

716. KING GEORGE III (after 1808), full length, standing on a dais in front of a Gothic stall or throne. He faces half right, is without Orders and wears a wig.

Black chalk with stump in plain border. $29\frac{1}{4} \times 20$ in. (74.4 × 40.9 cm.) (17610)

From Buckingham Palace (in store) and for many years at Windsor Castle hanging among prints, in a frame which bears no indication and is apparently not contemporary.

It is tempting to identify this with 'a drawing of His Majesty' bought by the Prince Regent on October 8, 1812, from Robert Bowyer for £52 10s. (Archives Invoice 26930) with an 'elegant burnish gold frame' for £6 6s. which was no doubt the 'Full length portrait of His late Majesty, by Bowyer, on paper, a drawing', No. 382 in the Carlton House Inventory of 1819 and after (also in the 1816 Inventory, No. 526, less fully detailed). Bowyer is said to have made a drawing of the King in his illness, surreptitiously on his thumbnail in chapel, and according to a family account (Ada Earland, *John Opie and his Circle*, 1911, p. 71) enlarged it, in concert with Bromley, into a sketch for an engraving. This sketch was taken to the Prince Regent who 'told Bowyer that the likeness was so affecting that he could not bear to have it published', and accordingly bought it for 50 guineas. For this portrait a wig was borrowed from the King's hairdresser. In 1820 Bowyer published a vignette portrait of the King after an original drawing by himself as Miniature Painter to His Majesty 'taken from the life in 1810' (proof in the Royal Library). This head is without a wig and not the same as in the present drawing. Both, however, shew marked indications of ill-health. This, with the price paid by the Regent in 1812 and the engraving-like nature of the present drawing, provides almost overwhelming circumstantial evidence for connecting it with Bowyer and the story, but the lack of a connecting link between it and the framed drawing at Carlton House forbids, at any rate in this place, an identification which, once made, would become absolute.

Robert Bowyer (1758–1834) is described in the R.A. Catalogues as 'Miniature Painter to His Majesty', and in his obituary notice in the *Gentleman's Magazine* as 'Portrait Painter in Watercolours to His Majesty'. He was credited by *The World* of February 27, 1790, with 'an extraordinary miniature of the King' having 'a flat diamond over it, half an inch square', and, in the issue of March 15, 'the whole substance of Fox's late long speech at the back of the Seal Ring'. This is confused in Chamber's *Book of Days*, i. 343, with the thumbnail story. A miniature by him of the King was engraved in 1797 (O'Donoghue, Vol. II, p. 302, No. 307), and in 1789 he had, it is said at the Queen's request, made and exhibited a miniature of Dr. Willis, another indication of his connexion with the King's illness.

No pencil work by him is available for comparison.

717. An inter-related group of portrait drawings, two character drawings, and a caricature, all mounted in twos and threes on soft, coloured paper, and uniformly priced at the back and inscribed in an old hand with names (twenty-two in all). (17711)

Mr. Barrington; Mr. Barwell; Mr. Brooks—a Sherriff's bailiff; Mr. (?) Burlem and Mr. Irwin; Mr. Fell and Jew Levi; Old Hall, the Cryer; Rev. Mr. Harvey; Mr. Hog at the Prince of Wa-; Mr. Leacroft; Capt. Lill; Mr. Jonas Junior; Govr. Morris (reproduced *Figure* 61), though scarcely to be connected with the distinguished American, Gouverneur Morris (1752–1821), who was in London in 17 . He had a wooden leg); Mr. Maule reading the Petition; Philosopher Storer; Small beer; and Going to see my Aunt.

The two last-named are in pen over pencil. All the others are in pen and watercolour and apparently by the same hand. They measure about $6 \times 3\frac{1}{2}$ in. (15 × 9 cm.).

With them are placed (23) a sleeping potman, in monochrome, uninscribed and mounted on heavier paper, and (24–26) three drawings on another sheet of that paper. One of these—Mr. Wheeler a night portrait—is inscribed in the same way as are the main group; the other two are illustrations, one sentimental, a boy in prison and the other, comic, somewhat in the manner of Elias Martin. This may

Fig. 61. 'Govnr. Morris' (Cat. No. 717)

Nor so far as has been ascertained do they correspond with any series of Fencing prints.

According to Angelo's own statement the original drawings of his plates were presented by him to the King after the publication of the book, each adorned with an elegant border, and the whole book bound in the most superb manner. (Letter of May 5, 1776, printed on p. 10 of the 1817 re-issue of the *Ecole*). There is a reference to some such presentation in the manuscript dedication (in the Royal Library, undated, but after 1765) to the Prince of Wales of a hand-coloured set of the reduced copies of Gwynn's plates made for the *Encyclopédie Universelle*. There is no trace in any of the old inventories, nor in the Catalogue of the King's Library at the British Museum, of the existence of the volume of original drawings. There may have been a confusion between 'desseins' and drawings.

720. PALM SUNDAY FESTIVITIES IN THE ISLAND OF MINORCA (*c*. 1775).

Pen and watercolour. $19\frac{3}{4} \times 26\frac{1}{4}$ in. (50.5 × 66.6 cm.)
(16491)

The price £4 4s. od. in pencil at the back identifies this drawing with 'A drawing the Fair at Mahon in the Island of Minorca' acquired for £4 4s. by the Prince of Wales from Colnaghi on March 17, 1804 (Archives Invoice 27255).
Possibly the work of a native practitioner but with evidence of the British Occupation. The title, 'The Fair at Mahon in the Island of Minorca,' is pencilled by an Assistant Librarian on the back of the washed mount, presumably from an older source.

721. A REVIEW OF THE FLEET (*c*. 1790).

Pen and watercolour within border. $17\frac{3}{8} \times 27\frac{3}{4}$ in. (44.1 × 70.4 cm.). (*Souvenir Album*, VI, p. 3).

Not by a professional artist.

II. CARICATURES

722. PETITION TO A BISHOP (*c*. 1750).

Pen and watercolour, incised with stylus and the back reddened with chalk; partly drawn for reversal. '5/–' at back. $6 \times 9\frac{1}{8}$ in. (15.4 × 23.4 cm.) (17698)

be by the same hand as the caricature 'Mr. Maule reading the Petition' mentioned above, and both drawings also shew similar perforations at the top and centre foot. See also No. 718.

Included with this group is a watercolour (27) $9\frac{1}{2} \times 6\frac{3}{4}$ in. showing, apparently, the last stand of Banditti under attack. It bears traces of similar mounting and still more of similar draughtsmanship.

718. 'AT THE DOG & DUCK'

Pen and watercolour. $7 \times 4\frac{3}{8}$ in. (17.7 × 11.1 cm.) (13762)
The connexion of this anonymous drawing with the Dog and Duck, a tavern of bad fame, pulled down 1812, is not apparent. Possibly the original mount was inscribed on the back in the same way as the twenty-two drawings described above.

719. Thirteen drawings of two figures in various positions of fencing (*c*. 1750). *Figure 62*

Red, black and white chalk on brown paper. *c*. $17\frac{3}{4} \times 23\frac{1}{2}$ in. (*c*. 45 × 59.6 cm.) (16676–16688)
Beyond reasonable doubt the 'Thirteen Drawings the Art of Fencing' acquired by the Prince of Wales from Colnaghi for £4 17s. 6d. on January 10, 1806 (Archives Invoice 27327). They are earlier in style than Gwyn's plates to Angelo's *Ecole des Armes*, 1763, and the positions do not correspond.

Fig. 62. A fencing position (Cat. No. 719)

723. THE GRACES, THE GRACES, THE GRACES, AT A GUINEA A LESSON PAR SIGN[R] L'OMAGGIO, *c.* 1770.

Pen, brown wash and watercolour on coarse brown paper. 13 × 18⅞ in. (33 × 47.8 cm.) (17699)

By an amateur.

The title as given, in ink below the drawing.

724. A MID-DAY MEAL (*c.* 1775).

Pen and grey wash. 6¼ × 6¾ in. (15.8 × 17.2 cm.) (13604)

A feeble, but possibly not amateur production, interesting only for the unusual representation of a humble room and furniture.

725. COMMODORE ST. IAGO RETURNING VICTORIOUS 1782.

Pencil, pen and watercolour, folded. 12½ × 7⅞ in. (31.7 × 20 cm.) (17700)

Engraved in reverse by Charles Bretherton Junior, published January 22, 1782 (B.M. Sat., V, No. 5960). Besides the title and legends, which are the same as in the print, there is a pencil inscription by a later hand, 'Sir Home Popham'. This is incorrect, the satire is on Johnstone's expedition against the Cape of Good Hope in 1781.

726. NECK OR NOTHING (*c.* 1779)

Pen and brown wash, the title, as given, inscribed at foot. 11½ × 18⅞ in. (29.2 × 47.5 cm.) (17702)

By an amateur. Folded and mended.

Priced '4/–'.

Lord North, riding a galloping horse, flogs it towards the brink of a high precipice. The King and another are also on the horse facing its tail. The King holds on to the Garter ribbon of the third man, who is clutching the branch of a tree at the foot of which Britannia is seated as an old hag with a tattered flag inscribed 'Geo.ge the T — by the Grace of — King of — ender of the faith &c.' Britannia is embraced by a man who is casting dice (marked A and E) on the chequered cover of a volume lettered 'Rise and Progress of the American War'. On the other side, above the precipice, an angel fastened to a huge anchor decorated with triple fleur-de-lys raises both arms towards a tropical and beflagged plantation seen in the distance beyond the sea. A signpost inscribed 'North End' and topped by a grinning skull is between the riders and the tree.

727. THE PROCESSION FROM THE HUSTINGS, UNDER THE DIRECTION OF MR. S–E (? Sawbridge, 1784)

Watercolour over red chalk. 7½ × 12⅝ in. (19 × 32 cm.) (17701)

By an amateur.

Fox in a blue coat seated on a garlanded chair, carried by four supporters. On the left eight horsemen ride away past a signpost 'To Tyburn Road', and on the right four horsemen and a boy are similarly seen riding off. The riders and Fox all wear blue coats, and cockades in their hats. Legends above them read from left to right:

'See the ball I hold &c'
'Let the Cynic toil like Ass's'
'Our fire their fire surpass's'
'And turns our schemes to Gold'.

728. THE WRITING ON THE WALL

Pen and watercolour. 9¾ × 8¼ in. (24.9 × 21 cm.) (17703)

On the left a man in blue looks through a quizzing glass apparently at an inscription 'War' in large letters. John Bull as a simple countryman gazes in horror at him. The legend reads: 'Sad humbug this Johnny upon the Stocks and so soon to follow with the confirmation of War.'

729. A FULL PIECE

Pen over black chalk, grey wash, on brown paper. 10⅜ × 17⅜ in. (28.8 × 44.2 cm.) (17704)

By an amateur.

Priced '3/6' on back.

A man (? Pitt) holds with both hands a flageolet to the lips of a young man who is playing the fiddle as he stands with one foot on a chair and the other firmly planted on the keys of an instrument. Another man hands him a French horn. There are no legends, but the title, as given, is written above.

730. THE MAGIC LANTHORN (*c.* 1802)

Pen and watercolour. 10 × 14 in. (25.5 × 35.5 cm.) (17705)

By an amateur.

Priced '4'.

Exhib.: B.F.A.C. 1931–32, No. 175.

Pitt with magic lantern shews Napoleon on a screen to two country bumpkins standing behind him (all with appropriate legends). Fox kneels in front of him with legend, 'Ah Master Billy you are humbuging poor Johnny at a fine rate.'

731. MAJOR BRYAN'S REFLECTION, 1821

Pen and watercolour. 10⅞ × 8½ in. (27.7 × 21.7 cm.) (17706)

Inscribed: '*Major Bryan*' in ink, and, in pencil, 'who attempted to get up a meeting in Ireland against the Queen —but was lucky to escape with life'. March, 1821, in pencil. Hunchback, in red and blue uniform, looking at himself in glass, devils and spirits to right; he says: 'See there the *Monster* comes again.' Female figure in green says: 'The Monster lives, my Love, but in thy Brain.' Numerous other legends, e.g.: 'Petition against Duke of Richmond', 'Kilkenny Resolutions', and references to Sir Capel Molineux, Todd and Toleration, O'Gorman, Scully, Sir Neil O'Donnell, Thomas Osborn, O'Connell.

732. A BARBER HOLDING A POWDER-PISTOL

Pen and watercolour. 5½ × 4⅛ in. (14 × 10.5 cm.) (17707)

733. AN OFFICER, PROFILE

Pen and watercolour. 4⅝ × 2⅞ in. (11.8 × 7.4 cm.) (17708)

The name 'Col. Robert Crawford' pencilled with a query, on the back.

734. BEGGARS

A group of ten watercolours, amateur or copy, about 1800, representing beggars of various kinds. Most are priced and two of them inscribed 'original drawing' in the Colnaghi hand. Five other drawings, similarly priced from 2/– to 4/–, are preserved with them. (17712)

735. A group of anonymous caricatures, social and theatrical. (Eight.)

Pen, pencil or watercolour. Some priced from 2/6 to 4/–. (17713)

Two are theatrical, one of them, according to inscriptions at the back, representing Palmer, Parsons, Mrs. Hopkins and

Mr. Dodd in a scene at a breakfast table. A 'Promenade' (much folded) has some kinship with No. 707. A caricature of Frenchmen purports to be signed by A. Grant, and an imitation mezzotint of a piper has the musical notation G. Sharp. There are a dance, an auction room and a dwarf inscribed 'shown in the Haymarket London 1765'.

736. A group of single-figure anonymous caricatures (14). Pencil, pen or watercolour. (17714)

By various hands, mainly amateur. Several are priced from 1/– to 3/6 showing that they were obtained by the Prince Regent from Colnaghi, no doubt among the 'gay' or 'curious' drawings which were acquired from time to time. Some have been folded as though sent through the post, as are those attributed to the Townshends (see Nos. 614–616). One is inscribed: '(?) Hanult Zerpis brother to the Empress of Russia when at Brussels in 1789' (? Prince Friedrich-August von Anhalt-Zerbst (1734–1793)). Others are 'Secretary Snout', 'Monsieur La Politesse', which is apparently signed 'Jacob Jallage Equis Delineavit' and 'Razor in the Upholsterer'.

III. WINDSOR TOPOGRAPHY

737. WINDSOR CASTLE AND TOWN, NORTH-WEST VIEW *Plate* 107

Pen and brown ink, grey wash. $7\frac{5}{8} \times 13\frac{3}{4}$ in. (19.1 × 34.7 cm.) (17412)

Late 17th century (manner of T. Wyck).

Inscribed in pencil: 'Windsor Castle'.

This able drawing and the following are by the same hand, the architecture largely fantastic, the town Italianate in character.

738. WINDSOR CASTLE AND TOWN; THE WEST FRONT

Pen and brown ink, grey wash. $8\frac{1}{8} \times 14\frac{1}{4}$ in. (20.5 × 36 cm.) (17413)

See on the preceding.

739. WINDSOR: A WOODEN TOWER, 1729; presumably the upper part of the old Curfew Tower.

Pen and watercolour. 7 × 10 in. (17.5 × 25.5 cm.) (17454)

Inscribed in ink, on the front, 'A Wooden Tower at Windsor, July 1729' and '90', 'N.10419' and '2:6' on the back.

An amateur performance; the separate building on the right, which bears some resemblance to the end of the Queen Elizabeth Gallery, may be a subsequent addition.

740. WINDSOR CASTLE AND TOWN FROM THE RIVER, LOOKING SOUTH-EAST (*c.* 1750)

Pen and brown and grey washes over pencil, the drawing of the Castle itself laid on another paper and enlarged at sides and bottom. $9\frac{5}{8} \times 15\frac{1}{8}$ in. (24.5 × 38.1 cm.) (17373)

Clearly concocted, presumably from prints; the north transept of St. George's Chapel has become a pediment on a Georgian front even more clearly than in the print by Schenk.

741. A FOREST SCENE, CALLED WINDSOR (*c.* 1780)

Pen and grey wash, much damaged and torn. $16\frac{7}{8} \times 23\frac{3}{8}$ in. (43 × 59.4 cm.) (14672)

Once ascribed to Paul Sandby, and with a false signature in the bottom right corner. (*Cf. Sandby Catalogue*, p. 56).

742. WINDSOR CASTLE: THE RUBBISH GATE WITH THE QUEEN'S HOUSE ON THE RIGHT (*c.* 1790)

Pen and grey wash. $6\frac{1}{8} \times 9\frac{1}{2}$ in. (15.5 × 24 cm.) (17396)

Companion to the following. Neat but puerile, of topographic interest.

743. WINDSOR CASTLE: THE EAST FRONT WITH THE QUEEN'S HOUSE ON THE LEFT (*c.* 1790)

Pen and grey wash. $6 \times 9\frac{1}{2}$ in. (15.5 × 24 cm.) (17397)

Companion to No. 742.

744. WINDSOR CASTLE: EDWARD III TOWER WITH THE KING'S (RUBBISH) GATE to the right and the Round Tower to left (*c.* 1800).

Pen and grey wash on laid paper. $9\frac{1}{4} \times 13\frac{3}{8}$ in. (23.3 × 33.9 cm.) (17515)

Has been ascribed to de Cort, but is by a stronger and more fluent architectural draughtsman.

745. WINDSOR CASTLE FROM THE RIVER LOOKING SOUTH-EAST (*c.* 1810)

Watercolour, gummed, much faded. $18\frac{1}{2} \times 25\frac{3}{4}$ in. (47.5 × 65 cm.) (17366)

A poor drawing, somewhat in the manner of F. Nicholson.

746. 'MR. GRIFFITHS' HOUSE AT OLD WINDSOR'

Watercolour over slight pencil. $3\frac{7}{8} \times 7$ in. (10 × 17.8 cm.) (17528)

The title as given inscribed on the back in pencil.

Mr. Griffiths bought Beaumont from Warren Hastings in 1789 and Emlyn of Windsor immediately rebuilt it. Griffiths sold it in 1805. The drawing may possibly be a retrospective reconstruction of the house before Emlyn rebuilt it, made for the purpose of extra-illustration.

The house is shewn in No. 256 (Farington).

747. Windsor Topography—a group of pencil drawings (*c.* 1810–1836).

(1) Windsor Castle: the Lower Ward, looking East.

Pencil. $7\frac{1}{4} \times 12$ in. (18.8 × 30.6 cm.) (17535)

(2) Distant view of Windsor from the South-West.

Pencil. $7\frac{1}{2} \times 11$ in. (19 × 28.1 cm.) (17541)

(3) The same.

Pencil, within ruled border. $8\frac{1}{4} \times 10\frac{1}{2}$ in. (21 × 26.8 cm.) (17540)

(4) Windsor Castle from the North.

Pencil. $7\frac{1}{8} \times 10\frac{1}{2}$ in. (18.4 × 26.5 cm.). Inscribed 'Windsor Buck Oct. 3 1820 from the Playing fields Eton'. (17376)

(5) Windsor Castle from the North.

Pencil. $7\frac{1}{4} \times 10\frac{5}{8}$ in. (18.4 × 26.8 cm.) (17377)

Inscribed 'Windsor Castle May 6 /25' on the front, and on the back in another hand, 'Shows the progress of the refacing of N. front—The Elizabeth Gallery just begun'.

(6) Windsor Castle from the Brocas.

Pencil. $7 \times 10\frac{1}{2}$ in. (17.7 × 26.6 cm.) (17378)

Inscribed and dated 'Windsor May 6 /25'.

(7) Windsor Castle from the end of Thames St.

Pencil. 7¼ × 10⅝ in. (18.3 × 27 cm.)   (17381)

Inscribed 'Windsor Buck Sept. 13 /30'.

(8) Thames Street and Curfew Tower.

Pencil. 6⅞ × 10¾ in. (17.3 × 27.4 cm.)   (17533)

Inscribed 'Windsor Berks Oct. 28 /36', and 'Mr. French No. 8 York Place' on the house to the left. Josiah French was a singer in the choir of St. George's Chapel.

(9) Lower part of Thames Street.

Pencil. 3¼ × 6⅜ in. (9.7 × 16.3 cm.)   (17382)

(10) St. George's Chapel and the Canon's houses seen from Thames Street.

Pencil. 3¼ × 6½ in. (9.7 × 16.6 cm.)   (17383)

Of these ten anonymous drawings, Nos. 1 and 2 on similar laid paper, may be by the same hand of *c.* 1810. In No. 1 the Round Tower is not yet heightened. Nos. 2 and 3, with identical inscriptions at the foot, are of the same view, No. 3 being the rougher sketch but disposed for a picture. Inscriptions at the top, pencilled notes and indications, mannerisms and paper bring together Nos. 4, 7 and 8, despite difference of date. Nos. 5 and 6 dated on the same day are clearly by another hand, though they shew points of similarity with both the other groups, and the leaves of a smaller sketch book, Nos. 9 and 10, may be by the same hand as Nos. 4, 7 and 8.

All the drawings, except No. 1, were acquired before 1916, but there is no indication of the sources.

V. LONDON AND RICHMOND TOPOGRAPHY

748. ST. JAMES'S PALACE: View of the Mall towards Buckingham House; St. James's Palace and a portion of Marlborough House to right (*c.* 1720).

Pen with brown ink and grey wash over pencil. 22⅝ × 40½ in. (57.4 × 104 cm.).

Given by Professor Tancred Borenius to H.M. Queen Mary, December, 1939, and by her to the Royal Library. Inscribed in pen on the reverse, 'St. James's Pallace,' and (more recent) at the top of the drawing, 'St. James Palace'. A red chalk perspective drawing on the reverse bears inscriptions: 'If the cloth is (?) 4 wide let this be the demensions of the palace,' 'or it would be better if the point of sight was lower'. Also (across) '& Kingsinton'.

Fig. 63. The Lord Mayor's Banqueting House, Tyburn Village (Cat. No. 749)

Fig. 64. The Lord Mayor's Banqueting House, Tyburn Village (Cat. No. 750)

749. THE LORD MAYOR'S BANQUETING HOUSE, TYBURN VILLAGE; huntsmen and hounds in the foreground (*c.* 1730).   *Figure* 63

Gouache. 11¼ × 17¾ in. (28.6 × 45.1 cm.)   (17715A)

Inscribed in pencil on the back, with the price '2/6' and, 'The Lord Mayor's Banqueting House stood where Stratford Place Oxford St. now stands'.

(*Cf.* Pennant's *London*, p. 152, who quotes Maitland.)

750. THE SAME, ANOTHER VIEW, cows in the foreground.   *Figure* 64

Gouache. 11¼ × 18 in. (28.6 × 45.7 cm.)   (17715B)

The same inscription and price.

751. MONTAGUE HOUSE, with a vignette of the new building at the Museum, erected 1804.

Watercolour on Whatman paper of 1811. 7⅛ × 11⅛ in. (18 × 28.6 cm.)   (17137, 17138)

Vignette: 2 × 5⅝ in. (5.2 × 14.2 cm.)

The two subjects are shewn as in the engraving by Busby (see early state of the plate in the Royal Collection) in Wilkinson's *Londina Illustrata*, Vol. I, No. 101, and the size is identical. The omission of details from the drawings indicates that they are copies, probably tracings from the prints for purposes of extra-illustration.

752. A PROJECT FOR BUCKINGHAM PALACE, ABOUT 1820

Pen and grey wash, a little watercolour. Damaged and mended. 18½ × 29½ in. (46.7 × 74.7 cm.)   (17182)

A fanciful project for the conversion of the Queen's House into the Palace, and scarcely by a practised architect.

Acquired from A. Mathew, June, 1943.

753. HIS MAJESTY'S VILLA IN RICHMOND PARK (the White Lodge) (*c.* 1775).

Pen and watercolour in lined border. 9⅝ × 13 in. (24.5 × 33.1 cm.)   (17157)

Inscribed in ink with the title as given, and with '7/–' on the back, in lower right corner.

Presumably the drawing 'His Majesty Villa Richmond' acquired by the Prince Regent from Colnaghi on April 6, 1812, for 7/– (Archives Invoice 27857).

SUPPLEMENT

Drawings by Paul and Thomas Sandby acquired since the completion of the Sandby Catalogue

The numbering follows the sequence of the *Catalogue of the Drawings of Paul and Thomas Sandby at Windsor Castle* by A. P. Oppé, 1947, and the cross-references are to that Catalogue, not to the earlier part of the present volume.

PAUL SANDBY

S.419. IN THE GARDEN AT WOOLMERS, BEDS.

Watercolour, some pen, indications of pencil or chalk, on lined and coloured mount. $6\frac{3}{8} \times 9\frac{3}{8}$ in. (16.3 × 23.8 cm.)

(17554)

Inscribed on the drawing in fine pen: 'Woolmers 1783', 'In the garden at Woolmers, Beds', in pencil on the mount. 'From P. Sandby Esq's Sale' (erased) and 'purchased at a sale by Mr. Sotheby, London, December 18, 1822, N. (or R.) H.' scrawled in pencil at the back of the mount.
Acquired from the Randall Davies Collection, Sotheby's, February 12, 1947, Lot 356, with the following two drawings, and three by Vivares.
A fully-coloured sketch of a gravel walk, lawns, trees, and an artificial ruin in a park. For Woolmers', *see Sandby Catalogue*, No. 321.

S.420. IN WINDSOR PARK.
Lawns and trees with a large brick house (? the Ranger's cottage) on the right and a fence with a road on the left. *Figure 65*

Pencil and watercolour. $18\frac{1}{2} \times 10\frac{7}{8}$ in. (16.6 × 27.6 cm.)

(17555)

Inscribed 'Windsor Park 1789' in the same manner as the preceding drawing. Acquired with No. 419.
Somewhat lighter in execution than the preceding. Careful and considered both for local colour and for atmosphere, and neatly executed with no marked precision; an excellent example of Sandby's mature naturalism.

S.421. THE SAME GARDEN LOOKING FROM THE HOUSE.
A lady and child at the foot of a ladder against a tree.

Pencil and watercolour. $6\frac{1}{2} \times 10\frac{7}{8}$ in. (16.6 × 27.8 cm.)

(17556)

Uniform with the preceding and from the same source.

S.422. THE DUKE OF CUMBERLAND WITH A GENTLEMAN, HIS GROOM ON HORSEBACK AND DOGS.
On the right a string of horses and two groups of riders on different planes. *Figure 66*

Fig. 65. Paul Sandby: A View in Windsor Park (Cat. No. S.420)

Fig. 66. Paul Sandby: The Duke of Cumberland and his horses (Cat. No. S.422)

Pencil, fine brush and watercolour over rough pencil; browned by exposure. 6¼ × 16¼ in. (16 × 41.4 cm.) (17549)
Acquired from Calmann in 1946 as by Wootton. The name 'Wootton' with 'Duke of Cumberland' in another hand both in pencil on the back.
The Duke in a green coat with the star of the Garter, much as he appears in No. 58 (*Sandby Catalogue*). The gentleman in attendance wears the same green coat; the attendant is in blue. The riders to the right on a much smaller scale wear red coats with green facings. Similarities with No. 58 suggest that this may have been an alternative sketch for that drawing. On the other hand, the string of horses and the groups connected with them suggest a composition more like that of No. 102. The spaniel is clearly the same as in No. 413, etc. The drawing is in the same manner as in No. 102 and No. 142, but still more careful.

S.423. TWO RACEHORSES, WITH RIDERS, EXERCISING
Pen or fine brush and watercolour over pencil. Browned by exposure. 4¾ × 10¼ in. (12.1 × 26 cm.) (17550)
Purchased with the preceding.
The riders wear red coats with green facings as in the preceding drawing; the saddlecloths, which are very elaborate in three pieces, are partly bordered in the same colours. The horses in the conventional galloping attitude are extremely neatly but equally badly drawn. They are similar to, but not identical with, those in No. 147 (*Sandby Catalogue*). Compare also the British Museum drawing L.B. 137, No. 55(a).

S.424. A LADY, three-quarter length, standing, in profile, to left; a band on the head tied under the chin, the hair tied with a ribbon, a frill round the neck with a bow behind, a vandyked fichu, and laced frills to sleeves. *Figure* 67
Pencil, top corners made up. 6⅛ × 3⅜ in. (17.3 × 8.5 cm.) (17585)
The costume and, indeed, the profile closely resemble No. 268, but with sufficient resemblance to Nos. 280 and 283 (called Mrs. Eyre), and the drawings of the 'Lady Chambers' or 'Miss Elliott' series, (Nos. 275, 278, etc.) to suggest that all alike are Mrs. Sandby. If the date on No. 268 is correct all these drawings would date from 1760.
Acquired with the following from Colnaghi, part of Lot 21, Sotheby's, October 15, 1947.

S.425. THE SAME, SEATED, half length, profile to left, wearing a cap, a ribbon without frills round the neck, and a plain scarf. Otherwise identical with the preceding, but the costume and profile are those of No. 279.
Pencil, the top corners made up. 5⅞ × 4⅛ in. (14.8 × 16.3 cm.) (17586)
Acquired with the preceding.

S.426. WINDSOR CASTLE FROM BISHOPSGATE, the distant castle through trees on the left.
Watercolour with traces of pencil and some pen; within coloured border on thin card. 12¼ × 9⅝ in. (30.7 × 24 cm.) (17594)
Signed: P.S. 1792 Windsor Park, on the trunk of a beech tree.
Acquired with the following from Messrs. Colnaghi in 1948.

S.427. WINDSOR CASTLE FROM TOWARDS PRIEST'S HILL, the Castle seen from the south-east. A carpet beater and knife grinder in the foreground; a farm and distant view to the right. *Plate* 117
Watercolour over pencil, some pen, within coloured border on thin card. 12⅛ × 9½ in. (30.5 × 24.1 cm.) (17593)
Signed: P.S. Old Windsor 1792.
Of the same date as Nos. 91–94 (*Sandby Catalogue*), but more picturesque and delicate in treatment and, if somewhat faded, among the best examples of Paul Sandby's late careful style.
Acquired with the preceding.

S.428. THE DEPUTY RANGER'S HOUSE *Plate* 115
Watercolour and gouache with washed mount on thick paper. 16¼ × 23⅜ in. (41.2 × 59.4 cm.) (17597)
With the following from the sale of the collection of H.R.H. Princess Helena Victoria and Princess Marie Louise at Schomberg House, bought Ellis and Smith. Exhibited Antique Dealers' Fair, 1947. Bought from Messrs. Sabin, 1948.
This and the following drawing are late examples, scarcely before 1800. The front of the house with the porch and two bows is the same as shewn in the drawings at the British Museum, etc., referred to on No. 109 (*Sandby Catalogue*). If, as seems probable, the view is from much the same point as No. 109, the whole of the main portion of the house with the porch must have been remodelled since the date, say 30

Fig. 67. Paul Sandby: A Lady standing (Cat. No. S.424)

years before, of Thomas Sandby's drawing, but the whole topography is obscure. The fir trees which occur in all these drawings are shown to the left of the house as in No. 109. The green in the coat of the rider, with red facings, may originally have been blue.

S.429. A VIEW IN THE GARDENS OF THE DEPUTY RANGER'S HOUSE   *Plate* 116

Gouache with washed mount, on thick paper torn at top and bottom. $15\frac{5}{8} \times 23\frac{1}{4}$ in. (29.7 × 59.2 cm.)   (17596)
See on the preceding. This drawing was kindly ceded to the Royal Library by its purchaser, Mr. Gilbert Davis.
The woman with parasol and the boy, both in black, and the somewhat noticeable small figures in black in the preceding drawing may perhaps mark the mourning for Thomas Sandby, who died in 1798 while his daughter and

young Paul Sandby were living with him. On the other hand, the child with her hand to her hat is a revival of a much earlier and frequently repeated figure, Nos. 313 and 314 (*Sandby Catalogue*), in reverse.

S.430. THE NORTH FRONT OF WINDSOR CASTLE FROM DATCHET LANE NEAR ROMNEY LOCK. Nocturne with fireworks and illuminations.   *Plate* 113

Gouache. $18\frac{3}{8} \times 28\frac{5}{8}$ in. (46.5 × 72.5 cm.)   (17598)
Signed in gold: P. Sandby 1768.
Presented by Lord Fairhaven to H.R.H. Princess Elizabeth, November, 1947, and by her to the Royal Library.
The view identical with that of No. 69 (*Sandby Catalogue*), and apparently the drawing referred to thereon as exhibited at Walker's Galleries in October, 1934. The size of the present drawing gives it a better claim than has No. 60, similarly signed and dated in gold, or No. 36, to be the drawing exhibited by Sandby at the Society of Artists in 1768 as 'Windsor Castle on a Rejoicing Night'.

S.431. MOUNTEBANKS AT NIGHT   *Plate* 114

Reed and watercolour. $11\frac{3}{4} \times 19\frac{1}{4}$ in. (29.8 × 48.8 cm.)
                                             (17600)

Signed: P. Sandby Inv. 1758, in minute characters on the overturned washtub. An inscription over the inn door reads 'Good Eating every day', and these words were originally placed on the inn sign but are almost obliterated.
Acquired at Christie's, June 11, 1948, Lot 47, in the sale of Lord Harcourt's pictures. In the old catalogue of the pictures at Nuneham this drawing was No. 264, 'Drawing of a Mountebank etc. by Paul Sandby, an early specimen of watercolour' (*Harcourt Papers*, Vol. III, p. 266).
This is the most considerable of Paul Sandby's more or less 'Hogarthian' drawings, and removes any doubt which may have been felt with regard to the 'Prison Scene' (*Sandby Catalogue*, No. 203) and the 'Magic Lantern' at the British Museum referred to thereon. The individual figures are on the same scale, and are of the same character as his etched London Cries of 1760, but their combination in a group makes this his most ambitious venture in that direction. The marked interest in artificial lighting, already shewn in a small etching of a stall among his Scottish plates, was developed at the evening meetings at his brother's house in Poultney Street. (*Cf. Sandby Catalogue*, p. 5, and the article by E. H. Ramsden in the *Burlington Magazine*, January, 1947.)
The portico and pediment of the church cannot be intended for St. Paul's, Covent Garden. Mr. Hugh Phillips suggests that the locality is Bloomsbury Market with St. George's in the background.

S.432. IN WINDSOR PARK   *Plate* 111

Watercolour. $6\frac{1}{4} \times 9\frac{1}{8}$ in. (15.6 × 23.2 cm.)   (17630)
Initialled (autograph) 'P.S.' on the back of the mount. 'Windsor Park' below the drawing and 'Drawn by Paul Sandby' on the back of the mount, both in another hand.

The loose and free watercolour in different shades of grey with no preliminary pencil work produces an effect of atmosphere and misty tonality, and possesses a charm which disappears from Sandby's more developed work. The drawing however clearly belongs to the series of light sketches dating from about 1790, for which see Nos. 95 and 185A (*Sandby Catalogue*).
Acquired from Messrs. Colnaghi, March, 1949.

THOMAS SANDBY

S.433. DESIGN FOR A BRIDGE AT VIRGINIA WATER IN THE FORM OF A RUINED ARCH

Pen and watercolour, the compass used for the two ornamental medallions and elsewhere. On thick Whatman paper, somewhat faded through exposure. $8\frac{3}{8} \times 18\frac{7}{8}$ in. (21.4×48 cm.)   (17608)

Inscribed at the back in pen, 'No. 5 bt. of Chapman' and numbered (?) '5' in the top left hand corner.
Acquired from Messrs. Spink, 1948.
The projected building shewn in this unusually complete and elaborate watercolour was evidently intended for a bridge; it is continued on the right by a wooden fence, above which part of the wheel and body of a coach appear at the end of the drawing. Further, the two medallions on the main piers seem to connect it with the bridge shewn on No. 123 and on the back of No. 124 (*Sandby Catalogue*). It is however even more clearly intended for a picturesque, partly ruined arch, and is indeed an adaptation and revision of that shewn on No. 122. The general disposition is the same, with flanking ruins and fragments on the left, the view through the arch over water is similar, and the light comes from the same direction. The main architectural features, where they differ, are in the same positions and of the same character, while some remain identical, e.g. the upper part of the ornamentation of the cornice. In both drawings some of the windows are bricked up while others remain free, and the foliage, which is fully carried out in the present drawing, is much as it is indicated in pencil on No. 122. The medallions, which connect the present drawing with Nos. 123 and 124, do not appear in No. 122, but they seem to be adapted from the ruined arch at Kew as shewn in Woollett's engraving after Kirby, which would appear to be the prototype of all these drawings (see especially the ruins, fragments and trees on both sides). Assuming that this finished watercolour represents the latest stage in the development of the design, it would appear that Sandby originally conceived a detached ruin at the end of Virginia Water on the lines of the arch at Kew, and then proposed to combine it with a road bridge which was required at somewhat the same spot and had been separately designed on another series of drawings. Some pencil lines in the foliage on the left hand side of No. 122 may indicate the genesis of the idea, but the general character of the arch shewn in that drawing (and still more in the alternative design, No. 121) and its completed continuations on both sides are entirely incompatible with a bridge.
The tower seen through the archway is loftier than that shewn in No. 122, but so far as can be discerned may also be the four-pinnacled erection projected on No. 145 and No. 146.

S.434. VIEW FROM SOMERSET HOUSE GARDENS WITH A RECONSTRUCTION OF INIGO JONES' WHITEHALL PALACE

Plate 110 and *Figure* 68 (*detail*)

Pencil, pen and grey wash and a little watercolour. Much use of the ruler, and compass in places. $19 \times 49\frac{1}{8}$ in. (48.2×125 cm.)   (17584)

On several pieces of paper, joined. The central portion only completed. The figures outlined in fine pen, the foliage in pencil, much left blank.
Inscribed in pencil 'from Old Somerset Gardens Terrace' and 'Drawn by Thomas Sandby—introducing Inigo Jones's intended design for the intended Palace at Whitehall of which the Banquet House was the only part executed', the latter perhaps in a 'Colnaghi' hand.

Acquired through Messrs. Colnaghi from a Grangerized *Pennant* in the Boney Sale (Lot 413, Sotheby's, October 8, 1947).
A looser version shewing the imaginary reconstruction at a slightly different angle and by afternoon light is at the British Museum (13×35 in., Crowle, *Pennant*, Vol. IV, No. 78 (L.B. 12)). The principal difference is that in it the open space in front of the southern end of the east front is obscured by houses and the northern end is left incomplete and partly obscured by the water-gate and trees. The present version would appear to be the later. The figures, which are prettily drawn, are probably by Paul Sandby.

T. SANDBY, Attributed to

S.435. THE EAST END OF ST. GEORGE'S CHAPEL. Unfinished.

Plate 112

Pen and grey wash over pencil, a little colour in the figures; compass and ruler used throughout. $22\frac{1}{8} \times 21\frac{1}{8}$ in. (56.3×53.8 cm.)   (17455)

The drawing is highly elaborated in some parts, e.g. the canopies on the left and the nearest on the right, some of the stalls, the pavement, the altar screen and the pulpit; other parts, e.g. the roof and the windows, are left partly finished, while others, principally the east and south walls, are completely blank. Such incompleteness first suggested to Miss Scott-Elliot the hand of Thomas Sandby, and this suggestion is supported by the constant use of the compasses for drawing segments of circles, and, though all the figures are more daintily drawn and coloured than is usual with him, the lady in the centre is almost identical with a woman in the foreground of No. 186 (*Sandby Catalogue*). The boy accompanying her recalls Gainsborough's portraits of Princes Adolphus and Augustus of 1783. At that date Thomas Sandby was engaged on the new reredos in St. George's, and it may have been in connexion with this work that he made or had made for him the many drawings of Gothic detail in the Chapel which formed Lots 102, 103, 104, 143, 151 and 203 in his sale of 1799. The present drawing may have been one of these. If large empty spaces were not a constant feature in Thomas Sandby's work, it might have been possible to suppose that the blank on the east wall of the chapel in this drawing was meant eventually to shew his own new design for the reredos. This possibility is strengthened by the tracery of the window above, which, so far as it is shewn, differs from that of Hollar's print (Parthey 1078) in the central light. The little ornament shewn in the smaller side light is the same as in Hollar. On the other hand, if the little tracery shewn were removed and the main mullions only retained, the result would be a bare framework such as once enclosed West's stained glass as shewn in F. Nash's print of 1804. In any case, the drawing represents a moment intermediate between the old arrangement and the reconstruction with West's window and Sandby's reredos. The altar rails shewn clearly in the drawing were removed as part of this rearrangement and were given to the Parish Church. They can there be recognized from this, the only known representation of them, for they are of early XVIII-century workmanship and subsequent to Hollar's print. There is now no trace, nor record, of the removal of the pulpit also shewn in this drawing, although in the contemporary account of the works done in the Chapel mention is made of furniture in Garter blue velvet given by the King for a pulpit which must, like the Communion Table and the Sovereign's and Princes' stalls, similarly adorned, have stood in the Chancel. No pulpit is shewn in this position in

Nash's print of 1804. The seating arrangements and reading desks are also shewn by Nash's print to have been modified. Altogether this drawing is of the greatest topographic importance since it gives, as far as it goes, the only representation of the Chapel as it stood before the changes of 1782 to 1788.

The drawing was acquired in 1909 from Palser. The existing attribution to F. Nash is impossible.

Three further drawings of details in St. George's Chapel may be considered in this connexion. They are of approximately the same date, but scarcely by the same hand. The nearest (17543) is an unfinished drawing of two stalls, in pencil, pen and grey wash, the line thicker and the details less elaborate than in No. 435. It has pencilled sketches apparently for a canopy on the reverse, a calculation and a pencilled inscription 'Berkshire', which it shares with No.

17542 and which proclaims them a comparatively recent purchase from a well-known dealer. No. 17542, on apparently the same paper, is an outline pencil and pen drawing of a perpendicular window at the south-west end of St. George's Chapel, with adjacent fan-vaulting. It has nothing on the reverse. Neither of these two drawings shows compass marks. No. 17638, on thicker paper, is a pen and watercolour drawing of the Dean's and two adjacent stalls, with the canopy of the former and parts of those of the latter. It is inscribed in the margin at foot in pencil 'By Nash'; on the reverse, where there are a small pen and wash detail of a stall with unfinished pencil continuation and a pencil sketch of an ornamental arch continuing as a bridge, the words 'Stalls at Windsor Chapell' are written in an old hand in pencil. The compass has been used freely for the principal drawing, and also for the pencilled arch on the reverse.

Fig. 68. Thomas Sandby: View from Somerset House Gardens with a reconstruction of Inigo Jones' Whitehall Palace. Detail. *Cf.* Plate 110 (Cat. No. S.434).

APPENDIX
PORTRAIT SKETCHES BY THE DIGHTONS

The titles in the first column are those written in an early hand in pencil on the drawings; subsequent manuscript explanations or additions are enclosed in square [ ], editorial comments in round ( ) brackets. The names of the artists in the second column when supplied from the print or detailed Archives Invoices are enclosed in angular ⟨ ⟩ brackets. In all other cases they are as given on the drawings. The engravings to which reference is made in the last column are in the Royal Library; in some cases dates have been supplied from the examples quoted by Sir Henry Hake in his articles in the *Print Collectors' Quarterly*, April, 1926, and October, 1926.

(Dighton del. = Robert Dighton)

		Vol.	p.	Engraved
Mr. Abbott of Covent Garden Theatre	Dighton 1805	I	2	
Colonel Affleck 16th	Dighton del.	I	3	1801
'Je ne vous entends pas' Monsieur Albin Dss of M—st's Friseur		I	4	
Lord Alvanley	Richard Dighton 1819	II	1	1819
An *Arden*-t Admirer of the Fair Sex. [M. Arden]	⟨Robert Dighton⟩	I	5	
Argyle, Duke of	Richard Dighton 1819	II	2	1819
'The Golden Ball' (John Ball)	Richard Dighton 1819	II	3	1819
Dr. Bankhead M.D. Brighton	⟨Robert Dighton⟩	I	6	
Dr. Barnes, Master of Peterhouse, Cambridge	⟨Robert Dighton⟩	I	8	1810
'A View from Baxter's Stables, Cambridge' (Jim Baxter)	Dighton del.	I	10	1810
John Bellingham	D. Dighton del.	II	4	1812
Mr. Bensley in the Tempest	R. Dighton del	I	11B	
Bank House—Bennett	⟨Robert Dighton⟩	I	11A	1803
Fifth Earl of Berkeley, A Noble Commander from South Gloucester	Dighton del.	I	7	1801
Earl of Blessington	Richard Dighton 1822	II	5B	
Mr. Boaden of the Royal Exchange	Richard Dighton 1820	II	5A	1820
Mr. Bobard, The Classical Oxford Coachman	Dighton	I	12	1808
Bodley	⟨Robert Dighton⟩	I	13	
General Bolton	Richard Dighton 1817	II	6A	1817
Mr. [Joseph] Booth in the Poor Soldier (2 versions)	R. Dighton del.	I	14	
Rev. Mr. Bowen of Bath	Dighton del.	I	15	
Mr. Braham as Henry Bertram in Guy Mannering	Richard Dighton 1819	II	6B	
Post Master of Bremen	⟨Robert Dighton⟩	I	130A	
Capt. Broome	⟨Robert Dighton⟩	I	16	
Marquis of Buckingham, *see* Lord Temple				
Mr. Bulkeley, Cleveland Row	Richard Dighton 1820	II	7A	
Sir Charles Bunbury	⟨Robert Dighton⟩	I	18	1802
Sir Francis Burdett	⟨Richard Dighton⟩	II	8	1820
Lord Burghersh	Richard Dighton 1822	II	7B	1822
Sir Charles Burrell, Bt. Sussex Militia	Dighton 1803	I	9	
Hon. Drummond Burrell, *see* Willoughby d'Eresby				
Mr. Byng	Richard Dighton 1820	II	9	1820
Calcraft, Mr., Major Dorset M ...	Dighton del.	I	19	
,, ,, An officer of Lord Paget's Regiment of Light Drag ... 7th	⟨Richard Dighton⟩	I	20	
,, ,, (On horseback, a sketch) 7th L.D.	⟨Richard Dighton⟩	I	20 v.	Eng. n.d.
[Cambridge, Duchess of] An Illustrious Consort Fig. 20	Richard Dighton 1818	II	10	1818
Lord Camelford (Pencil sketch, on reverse of Col. Erskine)		I	42	
Hon. Capt. Capel. (illegible inscription)	Dighton del.	I	21	
Lord Cathcart (incised with stylus)	⟨Richard Dighton⟩	I	22	Eng. n.d.
Mr. de la Chaumette. A view from the Royal Exchange	Richard Dighton 1817	II	27B	1817
Mr. Clarke, A Gentle ride from Exeter 'Change to Pimlico	⟨Robert Dighton⟩	I	24	1812
Dr. William Cleaver, Master of Brazen Nose Coll. Oxon, Bishop of St. Asaph	R. Dighton	I	25	1808
Lord Clermont (on horseback)	⟨Robert Dighton⟩	I	26	1802
,, ,, Brighton (on foot, brush outline, as in preceding from the waist)		I	16 v.	
Mrs. Clutterbuck as Agatha Friburg in Lovers' Vows	Robert Dighton Jun. del. 1805	I	27	
Lord Coleraine	⟨Robert Dighton⟩	I	28	Eng. n.d.
Sir John Colleton	Dighton del.	I	29	
Colonel Cooke	Richard Dighton 1819	II	11	1819
Mr. Copplestone—Proctor—Oxford	Dighton	I	30	
Earl Craven, Major General	Dighton del.	I	31	
Rev. Mr. Crow Public Orator Oxford. (incised and lettered, in reverse, with stylus, 'A celebrated Public Orator')	Dighton	I	32	1808
Major Cullen		I	33	
Mr. Curtis	Richard Dighton 1823	II	13	1823
Sir William Curtis, Bart., M.P.	Richard Dighton 1820	II	12	1820

		Vol.	p.	Engraved
General Dalrymple	Dighton del.	I	34	1804
Capt. F. Darby, 10th Hussars		I	35	
Matthew Day. A Gloomy Day	Dighton del.	I	36	1801
Mr. Delme. A celebrated Gentleman Jockey (sketch)		I	37	
Duke of Devonshire	Richard Dighton 1820	II	14	1820
Dighton Jnr. H.R.H. The Prince of Wales Volunteers	Dighton 1803	I	38	
General Donkin of Bath	Dighton del.	I	39B	1809
Major Downs. (on card; pencil sketch of the same on the reverse)		I	101	
,, ,, A St. James's Volunteer taken from the *Downs*. (Also, on horseback, outline on the reverse.) Exhib. B.F.A.C. 1931–32 No. 62	⟨Robert Dighton⟩	I	40	Eng. n.d.
Lt. General England. A *General* view of *Old England* taken from the Citadel at Plymouth	Dighton del.	I	41	1808
Colonel Erskine		II	42	
Prince Esterhazy	Richard Dighton 1822	II	15A	1822
Dr. Eveleigh. Master of Oriel Coll. Oxford	Dighton del.	I	43	1808
Earl of Fife	Richard Dighton 1821	II	15B	1821
A Fitzroy	Dighton 1809	I	44	
Dr. Ford. Master of Magdalen Hall Oxford	Dighton del.	I	45	1808
Lieut. Fry. 16th Lt. Dr(agoons)	Dighton del.	I	46	1801
Mrs. Fry, Reading to the Prisoners, in Newgate Fig. 21	Richard Dighton 1820	II	16	
Old George Goldsmidt	⟨Robert Dighton⟩	I	55	1802
Duke of Grafton. A Noble Duke (with a copy or replica)	Dighton del.	I	56	1801
Charles Grant. Merchant of London. This Gentleman appeared in Holland, in the British Uniform, and was the cause of the first Insurrection in Favour of the House of Orange	Richard Dighton 1818	II	17	1818
Lord G. Grenville. A Noble Student of Brazen Nose Coll. Oxford	Dighton del.	I	48	1808
Dr. Gretton. A View from Magdalen College, Cambridge	Dighton del.	I	47	1809
Mr. Grosvenor. The Almamater Surgeon Oxford (pencil sketch of same on reverse)	Dighton	I	49	1808
Martha Gunn	⟨Robert Dighton⟩	I	50	
Mr. Hudson Gurney M.P.	Richard Dighton 1820	II	18B	
Mr. Hall. View from the Swan Brewhouse Oxford	Dighton	I	51	1807
Mr. Hartley. Merton Coll. Oxford (incised and lettered, in reverse, with stylus)	Dighton	I	52	1808
Prince of Hesse Homburg	Richard Dighton 1819	II	21B	
Mr. Hilbers the Great Oil Merchant	Richard Dighton 1818	II	19	1818
Mr. Hobhouse	Richard Dighton 1819	II	20	1819
Dr. Horsley, Bishop of St. Asaph	⟨Robert Dighton⟩	I	54	1802
Mrs. House, Mother Goose of Oxford	Dighton del.	I	57	1807
Humphrey Howarth, Esq., M.P.	⟨Robert Dighton⟩	I	53	1803
Dr. Hughes. Master of Jesus Coll. Oxford	Dighton del.	I	58	1808
Mr. Ireland, Oxford. Ireland in Scotland or a trip from Oxford to the Land of Cakes	Dighton del.	I	59	1807
Dr. Jackson. The Dean of Christ Church Oxford	Dighton del.	I	60	1807
Rev. Mr. James. Magdalen Coll. Oxford	Dighton del.	I	61	
Lt. Col. Jenkinson . . . Field Officer	Dighton del.	I	62	1804
Col. Jolliffe. The Hero of the Chase	Richard Dighton 1819	II	22	1819
Sir Tyrwhitt Jones Bart	Richard Dighton 1824	II	23	
Mr. Kean as Lucius Junius, in Brutus	Richard Dighton 1818	II	24	
Mr. Charles Kemble of Covent Garden Theatre	Richard Dighton 1821	II	25	
Rev. Mr. Kett, Trinity Coll. Oxford	Dighton del.	I	63	1807
Mr. Kilner, Senior Fellow of Merton College Oxford	Dighton	I	64	1808
Sir John Lade. Bt. Sir John = a dashing Lad Fig. 19	Dighton del.	I	65	1801
Lord Lake	Richard Dighton 1818	II	26	1818
The Hon. George Lamb	Richard Dighton	II	27A	1819
[Lt. Col.] Geo. Leigh	By R. Dighton, Jun.	I	66	1801
(?) Leigh (sketch, pen)		I	142	
,, (mounted, sketch, pencil)		I	143	
Lt. Col. Leighton, and Lt. Barnes, 4th Dragoons	⟨Robert Dighton⟩	I	67	
Mr. Liston in Love Law and Physic	Richard Dighton 1819	II	28	1819
'Soloman Loan'	⟨Robert Dighton⟩	I	68	1802
J. F. Lockhart M.P. A Friend to Liberty—and Independant Freeman of the City of Oxford		I	69	
The Marquis of Londonderry	Richard Dighton 1821	II	29	Eng. n.d.
Louis XVI (?)	[? Dighton]	I	141	
Sir John Lubbock Bart	Richard Dighton 1824	II	30	
Col. Lygon	Richard Dighton 1822	II	31	1822
Col. Macdermott. An Officer of the 10th Light Dragoons. (Exhib. B.F.A.C. 1931–32, No. 63)		I	70	
Paymaster Manby, 10 Hussars	Dighton del.	I	71	
Mr. Manners	Richard Dighton 1821	II	32	1822
The Bishop of Bristol — Master of Trinity Coll. Cambridge (William Lort Mansell)	⟨Robert Dighton⟩	I	72	Eng. 1810
Sir Murray Maxwell, K.C.B.	Richard Dighton 1818	II	33	Eng. n.d.
Mr. Mellish	Richard Dighton 1822	II	34A	1822

		Vol.	p.	Engraved
Philip Metcalfe Esq., M.P.	Dighton del.	I	73	
Mr. Mills	Richard Dighton 1820	II	34B	
Mr. Montefiore. A view on the Royal Exchange	Richard Dighton 1818	II	35	1818
Dr. John Moore, Ld. Archbp of Canterbury		I	74	
Councellor Morris—of Bath	Dighton del.	I	75	1809
Munden. Wife ! Did you say, Wife?. . . say it again. Speed the Plough	Dighton 1800	I	76	
Beau Nash. (incised with stylus)	Dighton	I	77	1802
Naval Pillar. 1799		I	39A	
Capt. Neville, An Officer in the 2nd Regt. of Life Guards	R. Dighton, Jun.	II	36	
Lord Nugent	Richard Dighton 1822	II	18A	Eng. n.d.
Mr. Otto. Brighton	Dighton del.	I	78	
„ (? Jun.) Sussex M . . . a	Dighton del.	I	79	
Mr. Overend, the famous Bill Broker 'They'll be done, we are obliged to thee'	Richard Dighton 1820	II	37A	1820
'Mr. Paddle'	⟨Robert Dighton⟩	II	37B	
Lord Paget. A Commander of Light Dragoons. (Pencil, and the same on reverse. Exhib. B.F.A.C. 1931–32, No. 77)	R. Dighton, Jun.	I	80	
Mr. Paine of (illegible) Brighton	⟨Robert Dighton⟩	I	81	
Dr. Parsons. Vice Chancellor of Oxford, Master of Baliol Coll. Oxford	Dighton del.	I	82	1808
Admiral Payne. 'Jack P. the little Admiral'	Dighton del.	I	83	1801
Mr. Rd. (?) Pearson, Brighton		I	84	
T. Pelham (Earl of Chichester) Sussex M . . . a	Dighton del.	I	23	
Persian Ambassador	Richard Dighton 1819	II	59 v.	1819
Lord Petersham	R. Dighton, Jun.	II	38	
Capt. Pitt. South Hants M . . . a	Dighton del.	I	85	
Lord Pomfret	Richard Dighton 1823	II	40	
Rev. Mr. Porteous, Brighton	⟨Robert Dighton⟩	I	86	
Mr. Powell inscribed	R. Dighton, Jun.	II	41A	
Lt. Genl. Sir J. Pultney	Dighton del.	I	87	
Raikes Esq., One of the Rakes of London	Richard Dighton 1818	II	41B	1818
Sir Thomas Reid Bart	Richard Dighton 1824	II	42A	
Bill Richmond (A *Striking* view)	Dighton del.	I	88	1810
Sir Samuel Romilly, The late	Richard Dighton 1818	II	42B	
Mr. Rothschild, A View from the Royal Exchange	Richard Dighton 1817	II	43A	1817
Mr. Rowcroft, Consul General for Peru	Richard Dighton 1824	II	43B	1823
Lord Sefton (sketch)	Dighton del.	I	89	1801
„	Richard Dighton 1818	II	44	1818
Lord Seymour	Richard Dighton 1820	II	45	Eng. n.d.
Sir Horace Seymour, A View from Knightsbridge Barracks	Richard Dighton	II	46	1817
Alderman Sir James Shaw	Richard Dighton 1819	II	47	1819
Rev. Dr. Shepherd—of Bath	Dighton del.	I	90	1809
Major Genl. Slade	⟨Robert Dighton⟩	I	91	1802
Dr. Smith. Master of Pembroke Coll. Oxford	R. Dighton	I	92	1808
Starkey, Staffordshire	⟨Robert Dighton⟩	I	93	
Sir Walter Stirling Bart.	Richard Dighton 1824	II	48A	1824
G. F. Stratton; Rangers Lodge near Enstone Oxon		I	94	
Mr. Stump—Stock Broker—Exchange Alley	Dighton	I	95	1803
Styles, Auctioneer, Brighton	Dighton del.	I	96	
Mr. Talbot	Richard Dighton 1818	II	48B	1818
Mr. Tattersall	Dighton del.	I	97	1802
„	Richard Dighton 1822	II	49A	1822
Capt. G. F. Teasdale	Dighton 1805	I	98	
Lord Temple, a View of a Temple near Buckingham	Dighton del. 1811	I	17	1811
Arthur Thistlewood taken at the Old Bailey Monday April 17, 1820	Richard Dighton 1820	II	49B	
Mr. Tongue	Richard Dighton 1822	II	50	
Townsend	Dighton del.	I	99	1804
Mr. P. Travers (or Trevor) Senr. A Fashionable Jew Travers-ing the Steyne at Brighton	Dighton del.	I	100	1801
Miss M. Tree of Covent Garden Theatre	Richard Dighton 1821	II	51	
Trevis jnr. (sketch on *verso*)	Dighton del.	I	117	
Col. Upton	Richard Dighton 1817	II	52A	1817
M. Paul de Vallabrigues Husband of Madame Catalani		II	52B	
Dick Vaughan. The Cambridge Telegraph. Dick Vaughan or Hell Fire Dick	Dighton del.	I	102	1809
Mr. Wade Master of the Ceremonies, Brighton	⟨Robert Dighton⟩	I	103	1803
Mr. Waithman	Richard Dighton 1818	II	53	1818
Lt. Col. Wall, Sth. Glos. M . . . a	Dighton del.	I	104	
Capt. Walwyn „ „ „	Dighton del.	I	105	
Mr. Want	⟨Robert Dighton⟩	I	106	
Marquess Wellesley, a Great Coat	R.D. Jnr.	II	54A	
The Duke of Wellington	Richard Dighton 1819	II	54B	1819
The Earl of Westmorland	Richard Dighton 1821	II	55	1821
Lord Willoughby de Eresby	Richard Dighton 1818	II	56	1818
Sir Robert Wilson	Richard Dighton 1821	II	57A	1821
Miss Wilson in Artaxerxes	Richard Dighton 1821	II	58A	

		Vol.	p.	Engraved
Thomas Wilson Esq., M.P. . . . . Richard Dighton 1823 .		II	57B	1824
Mr. Wombwell . . . . Richard Dighton 1820 .		II	58B	1820
Rev. Mr. Wood, St John's Coll. Cambridge . . . . Dighton . . .	I	107	1809
Alderman Wood (Sir Matthew) . . . . . . Richard Dighton 1819 .		II	58 v.	1819
Sir Rd. Worsley, South Hants. M . . . a . . . . . Dighton del. . .	I	108	
Lord Yarmouth . . . . Richard Dighton 1818 .		II	59	1818

and forty-two unidentified portrait drawings: Officers in uniform, Vol. I, pp. 1, 109–116, 118–126, 140, of which Nos. 114, 121 and 125 are signed R. Dighton, Jun., and No. 116, R. Dighton, Jun., 1805. No. 122, 'Views at Camp', is engraved with signature Dighton, Jun.; Civilians, Vol. I, pp. 127–131, and Vol. II, pp. 39 and 60.

Also the following subject drawings:

		Vol.	p.
'Vat you ax for this cane' 'Jew and Doctor' . . . . Dighton 1800 . .		I	132A
Turnpike Gate—Knight—1799		I	132B
Characters from Roderick Random (9) . . . . Dighton del. . . .		I	133–135
The Contrast, The Salutation, Sally Rescued by Thomas . . Dighton del. . . .		I	136
Two or a Trade can never agree: (Fishwives) . . . Dighton del. . . .		I	137
,, ,, ,, (Orange sellers) . . .		I	138
Flower girl and Buck . . . . Dighton 1807 . .		I	139

Seven drawings by the Dightons are in *Military Drawings*, Vol. V, all of 1807 and 1808. One of these is signed Robert Dighton, Jun.; three, R. Dighton, Jun. Vol. XI has nine by the Dightons and Vol. XII, two. Three of those in Vol. XI are signed Robert Dighton, Jun., 1805; four, R. Dighton, Jun., 1804 or 1805. Six of these signatures in Vol. XI, those on the unidentified portrait drawings (Nos. 114, etc.) mentioned above and on Neville (II, 36), Lord Paget (I, 80), and Lord Petersham (II, 38), correspond with the hand of the invoice from Robert Dighton, Jun., which is receipted 'R. J. Dighton', and that of the signed prints.

PLATES

I. SAMUEL COOPER: KING CHARLES II. 1661 (Cat. No. 133)

2. BENJAMIN WEST: KING GEORGE III. About 1777
(Cat. No. 639)

3. BENJAMIN WEST: QUEEN CHARLOTTE. 1777
(Cat. No. 640)

4. JOHN DOWNMAN: EDWARD, DUKE OF KENT. About 1785 (Cat. No. 188)

5. HUGH DOUGLAS HAMILTON: KING GEORGE III.
1769 (Cat. No. 283)

6. HUGH DOUGLAS HAMILTON: QUEEN CHARLOTTE.
1771 (Cat. No. 288)

7. HUGH DOUGLAS HAMILTON:
GEORGE, PRINCE OF WALES. 1769 (Cat. No. 284)

8. HUGH DOUGLAS HAMILTON:
FREDERICK, DUKE OF YORK. 1769 (Cat. No. 285)

9.   SIR THOMAS LAWRENCE: THE PRINCE REGENT. 1814 (Cat. No. 412)

10. HENRY EDRIDGE: QUEEN CHARLOTTE.
1803 (Cat. No. 198)

11. HENRY EDRIDGE: KING GEORGE III.
1803 (Cat. No. 197)

12. HENRY EDRIDGE: PRINCESS AUGUSTA.
1802 (Cat. No. 206)

13. HENRY EDRIDGE: PRINCESS MARY.
1802 (Cat. No. 219)

14. HENRY EDRIDGE: PRINCESS ELIZABETH.
1804 (Cat. No. 210)

15. HENRY EDRIDGE: PRINCESS SOPHIA.
About 1802 (Cat. No. 222)

16. HENRY EDRIDGE: PRINCESS AMELIA.
1804 (Cat. No. 225)

17. HENRY EDRIDGE: PRINCESS AMELIA.
About 1802 (Cat. No. 226)

18. HENRY EDRIDGE: ADOLPHUS, DUKE OF
CAMBRIDGE. 1802 (Cat. No. 216)

19. HENRY EDRIDGE: ERNEST, DUKE OF
CUMBERLAND. 1802 (Cat. No. 214)

20. HENRY EDRIDGE: AUGUSTUS, DUKE OF
SUSSEX. 1806 (Cat. No. 215)

21. HENRY EDRIDGE: EDWARD, DUKE OF
KENT. 1802 (Cat. No. 201)

22. HENRY EDRIDGE: PRINCESS SOPHIA. 1802 (Cat. No. 220)

23. RICHARD COSWAY: THE GLOUCESTER FAMILY. About 1805 (Cat. No. 150)

24. ROBERT ADAM: A CASTELLATED BRIDGE. About 1780 (Cat. No. 17)

General Design of a Transparent Illumination proposed to have been executed in the Queens Garden for Honour of His Majestys Birth Day the 4.th June 1763.

25. ROBERT ADAM and (?) G. B. CIPRIANI: THE ILLUMINATION IN THE QUEEN'S GARDEN. June 4 1763
(Cat. No. 18)

26.　DAVID ALLAN: PIAZZA DI SPAGNA DURING THE CARNIVAL. 1775 (Cat. No. 25)

27.　DAVID ALLAN: FRENCH GAIETY AND ITALIAN MAGNIFICENCE. 1775 (Cat. No. 28)

28. DAVID ALLAN: PIAZZA MONTANARA DURING THE CARNIVAL. 1775 (Cat. No. 29)

29. DAVID ALLAN: MUSICIANS IN THE CORSO DURING THE CARNIVAL. 1775 (Cat. No. 30)

30.   LORD AYLESFORD: VIEW ON THE MEDWAY. About 1790 (Cat. No. 32)

31.   LORD AYLESFORD: VIEW OF ROCHESTER. About 1790 (Cat. No. 32)

32.   GEORGE BARRET: COAST SCENE. About 1815 (Cat. No. 41)

33. LOUIS PHILIPPE BOITARD: A TAILOR'S SHOP. Engraved 1749 (Cat. No. 71)

34. HENRY WILLIAM BUNBURY: THE COUNTRY CLUB. Engraved 1788 (Cat. No. 102)

35. JAMES BRUCE and LUIGI BALUGANI: THE TEMPLES AT SUFFETULA.
About 1770 (Cat. No. 94)

36. JAMES BRUCE and LUIGI BALUGANI: ENTRANCE TO THE HIERON AT SUFFETULA.
About 1770 (Cat. No. 94)

37. JAMES BRUCE and LUIGI BALUGANI: THE TEMPLE OF JUPITER AT TEBESSA.
About 1770 (Cat. No. 94)

38. JAMES BRUCE and LUIGI BALUGANI: THE AMPHITHEATRE AT THISDRUS.
About 1770 (Cat. No. 94)

39. FRANCESCO BARTOLOZZI: DR. ARNE. Engraved 1782 (Cat. No. 47)

40. G. B. CIPRIANI: BARTOLOZZI ASLEEP. About 1770 (Cat. No. 125)

The Forepart of the
First Coach

41. SIR WILLIAM CHAMBERS and G. B. CIPRIANI: DESIGN FOR THE ROYAL COACH. About 1760
(Cat. No. 116)

42. G. B. CIPRIANI: DESIGN FOR THE MONUMENT AT SOMERSET HOUSE. About 1775 (Cat. No. 120)

43. J. B. C. CHATELAIN: LANDSCAPE. About 1760 (Cat. No. 119)

44. J. R. COZENS: AN ENGLISH COUNTRY HOUSE. About 1785 (Cat. No. 158)

45. ROBERT CRONE: CLASSICAL LANDSCAPE. About 1770 (Cat. No. 161)

46. THOMAS GAINSBOROUGH: LANDSCAPE COMPOSITION. About 1770 (Cat. No. 269)

47. ROBERT DIGHTON: ELECTION SCENE IN COVENT GARDEN. 1784 (Cat. No. 183)

48. DENIS DIGHTON: CORONATION BANQUET, 1821. (Cat. No. 182)

49. JOHANNES ECKSTEIN: THE CAMEL AT EXETER 'CHANGE. 1798 (Cat. No. 194)

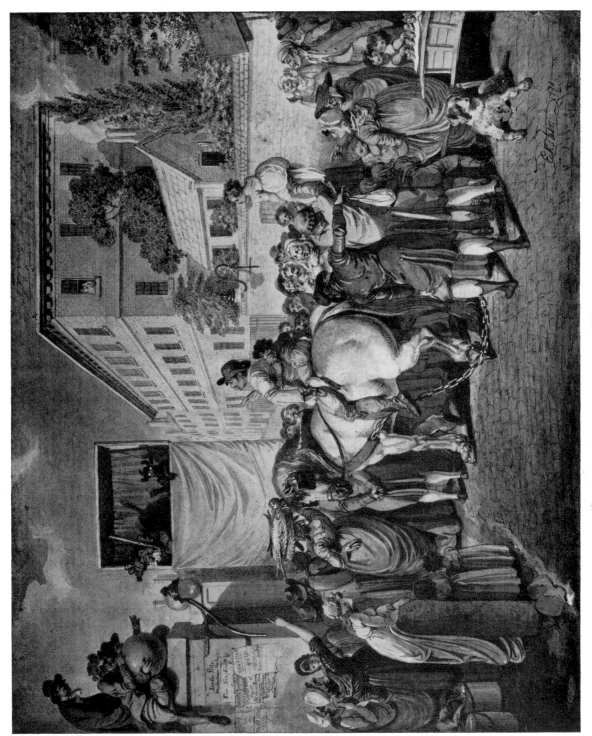

50. JOHANNES ECKSTEIN: PUNCH AND JUDY. 1798 (Cat. No. 193)

51. JOSEPH FARINGTON: WINDSOR FROM ST. LEONARD'S. About 1790 (Cat. No. 255).

52. JOSEPH FARINGTON: WINDSOR FROM THE NORTH-WEST. About 1790 (Cat. No. 243)

53. JOSEPH FARINGTON: WINDSOR FROM ETON. About 1790 (Cat. No. 247)

54. JOSEPH FARINGTON: WINDSOR FROM ETON MEADOWS. About 1790 (Cat. No. 251)

55. JOSEPH FARINGTON and MARY SMIRKE: VIEW OF WORCESTER. 1821 (Cat. No. 260)

56. THOMAS HEARNE: WINDSOR CASTLE: THE SOUTH FRONT. About 1775 (Cat. No. 322)

57. WILLIAM HOGARTH: FALSTAFF EXAMINING HIS RECRUITS. About 1730 (Cat. No. 345)

58.   WILLIAM HOGARTH: SCENE IN THE BEGGAR'S OPERA.   About 1730 (Cat. No. 344)

59. WILLIAM HOGARTH: THE SOUTH SEA BUBBLE. 1721 (Cat. No. 330)

60. WILLIAM HOGARTH: THE BATHOS. 1764 (Cat. No. 356)

61. WILLIAM HOGARTH: THE PROPORTIONS OF GARRICK AND QUIN. 1746 (Cat. No. 351)

62. WILLIAM HOGARTH: HEADPIECE TO THE JACOBITE'S JOURNAL. 1747 (Cat. No. 352)

63. WENCESLAUS HOLLAR: WINDSOR FROM THE NORTH-EAST. About 1640 (Cat. No. 369)

64. WENCESLAUS HOLLAR: THE NORTH BANK OF THE THAMES FROM WESTMINSTER. About 1640
(Cat. No. 371)

65.   WENCESLAUS HOLLAR: VIEW OF RICHMOND. 1638 (Cat. No. 373)

66.   WENCESLAUS HOLLAR: VIEW OF ROEROORT (RUHRORT). 1634 (Cat. No. 375)

67. WILLIAM LANE: STUDY FOR A GROUP OF MUSICIANS. 1810 (Cat. No. 408)

68. MARCELLUS LAROON: A FRENCHMAN AT BOW-STREET. 1740 (Cat. No. 409)

69. SAWREY GILPIN: A SADDLE HORSE WITH GROOM. About 1760 (Cat. No. 272)

70. FRANCIS SMITH: THE AUDIENCE OF THE GRAND SIGNIOR. About 1764 (Cat. No. 592)

71.   SAWREY GILPIN: THE PAD. Engraved 1760 (Cat. No. 273)

72.   FRANCIS SMITH: THE AUDIENCE OF THE GRAND VIZIER. About 1764 (Cat. No. 593)

73. ISAAC OLIVER: MOSES STRIKING THE ROCK. About 1625 (Cat. No. 459)

74. BERNARD LENS II: WINDSOR CASTLE FROM THE NORTH. About 1700 (Cat. No. 418)

75.   ISAAC OLIVER: NYMPHS AND SATYRS. About 1625 (Cat. No. 460)

76.   LADY MORDAUNT: WINDSOR CASTLE FROM THE NORTH-WEST. 1819 (Cat. No. 439)

77. THOMAS ROWLANDSON: THE ENGLISH REVIEW. 1786 (Cat. No. 517)

78. THOMAS ROWLANDSON : THE FRENCH REVIEW . 1786 (Cat. No. 518)

79. THOMAS ROWLANDSON: THE SCHOOL OF ELOQUENCE. About 1775 (Cat. No. 510)

80. THOMAS ROWLANDSON: BOOKSELLER AND AUTHOR. 1784 (Cat. No. 513)

81. THOMAS ROWLANDSON: SUNDAY MORNING. 1798 (Cat. No. 524)

82. THOMAS ROWLANDSON: OVERSET. About 1785 (Cat. No. 516)

83. THOMAS ROWLANDSON: 'HIGH SPIRITS'. About 1790 (Cat. No. 521)

84. THOMAS ROWLANDSON: HAYMAKERS AT REST. 1798 (Cat. No. 525)

85. THOMAS ROWLANDSON: THE CHAMBER OF GENIUS. Engraved 1812 (Cat. No. 541)

86. THOMAS ROWLANDSON: TWO MEN ASLEEP ON A SOFA. About 1785 (Cat. No. 514)

87. THOMAS ROWLANDSON: RAG FAIR. About 1801 (Cat. No. 528)

88. THOMAS ROWLANDSON: TARR POINT (TORPOINT). About 1805 (Cat. No. 532)

89. THOMAS ROWLANDSON: HAMPTON COURT, THE WEST FRONT. About 1810 (Cat. No. 537)

90. THOMAS ROWLANDSON: HAMPTON COURT FROM THE RIVER. About 1810 (Cat. No. 536)

91.   AUGUSTUS CHARLES PUGIN: LOWER REGENT STREET. 1817 (Cat. No. 482)

92.   JOHN INIGO RICHARDS: A GOTHIC HALL. 1794 (Cat. No. 492)

93. THOMAS STOTHARD: DESIGN FOR A TRANSPARENCY. 1810 (Cat. No. 606)

94. BENJAMIN WEST, ascribed to: 'THE APOTHEOSIS OF PRINCESS CHARLOTTE'. About 1817
(Cat. No. 642)

95. J. RIGAUD, attributed to: CLAREMONT. About 1750 (Cat. No. 506)

96. WILLIAM WOOLLETT: VIEW OF TWO FARMHOUSES. About 1770 (Cat. No. 688)

97.   GEORGE VERTUE: WILLIAM PINKETHMAN IN 'LOVE MAKES A MAN'.
About 1720 (Cat. No. 624)

98. SAMUEL DE WILDE: SARAH HARLOWE IN 'THE ANATOMIST'. 1805 (Cat. No. 659)

99. SIR JAMES THORNHILL: DESIGN FOR A CEILING. About 1715 (Cat. No. 610)

100. RICHARD WESTALL, attributed to: THE MARRIAGE OF PRINCESS CHARLOTTE OF WALES AND PRINCE LEOPOLD. 1816

(Cat. No. 647)

101. SIR DAVID WILKIE: A COTTAGE GIRL SEATED.
About 1819 (Cat. No. 661)

102. SIR DAVID WILKIE: ARRIVAL OF KING GEORGE IV AT HOLYROOD. 1822 (Cat. No. 663)

103. SIR DAVID WILKIE: KING GEORGE IV HOLDING A DRAWING-ROOM. 1822 (Cat. No. 664)

104. JOHN WOOTTON: HUNTING SCENE. 1734 (Cat. No. 691)

105. J. M.: THE LONG-WAYS DANCE. 1785 (Cat. No. 707)

106. JOHN WYCK, attributed to: WINDSOR CASTLE FROM THE SOUTH-WEST. About 1700 (Cat. No. 697)

107. ANONYMOUS: WINDSOR FROM THE NORTH-WEST. About 1675 (Cat. No. 737)

108. JOHANN ZOFFANY: VENUS, CUPIDS AND SATYRS. About 1779 (Cat. No. 700)

109. JOHANN ZOFFANY: TRITON AND NEREID. About 1779 (Cat. No. 701)

110. THOMAS SANDBY: VIEW FROM SOMERSET HOUSE GARDENS WITH A RECONSTRUCTION OF WHITEHALL PALACE. About 1780 (Supplement No. 434)

111. PAUL SANDBY: A VIEW IN WINDSOR PARK. About 1790 (Supplement No. 432)

112.   THOMAS SANDBY, attributed to: THE EAST END OF ST. GEORGE'S CHAPEL. About 1782
(Supplement No. 435)

113. PAUL SANDBY: WINDSOR CASTLE FROM DATCHET LANE. 1768 (Supplement No. 430)

114. PAUL SANDBY: MOUNTEBANKS. 1758 (Supplement No. 431)

115. PAUL SANDBY: THE DEPUTY RANGER'S HOUSE, WINDSOR PARK. About 1800 (Supplement No. 428)

116. PAUL SANDBY: VIEW IN THE GARDENS OF THE DEPUTY RANGER'S HOUSE. About 1800
(Supplement No. 429)

117. PAUL SANDBY: WINDSOR CASTLE FROM PRIEST HILL. 1792 (Supplement No. 427)

CONCORDANCE

INDEX OF PERSONS AND SUBJECTS

INDEX OF PLACES

CONCORDANCE

Windsor Inventory No.	Oppé Catalogue No.	Windsor Inventory No.	Oppé Catalogue No.	Windsor Inventory No.	Oppé Catalogue No.	Windsor Inventory No.	Oppé Catalogue No.	Windsor Inventory No.	Oppé Catalogue No.
2516	56	13355	27	13494	353	13632	257	13862	217
6643	612	13356	28	13495	361	13633	258	13863	227
6649	119	13357	30	13496	366	13634	250	13864	197
6650	161	13358	22	13497	343	13635	247	13865	198
11610–11714 }	94	13359	23	13498	367	13636	249	13866	225
12872	171	13360	24	13500	408	13637	245	13867	211
13030	61	13371	41	13501	413	13638	244	13868	200
13245	111	13372	42	13502	414	13639	243	13869	215
13246	115	13373	43	13512	424	13640	252	13874	694
13247	112	13374	40	13525	471	13641	253	13875	695
13248	120	13375	59	13526	467	13642	246	13876	696
13249	37	13379	63	13527	468	13643	255	13883	283
13250	162	13380	69	13528	460	13644	254	13884	288
13251	38	13381	70	13529	459	13645	256	13885	284
13252	39	13382	68	13537	483	13685	535	13886	285
13253	405	13385	232	13538	493	13686	531	13887	286
13257	279	13386	233	13539	494	13687	533	13888	287
13258	82	13408	152	13540	495	13688	532	13891	268
13259	81	13411	167	13541	496	13689	534	13892	174
13262	377	13412	165	13545	500	13690	537	13893	137
13263	369	13413	166	13550	473	13691	536	13894	160
13264	370	13414	660	13553	578	13692	528	13898	666
13265	378	13415	659	13554	576	13693	539	13901	290
13266	371	13416	183	13555	580	13694	523	13902	291
13267	373	13420	251	13556	573	13695	514	13903	292
13268	372	13421	248	13557	579	13696	519	13904	293
13269	379	13426	380	13558	577	13697	520	13905	294
13270	374	13427	270	13559	574	13698	526	13906	295
13271	375	13428	269	13560	575	13699	512	13907	296
13272	376	13432	272	13563	596	13700	547	13908	297
13279	71	13433–13440 }	273	13564	597	13701	530	13909	298
13280	325	13445	314	13565	594	13702	542	13910	299
13281	703	13456	354	13566	595	13703	524	13911	300
13282	701	13457	352	13567	60	13704	513	13912	301
13283	702	13458	355	13568–13571 }	598	13705	540	13913	302
13284	699	13459	332	13573	599	13706	541	13914	303
13285	700	13460	333	13574	607	13707	516	13915	304
13286	698	13461	334	13575	608	13708	525	13916	305
13287	411	13462	335	13579	624	13709	521	13917	306
13288	572	13463	336	13580	626	13710	546	13918	307
13290	388	13464	337	13581	625	13711	522	13919	308
13291	121	13465	338	13586	641	13712	515	13920	309
13292	122	13466	356	13589	658	13713	511	13921	498
13293	126	13467–13470 }	328	13590	669	13714	544	13924	93
13294	125	13471	349	13591	667	13715	545	13928	550
13295	50	13472	341	13592	668	13716	549	13930	484
13296	47	13473	360	13593	663	13717	527	13931	485
13297	58	13474	342	13594	688	13718	529	13932	713
13298	54	13475	357	13595	689	13719	510	13933	177
13299	53	13476	331	13596	691	13720	517	13934	154
13300	57	13477	351	13598	64	13721	518	13935	186
13301	52	13478	340	13599	65	13760	620	13936	97
13302	55	13479	330	13600	66	13761	630	13937	96
13303	49	13480	364	13603	135	13762	718	13938	490
13304	588	13481	329	13604	724	13763	707	13985	212
13305	48	13482	346	13605	543	13848	229	13986	213
13306	51	13483	359	13606	181	13849	228	13987	208
13307	105	13484	358	13607	704	13850	202	13988	226
13308	410	13485	365	13608	499	13851	201	13990	670
13309	409	13486	339	13609	242	13852	214	13991	644
13310	404	13487	344	13610	715	13853	209	13999	117
13312	192	13488	348	13611	327	13854	206	14000	116
13313	193	13489	347	13612	416	13855	223	14035	472
13314	149	13490	350	13613	417	13856	224	14039	134
13351	21	13491	345	13624	128	13857	220	14040	133
13352	25	13492	362	13625	129	13858	218	14043	241
13353	26	13493	363	13626	130	13859	219	14203	169
13354	29			13630	182	13860	203	14209	67
						13861	204	14225	136

Windsor Inventory No.	Oppé Catalogue No.	Windsor Inventory No.	Oppé Catalogue No.	Windsor Inventory No.	Oppé Catalogue No.	Windsor Inventory No.	Oppé Catalogue No.	Windsor Inventory No.	Oppé Catalogue No.
14230	172	17072	584	17336	604	17529	234	17661	83
14246	216	17073	582	17337–17349	163	17530	235	17662	84
14247	210	17079	486	17353	601	17531	236	17663	85
14248	207	17080	487	17354	157	17532	237	17664	86
14266	289	17090	489	17355–17364	164	17533	747(8)	17665	187
14300	476	17091	488	17366	745	17535	747(1)	17666A	89
14313	538	17092	481	17367	501	17540	747(3)	17666B	90
14587	141	17093	482	17368	502	17541	747(2)	17666C	91
14564	265	17094	627	17369	95	17546	259	17667	92
14611	142	17095	628	17370	455	17551	156	17668	453
14672	741	17096	629	17371	138	17553	140	17669	456
14710	264	17098	153	17372	139	17557	633	17670	102
14714	426	17099	222	17373	740	17558	634	17671	103
14735	581	17123	492	17374	565	17559	635	17672	104
14737	589	17124	110	17375	564	17560	34	17673	106
14738	590	17125–17129	444	17376	747(4)	17561	35	17674	107
14749	610	17130	585	17377	747(5)	17562	36	17675	108
14750	159	17131	568	17378	747(6)	17563	661	17676	109
14751	621	17132	566	17379	239	17564	603	17677	673
14752	622	17133	567	17380	231	17566	276	17678	675
14765	180	17134	649	17381	747(7)	17567	277	17679	676
14767	671	17135	651	17382	747(9)	17571	442	17680	677
14768	664	17136	650	17383	747(10)	17576	240	17681	678
14769	665	17137–17138	751	17385	636	17577	205	17682	679
14983	146	17139	587	17386	450	17590	609	17683	680
14984	147	17140	274	17387	451	17591	639	17684	681
14985	143	17141	586	17388	447	17592	640	17685	682
16405–16406	271	17142	593	17389	448	17595	591	17686	683
16491	720	17143	592	17390	449	17599	383	17687	684
16598	175	17144	368	17395	406	17601	652	17688	685
16601	280	17155	613	17396	742	17602	653	17689	686
16602	281	17157	753	17397	743	17603	654	17690	674
16666–16675	437	17159	690	17398	381	17604	655	17691	687
16676–16688	719	17160	632	17399	322	17605	656	17692	548
17010	88	17161	631	17400–17404	323	17606	605	17693	706
17011	429	17178	261	17405	99	17610	716	17694	708
17012	428	17179	260	17406	98	17612	324	17695	709
17013	474	17182	752	17407	100	17614	72	17696	710
17016	384	17194	385	17408	637	17617	46	17697	711
17017	638	17195	386	17412	737	17619	646	17698	722
17018	457	17196	714	17413	738	17620	11	17699	723
17019	188	17235	423	17414	418	17621	438	17700	725
17020	191	17236	195	17415	697	17622	439	17701	727
17021	190	17237	196	17416	262	17623	440	17702	726
17022	189	17239	33	17417	407	17624	441	17703	728
17023	504	17252	326	17418	672	17626	662	17704	729
17024	503	17253–17254	422	17420	238	17627	118	17705	730
17025	505	17255	316	17442	155	17628	469	17706	731
17026	475	17256	310	17444	509	17629	647	17707	732
17027	497	17257	317	17445	507	17631	657	17708	733
17028	267	17258	712	17446	508	17634	611	17711	717
17029	692	17259	387	17447	617	17636	606	17712	734
17030	693	17260	311	17448	583	17637	184	17713	735
17032	150	17264	313	17453	178	17643A	18	17714	736
17033	151	17265	312	17454	739	17643B	19	17715A	749
17034	479	17266	315	17456	452	17643C	20	17715B	750
17035	480	17272	434	17460	131	17644	382	17716	614
17044	44	17273	433	17461	619	17645	230	17717–17719	615
17045	45	17274	435	17462	446	17646	132	17720	616
17051	158	17275	436	17463	506	17647	168	17721	641
17054	176	17299	17	17484	425	17648	170	17962A, B, C	87
17055	192	17301	319	17486	623	17649	62	17963	148
17058	266	17309	445	17489	648	17650	101	17964	127
17063	427	17311	263	17500	144	17651	73	17965	419
17064	454	17314–17321	278	17501–17513	179	17652	74	17969	123
17067	491	17322	600	17514	320	17653	75	17970	124
17068	563	17323	199	17515	744	17654	76	17983	400
17069	569	17324	221	17527	145	17655	77	17984	390
17070	571	17327	602	17528	746	17656	78	17985	392
17071	570					17657	79	17986	396
						17658	80	17987	402
						17659	282	17988	394
						17660	443		

Windsor Inventory No.	Oppé Catalogue No.
17989	389
17990	395
17991	393
17992	399
17993	391
17994	397
17995	401
17996	398
17997 17998	403
17999	618
18000	275
L.C.D.	
668	113
669	114
702	643
704	412
1337	271
1838	645
2354	415

Windsor Souvenir Volume	Oppé Catalogue No.
IV, p. 23a	554
IV, p. 23b	555
V, p. 31	558
V, p. 33	559
VI, p. 1	31
VI, p. 2a	477
VI, p. 2b	478
VI, p. 2c	552
VI, p. 2d	553
VI, p. 3	721
VI, p. 4	318
VI, p. 9	556
VI, p. 10	557
VI, p. 13	560
VI, p. 16	561
VI, p. 22	562
VI, p. 68	430
VI, p. 69	431

Windsor Inventory No.	Sandby Supplem't No.
17455	435
17542 17543	435
17549	422
17550	423
17554	419
17555	420
17556	421
17584	434
17585	424
17586	425
17593	427
17594	426
17596	429
17597	428
17598	430
17600	431
17608	433
17630	432
17638	435

For persons represented in the series of character studies by the Dightons, see the Appendix on pages 118–121.

	Cat. Nos.		Cat. Nos.
Aboukir, Landing at	175	Billington, Mrs.	53
Academy Figures	346, 348	'Bishop, Anna'	417
Actor, Progress of an	687	*Bishop, Petition to a*	722
Alexander I of Russia	67	*Blackguards, a Brace of*	546
Alfred, Prince	302	Bloodworth, Capt.	691
All Fours	106	Boaden, Miss, 68	68
Allen, T.	92	*Bookseller and Author*	513
Amelia, Princess	136, 225, 226, 309, 498, 589	*Boys Peeping at Nature*	343
American War, caricature on	726	*Bridge, A Roman*	476
Amherst, William Lord	715	*Britannia offering a Crown*	618
Analysis of Beauty, Vignette for	354	Brooks, Mr.	717
'Angelica and Medor'	52	Bruce, James	Introd., p. 8
Anhalt Zerbst, Prince of (?)	736	*Bruiser, The*	355
ANIMALS		*Bryan's, Major, Reflection*	731
camel	194	*Buck's Beauty and Rowlandson's Con-*	
cow	607	noisseur	526
dog	573	Burlem	717
fowls	580		
dead hare	578		
horses	272, 273, 572 ff.	*Calves' Head Club, The*	358, 359
lion	608	Cambridge, Adolphus D. of	216, 301
Anne, Princess Royal	695	CARICATURES	
Anne, Queen	267	Military	128, 132
ANONYMOUS PORTRAITS	49, 69, 60, 115, 135, 313, 380, 484, 485, 512, 581, 694	Political	62, 76, 81, 453, 512, 551, 675, 682, 706, 725–731
Anspach, Elizabeth, Margravine of	152	Social	73–6, 79, 82–6, 101–4, 106–9, 129,
Antiope and Jupiter	463		130, 132, 170, 187,
Anything will do for an officer	522		196, 279, 423, 456,
ARCHITECTURAL DRAWINGS	1, 3, 4, 17–20, 599–602, 609–611, 699, 701, 705		614–6, 673, 674, 676–81, 683, 707, 708–11, 715, 717,
Arne, Dr.	47		723, 724, 735, 736
Ashe	408	Theatrical	77, 78, 105, 456,
Assumption, The	63		687, 716, 735
Astronomers, The Mock	196	Caroline, Queen	151, 293
Aubrey, J.	424	Cart and horses	270
Auction, The	364	Cartwright, Major J. (?)	512
Audiences of Grand Signior and Grand Vizier	592, 593	Cavendish, Col. C.	316
Augusta, Princess	203–8, 305	*Chamber of Genius*	541
Augusta, Princess of Wales	39	'Charke, Charlotte'	505
Author and Bookseller	513	Charles I, King	469, 626
Azoff-ud-Dowlah	698	Charles II, King	33, 133, 134, 629
		Charles Edward, Prince	385, 386, 714
		Charlotte of Wales, Princess, *see* Wales	
Balugani, Luigi	94	Charlotte, Princess Royal	200, 304
Barber, A.	732	Charlotte, Queen	154, 198, 199, 268, 288, 290, 640
Barrington, Mr.	717		
Bartolozzi, F.	125, 588	*Chelsea Pensioner, A*	357
Barwell, Mr.	717	Churchill, C.	355
Bathos, The	356	Cibber, Colley	503
Battle of the Nile	31	Theophilus	504, 692
'Beauclerk, Lady D.'	55	Cipriani, G. B.	50
Before	361	Clare, Lord	614
Beggars	734	CLASSICAL SUBJECTS	57, 122, 126, 389–
and riders	410		403, 460, 463
Beggars' Opera, Scene in	344	Coach, State	116, 117, 123, 124
Beggars' Opera Burlesqued	339	Cockermouth Post Coach	516
Belgians, King of, *see* Leopold, Prince		*Consultation, The*	547
Bethesda, Pool of, figure for	346	*Contretemps, A*	545

	Cat. Nos.
Conversation, A	411
Conversation, A Midnight	511
Cornwallis, M.P.	691
Coronation scenes	181, 182, 658
Correggio, drawings after	463, 464
Country Club, The	102
Cozens, Alexander	Introd., p. 10
Craggs, R. Nugent	614
Craven, Elizabeth Lady, see Anspach	
Crawford, Col. R.	733
Cricket Match	636
Cruelty, Reward of	353
Cumberland, Ernest D. of	214, 299
Cumberland, William D. of	Supplement S.422
Cupid and Psyche	702
Dalton, Richard	Introd., pp. 7, 8
Dance of Death	458
D'Avalos Allegory	461
Debating Society, The Grand	510
Della Sommaglia, Cardinal	272
Derby, Earl of	681
DESIGNS	
a bridge	Supplement S.433
ceiling	610, 699
diploma	603
frieze	599, 701
frontispiece	275, 376, 389
lunette	600, 601
pediment	705
ticket	604
title-page	618
transparency	606
tympanum	602
Devonshire, Duchess of, Elizabeth	415
Georgina	60
Dighton, Denis	Introd., p. 11
Doctors in Harlot's Progress	340
Dodd, Mr.	735
'Dog and Duck, At the'	718
Duel, The	683
Dugdale, Monasticon, frontispiece	376
Dundas	551
Edward VI, King	627
Edwin, Mr.	77, 78
Election Scenes	183, 706, 727
Election, The Mock	321
Elizabeth, Princess, see Hesse-Homburg	
Elizabeth, Queen	457
Eloquence, School of	510
Elvill, Sir John, house of	426
Encampments of 1780	280, 281
English Apathy	676
English Review, The	517
Fair at Mahon	720
Falkland, Viscount H.	312
Falstaff's Arrest	685
Falstaff examining his recruits	345, 686
Falstaff playing the Prince	105
Farinelli, see Senesino	
Farren, Elizabeth	497, 681
Fell, Mr.	717
Fencing	719
	Cat. Nos.
Fielding, Col. R.	317
Fleet, Review of	720
Flowers, drawings of	432
Fortune Teller, A	195
Fox, C. J.	81, 675, 706, 727
French Review, The	518
Frenchman at Bow Street, A	409
Front-is-piss	366
Full Piece, A	729
Gainsborough, T.	Introd., p. 9
Game at Hazard, see Hazard Table	
Garrick	242, 351, 499, 704
Genius, Chamber of	541
George I, King	405, 618, 712
George III, King	37, 162, 177, 197, 283, 291, 387, 550, 639, 716
medallion	121
monument of	120, 445, 648
'playing at soldiers'	713
Regency Bill 1788	641
'returning from hunting'	527
transparency	606
George IV, King	93, 184, 272, 284, 292, 412, 490, 663, 665
coronation	181, 182, 658
drawing-room	664
embarkation	318
lying-in-state	483
George, Miss	77
Gilpin, John, Ride of	109
Gloucester, Henry, Duke of	628
Gloucester, Maria, Duchess of	150
Gloucester, Princess Mary, Duchess of	136, 150, 160, 217–9, 307
Gloucester, Princess Sophia of	150
Gothic Hall, A	492
Graces, The	723
Grant, A.	735
Grenadier, A	422
Griffith, Mr., house of	746
'Grog on Board'	515
Grueber, Mrs.	591
Guercino, drawings after	56, 594-7
Guido, drawing after	57
Hall, the Cryer	717
Happy Marriage, Design for	340
Harlot's Progress, Doctors in	340
Harlowe, Mrs.	659
Harvey, Rev.	717
Haymakers at Rest	525
Hazard Table, The	342
Headdresses	421
Henley, Orator	360
Henrietta, Maria, Queen	271, 469
Hercules	611
Hesse Homburg, Princess Elizabeth, Landgravine of	209–13, 306
Hieroglyphic Letter	442
'High Spirits'	521
Hog, Mr.	717

	Cat. Nos.
Hogarth's Lodging	367
Holbein, drawings after . .	458, 625, 627
Holmes, Sir Richard . .	Introd., pp. 7, 13
Hood, Admiral . . .	706
Hopkins, Mrs.	735
Howson, Bishop . . .	314
Huddesford	703
Hudibras, drawings for . .	332–8
'Humbug upon the Stocks' .	728
Hunting scenes . . .	33, 539, 691
'Hutchinson, General' . .	49
Indignant Husband, An . .	540
Irish Perseverance . . .	677
Irois, Relief of . . .	431
Irwin, Mr.	717
Jack in Office . . .	365
Jacob Jallage . . .	736
Jacobite's Journal, Headpiece	352
Jamaica, H.M.S. . . .	431
James II, King . . .	241
Jennings, Mrs., house of .	446
Johnstone, Commodore George	725
Jonas, junior, Mr. . .	717
Kemble	479
Kent, Edward Duke of . .	188, 201, 202, 287, 298
Victoria, Duchess of . .	111
King's Champion . .	182, 183
King's Maps . . .	Introd., pp. 7, 8
'Last Annuity Paid' . .	710
Lawrence, Sir T. . .	Introd., p. 13
Leacroft, Mr. . . .	717
Leatherworker, A . .	59
Leo XII	282
Leopold, Prince . .	174, 646, 647
Leslie, Sir Edward, Seat of .	44, 45
Letter, Hieroglyphic . .	442
Levi	717
Lill, Capt. . . .	717
Linley	408
Longways Dance . .	707
'Lord Swell's Advice' .	708
Lottery, The . . .	329
Louis XIV . . .	404
Lovers, The . . .	465
Magic Lanthorn, The . .	730
Maratta, drawing after . .	118
'Marie Antoinette, Arrest of'	48
Marlborough, Duke of . .	240
Marriage à la Mode . .	362, 363
Masquerade Ticket . .	325
Maule, Mr. . . .	717
Mensdorf, Alexander . .	113
Method! . . .	678
Midnight Conversation, A .	511
Miles's, Capt., Revenge .	279
Milton, John . . .	496

	Cat. Nos.
Misaubin, Dr., and Dr. Ward	341
'Moggadorio' . . .	423
Monsey, Dr. . . .	544
Moore, Dr. John . . .	281
Morris, Gov. . . .	717
Morsels of Melody . .	673
Moses Striking the Rock .	459
Mountebanks . . .	Supplement S.431
Musicians . . .	408, 443, 456, 673
Napoleon . . .	474, 638
Nash, 'Beau' . . .	693
Nature Unveiled . .	343
NAVAL SUBJECTS . .	31, 88, 430, 431, 477, 478, 552–7, 560, 562
Neck or Nothing . .	726
Nemours, Victoire, Duchesse de	112
New South Sea Fishery .	551
Newcastle, Duke of . .	506
Nile, Battle of the . .	31
Nocturnes . . .	Supplement S.430, S.431
Normanby, Marquess of .	413
North, Lord . . .	726
Nymphs & Satyrs . .	460
Octavius, Prince . .	303
O'Neil, Eliza . . .	416
Opera Singer, An . .	331
Orange, Frederica, Princess of	227
Orion, H.M.S. . . .	478
Orléans, Duc d'(Egalité) .	388
Oudh, Nabob of . . .	698
Overset	516
Palmer, Mr. . . .	735
Pantheon, King's . .	328
Parke	408
Parsons, Mr. . . .	735
Penderel (Pendrill), W. .	311
Penny Wedding, Girl in the	661
Petition to a Bishop .	722
Piazzetta, drawings after .	13, 14
Pike and Musket Drill .	437
Pinkethman, William . .	624
Pinto	408
Pitt, W. . . .	551, 729, 730
Plumer Ward, R. . .	414
Pope, Alexander . .	493–5
'Portsmouth, Duchess of' .	33
Post House, The . .	529
Pote, Dr. . . .	165
Poverty Struck Pride .	680
Procession from the Hustings .	727
Proportions of Garrick and Quin .	351
Punch and Judy . .	193
Putti . . .	471
Quaker in a Quake, A .	530
Quin . . .	351
Quixote, Don, drawings for .	349, 350

	Cat. Nos.
R., Mrs.	519
Rag Fair	528
Ramsbottom, Mr., house of	448
Randles, Edward	189
Raphael, after	278, 464, 468
Razor in the Upholsterer	736
Regatta at Spithead	88
RELIGIOUS SUBJECTS	56, 63–66, 118, 462, 466, 468, 470
Return from the Grand Tour	711
Reviews	517, 518, 555, 556, 560, 721
Ricci, Marco, after	157
Rochester, Bishop of	682
Rowlandson, T.	Introd., pp. 11, 12
Royal Academicians, group of	703
Royal Family, groups	186, 605
see also under individual names	
Russell, Dr. Patrick	167
Sadler's Flying Artillery	548
Sagacity!	679
Salomon	408
Sandby, P.	473
Sandby, Mrs. (?)	Supplement S.424, S.425
Saxe-Coburg, Princes of	113, 114
Saxe-Weimar, Prince Edward of	590
Schomberg, Isaac	191
School of Eloquence	510
Senesino	331
Sharp, G.	735
Shield	408
Shrimp Girl	542
Siddons, Mrs.	166, 480, 500
Simmons, Samuel	660
Sligo, Marchioness of	472
Smart, A	674
Sophia, Princess	136, 220–4, 308
South Sea Bubble, The	330
South Sea Fishery, a New	551
St. George & Dragon	464, 471
'St. Iago, Commodore'	725
Statues, Antique	163
Stolen Kiss	520
Storer, Philosopher	717
'Stubbs, George'	169
Sunday morning	524
Superb, H.M.S.	557
Susanna and the Elders	347
Sussex, Augustus, Duke of	215, 300

	Cat. Nos.
Tailor's Shop	71
Tamborina	549
Tartuff's Banquet	360
Tea party in a pergola, A	696
Three Figures	347
Titian, after	461, 462, 465–7
Travellers	74, 523
Two men asleep	514
Undaunted, H.M.S.	430
Unwelcome Visitor, The	530
Van Dyck, after	469, 626
Venus, attired by the Graces	75
and Cupid	702
and satyrs	600, 700
Cupid and Mercury	462
sleeping	463
toilet of	126
Victoria, Queen	643–5, 667–70
Victory, H.M.S.	477
Virgin & Child	470
Wales, Charlotte Princess of	96, 151, 174, 294
'apotheosis'	642
marriage of	646, 647
Wales, Frederick, Prince of	38, 342, 691, 694
Ward, Dr., and Dr. Misaubin	341
Weischell	408
Wellesley, Marquess of	228
Marchioness of	229
Wheeler, Mr.	717
Whitehall fresco	625
William IV, King	153, 190, 286, 297, 666
Woffington, Peg	475, 543
Wotton, Sir H.	315
Wray, Sir C.	62
York, Edward, Duke of	5
Frederica, Duchess of	296
Frederick, Duke of	95, 127, 137, 285, 295
Zell, William, Duke of	310

INDEX OF PLACES

Cat. Nos.

Ideal landscapes	.	.	17, 40, 42, 43, 72, 119, 157, 161, 269, 270, 539, 622, 634, 635
Unidentified landscapes.	.	.	41, 100, 158, 277, 374, 379, 492, 535, 539, 612, 633, 688, 689
Aboukir, Landing at	.	.	175
Africa, North	.	.	94
Baalbec	.	.	94
Beaumont	.	.	746
Belvoir	.	.	563
Bolton Abbey	.	.	100
Bridgnorth	.	.	420
Brighton	.	.	489, 534
Carisbroke Castle	.	.	427
Carthage	.	.	94
Chiselhurst	.	.	100
Claremont	.	.	506
Colchester	.	.	535
Douglas, I.O.M.	.	.	559
Dover	.	.	173
Eastbourne	.	.	263, 264
Edinburgh	.	.	427
Egypt	.	.	164
Englefield Green	.	.	426
Eton (*see also under* Windsor)	.	257, 258, 320
Ferry Bridge	.	.	531
Fort Royal	.	.	428
Gibraltar	.	.	420
Greece	.	.	164; p. 52
Greenwich	.	.	631
Hampton Court	.	.	173, 278, 437, 536, 537
Harrogate	.	.	533
Heligoland, Battle of	.	.	562
Holyrood Palace	.	.	662, 663
India	.	.	171, 172
Italy, views in	.	.	173, 420; p. 52
Kew	.	.	146, 147, 266, 538
Knole	.	.	148
Lambesa	.	.	94
Leptis Magna (Lebida)	.	.	192
LONDON			
Arundel House	.	.	372
Banqueting House	.	.	749, 750
Bear Garden	.	.	586
Buckingham House	.	.	18ff., 274, 324, 434, 436, 599-602
project for	.	.	752
Carlton House	.	.	61, 368, 481, 488, 489, 654-7
Covent Garden Theatre	.	.	568, 650
Crosby Hall	.	.	571
Drury Lane Theatre	.	.	566, 567, 651
'Eleanor Gwynn's House'	.	.	587
Exeter Change	.	.	194
Fortune Playhouse	.	.	582
Great Aliff Street Theatre	.	110
Grocers' Hall	.	.	585
Kensington Palace	.	.	444, 445
King's Theatre, Haymarket	.	570

Cat. Nos.

Lambeth, View from	.	.	378
'Hogarth's Lodging in'	.	.	367
Marlborough House	.	.	748
Melbourne House	.	.	444
Montague House	.	.	280, 751
North bank of the Thames	.	371
Old Playhouse	.	.	584
Opera House	.	.	486, 487
Ranelagh	.	.	454
Regency Theatre	.	.	569
Regent Street, Lower	.	.	482
St. James's Palace	.	.	370, 433, 511, 611, 748
St. James's Park	.	.	434, 435, 444, 491, 748
St. Stephen's, Walbrook	.	.	444
Somerset House	.	.	120, 121
Gardens	.	.	Supplement S.434
Tower, Armoury in	.	.	613
Veterinary College, St. Pancras	.	46
Westminster	.	.	370, 371, 452, 649
King's Gate	.	.	630
Whitehall	.	.	Supplement S.434
Man, Isle of	.	.	559
Medway	.	.	32
Minorca	.	.	720
Montpellier, *see* p. 78			
New Timber, Sussex	.	.	149
Oatlands	.	.	87
Orchardleigh	.	.	100
Palmyra	.	.	94
Paris	.	.	232, 233
Ptolometa	.	.	94
Reigate	.	.	180
Ribchester	.	.	100
Richmond	.	.	173, 176, 373, 632, 690, 753
Rochester	.	.	32
Rome	.	.	21-30
Ruhrort	.	.	375
St. Albans	.	.	620
St. Domingo	.	.	429
St. Helena	.	.	384, 474
Shrewsbury	.	.	261
Spithead	.	.	88, 555, 556, 560
Taplow	.	.	259
Tarbert	.	.	44, 45
Timgad	.	.	94
Torpoint	.	.	532
Twickenham	.	.	327
Warwick	.	.	100
West Indies	.	.	428-31
Wight, Isle of	.	.	41, 427
Windermere	.	.	289
Windsor, *see below*			
Woolmers	.	.	Supplement S.419
Worcester	.	.	260
WINDSOR			
Castle and Town			
Distant views	.	.	155, 248
From the North and North-East		35, 36, 97, 141, 231, 369, 406, 407, 440, 441, Supplt. S.430

Cat. Nos.

WINDSOR

Castle and Town

From East and South-East . 99, 377, 672, 743

From South and South-West . 138, 98, 322, 697, 747

From West and North-West . 140, 239, 243, 262 418, 419, 439, 455 501, 621, 737, 738 740, 745, 747

From Bishopsgate . . 276, 438, Supplement S.426, S.427

From Brocas, *see* from North-West

From Clewer Fields . . 244

From Cranbourne Lodge . 142

From Eton . . . 245–253, 326

From the Great Park . . 254

From Lord Shuldham's . . 256

From the river . . . 636

From Romney Island . . 319

From St. Leonard's . . 34, 255

From Snow Hill . . 159

Windsor Castle, Details

Bell Tower . . . 447

Black Rod . . . 265

Castle Hill . . . 381

Curfew Tower . . . 739, 747

Dentons Commons . . 425

East Front . . . 743

Garter Throne Room . . 671

Hundred Steps . . . 448

Cat. Nos.

Lower Ward 747

Maids of Honour Tower . . 144

Norman Gate . . . 449, 637

North Terrace . . . 509

Quadrangle . . . 143, 583, 617, 744

Queen's Lodge . . . 322, 381, 502, 565, 742, 743

St. George's Chapel . . 139, 178, 564, 652, 653, 747, Supplement S.435

Windsor Park . . . 741, Supplt. S.432

Belvedere 507, 508

Boat House 619

Cottages 131, 323, 623

Deputy Ranger's House . . Supplement S.420, S.421, S.428, S.429

Engine House . . . 237

Frogmore 100, 145, 209, 230, 382, 383

George III Statue . . . 445, 648

Herne's Oak 156

Mr. Griffith's House . . 746

Mrs. Jenning's House . . 446

Virginia Water . . . 179, Supplement S.433

Windsor Town

Bridge 238, 245, 450, 451

Charity School . . . 236

Parish Church . . . 235

Thames Street . . . 747

Town Hall 234, 452

WIMBLEDON SCHOOL OF ART LIBRARY